GOLD MEDAL PLAYS
for
HOLIDAYS

Gold Medal Plays for Holidays

Thirty royalty-free, one-act plays for children

by

HELEN LOUISE MILLER

Publishers PLAYS, INC. *Boston*

CAUTION

All material in this volume is fully protected by copyright law. All rights, including motion picture, recitation, television, public reading, radio broadcasting, and rights of translation into foreign languages, are strictly reserved.

NOTICE FOR AMATEUR PRODUCTION

These plays may be produced by schools, clubs, and similar amateur groups without payment of a royalty fee.

NOTICE FOR PROFESSIONAL PRODUCTION

For any form of non-amateur presentation (professional stage, radio or television), permission must be obtained in writing from the publisher. Inquiries should be addressed to PLAYS, INC., 8 Arlington Street, Boston 16, Massachusetts.

Library of Congress Catalog Card Number: 58-5793

MANUFACTURED IN THE UNITED STATES OF AMERICA

Contents

GOLD MEDAL PLAYS
for
HOLIDAYS

The Greedy Goblin

Characters

Mr. Strudel, *baker*
Mr. Whitman, *city detective*
Mrs. Whitman, *his wife*
Jasper Whitman, *their son*
Joe Hawkins, Jerry Ames, Karen Keller, Betsy Bryan — *students*
The Greedy Goblin

Setting: *Living room of the Whitman home, the evening before Halloween.*

At Rise: Mr. Whitman *is talking with* Mr. Strudel. Jasper Whitman *listens to them as he looks at the evening paper.*

Mr. Strudel: I'm telling of you, Mr. Vhitman, this is—how you say—der last straw! Der straw vot is breaking mit der back of der camel, und I am dot camel! More I cannot stand! Five hundred pies I bake this day, und how many get stolen from off der vagon und from off der shelves? You I am asking, Mr. Vhitman. How many you tink?

MR. WHITMAN: Well, Charlie, it's a safe bet I can hit the nail right on the head. You tell me how many of those pies were pumpkin custards, and I'll tell you how many were stolen.

MR. STRUDEL: Four hundred fifty pumpkin custards I bake on special orders for Halloween!

MR. WHITMAN: Then four hundred fifty pies were stolen! It's the same story! No pumpkin pie is safe in this whole town!

MR. STRUDEL: Und now I am asking vy you do not catch up mit der gang vot iss stealing der pies! Vot are you, a city detecatif or a willage blacksmith?

MR. WHITMAN: Don't worry, Charlie. We're doing all we can do. Go on back to your bakery and try to keep up your steam. We're bound to break this case in another 12 hours. (*Phone rings and* MRS. WHITMAN *comes in and answers it.*)

MR. STRUDEL: Twelf more hours und I vill be a broken man!

MRS. WHITMAN (*At phone*): Yes, he's here. Oh, that's too bad! Yes, I'll tell him right away. (*Hangs up*) Mr. Strudel, that was your wife. She wants you to come home right away. The first batch of pumpkin pies disappeared off the cooling racks.

MR. STRUDEL (*Uttering a yell of despair*) : Ach du lieber! Ach du lieber Augustine! You hear? All mine first batch, stolen already yet off der pie racks! Ach du lieber! (*Exits*)

MRS. WHITMAN: This is really terrible, John. Can't you do anything about it?

MR. WHITMAN: Don't *you* start asking foolish questions,

Mary. We're all knocking ourselves out down at headquarters. If we don't catch this gang of hoodlums before tomorrow, the whole police force will be the laughing stock of the town.

JASPER: Don't you have any clues at all, Pop?

MR. WHITMAN: No more than what you see in the paper! Those reporters know as much as we do.

JASPER: "THE GREEDY GOBLIN STRIKES AGAIN"—that's the headline in tonight's paper, Dad.

MR. WHITMAN: Very clever of the newsboys! They got that headline from the notes that were left at the scene of some of the crimes.

JASPER: But can't you get fingerprints off the notes, Dad?

MR. WHITMAN: It isn't as simple as all that, son. There just aren't any fingerprints. Just the name in that greenish kind of ink that the crime lab can't even seem to analyze.

JASPER: Gee, that's funny! No fingerprints at all on the notes?

MR. WHITMAN: None. And there's not a section of town that hasn't been touched. Stores, church basements, schools, bakeries, hotels, private homes, any place where there is a pumpkin pie is a target for those boys.

JASPER: We're having a committee meeting here tonight, Dad, to replan our school Halloween party. If we can't count on pumpkin pies, I guess we'll have to switch over to cider and doughnuts. But gee whiz! What's a Halloween party without pumpkin pie?

MR. WHITMAN: Things are tough all around, son. But don't worry. We'll get those thugs, if it takes every man on our force. (*Begins to put on coat and hat*) Don't worry if I'm a bit late, Mary. We're going to pour all the heat we've got on this thing tonight.

MRS. WHITMAN: Oh, dear! *Must* you go back to the office tonight?

MR. WHITMAN: Tonight and every night, till we get this case wrapped up.

JASPER: You know, Dad, I've got a theory on this thing . . .

MR. WHITMAN: Sorry, Jasper, I've no time for theories tonight. They're a dime a dozen. Tonight we've got to get action. Save it and tell me tomorrow. So long, Mary. Don't wait up for me. (*Exits.*)

JASPER: I wish he had waited to hear my idea.

MRS. WHITMAN: He's too busy and too worried, Jasper. This whole pumpkin pie business makes him look and feel awfully silly. Now tell me, how many people are coming to your committee meeting?

JASPER: Just four. Jerry, and Joe, Karen and Betsy. Why?

MRS. WHITMAN (*Smiling*): Oh, nothing . . . only . . . well, I just might have a little surprise for you, that's all. That is, if everything goes right.

JASPER: What's the big secret, Mom?

MRS. WHITMAN: Well, I know these committee meetings make you boys and girls terribly hungry and so I just thought I'd try feeding you up on a . . . (*Looking around nervously*) I almost hate to say this . . . but just before supper I baked a . . . you know what . . .

JASPER: Mom, you never had the nerve to bake a . . .

MRS. WHITMAN: Sh! Not so loud! Yes, I did.

JASPER: But where is it?

MRS. WHITMAN: It's out in the refrigerator. At least it was a few minutes ago.

JASPER: Well for Pete's sake! Don't leave it unguarded a single minute. I'll go look and see if it's still there. (*Exits*)

MRS. WHITMAN (*Calling after him*): Now mind you don't cut into it while it's still warm. (*Doorbell rings,* MRS. WHITMAN *goes to door. Enter* JERRY *and* JOE.) Hello, Joe. How are you, Jerry?

BOYS: Hello, Mrs. Whitman, fine, thank you (*etc.*).

JERRY: Is Jasper in?

MRS. WHITMAN: Jasper will be here in a minute. He had some urgent business in the kitchen. Jasper! (*Calling*) Your friends are here. (*Enter* JASPER)

JASPER: It's still there, Mom, but you'd better stand watch a while. Hiya, fellows. Anything new about the Greedy Goblin? (*Exit* MRS. WHITMAN.)

JOE: Not a thing.

JERRY: I guess we'll have to change our refreshments, all right. (*Doorbell rings.*) That's probably the girls. (*Goes to door. Enter* BETSY *and* KAREN.)

JASPER: Hi! The boys are already here, so we can get started right away. (*Boys and girls exchange greetings.*)

KAREN: Did your Dad hear any more on the pumpkin pie stealing, Jasper?

JASPER: That's all he hears about from morning till night.

BETSY: But doesn't he have any more clues? I've always thought your Dad was a pretty smart detective.

JASPER (*On defensive*): He's *still* a pretty smart detective, you'll see.

KAREN: My dad says he thinks it's funny the whole police force and detective bureau can't round up a gang of boys.

JOE: What makes him so sure it's *boys?*

JERRY: Yeah, where did he get his tip that there's a gang involved? The notes all say *The Greedy Goblin.*

BETSY: But it would have to be more than one person. Look how many pies have been stolen, from all parts of town and at all hours of the day and night. *One* boy couldn't possibly cover all that territory.

JOE: There you go again, *"boy"!* Why couldn't it be a girl?

JASPER: Look! Are we here to replan the school party or solve the mystery of the Greedy Goblin?

BETSY: It would be wonderful if we could do both.

KAREN: Replanning the party is easy. Betsy and I have lined up ten dozen doughnuts and all the cider we can drink.

JERRY: I still think we should hold out for pumpkin pies. Strudel's bakery is running an extra shift. Maybe we can get some pies after all.

JASPER: No soap! Mrs. Strudel just called my dad before he left and told him that the first batch had already been stolen off the cooling racks.

JOE: Well how do you like that? Some police force we got in this town. Excuse me, Jasper, I keep forgetting your dad is on the force.

JASPER: Well, you better try hard to remember. I'm sick of hearing all the cracks people make about the police force and the detective bureau. My dad's all upset over this case.

KAREN: But why aren't there any clues, Jasper? There must be some, only the police aren't smart enough to see them.

JASPER: That's because they don't really understand the case.

JOE: Now who's criticizing the police force?

JASPER: I'm not criticizing them. I'm just saying they don't understand the case.

JERRY (*With sarcasm*): And I suppose *you* do!

JASPER: I *think* I do. At least, I have a theory.

ALL: You do? What is it? (*Etc. They gather eagerly around* JASPER.)

JASPER: Well . . . it's really very simple. You see, there are no fingerprints. The thefts take place in widely separated parts of town at almost the same time.

JOE: So what? What's the answer?

JASPER: Well, don't you see? It isn't natural.

KAREN: I know it isn't natural, but what's your theory?

JASPER: If it isn't natural, it must be supernatural.

BETSY: What's that—"supernatural"?

JASPER: Something that's beyond or above the natural.

JOE: Stop talking in riddles. You read too many books. I don't get it.

JASPER: Well, Joe, in plain English, I think the Greedy Goblin is just exactly who he says he is . . . a greedy goblin.

BETSY: I still don't understand.

JASPER: I think the Greedy Goblin is a real, sure-enough *goblin* instead of a *person*. He doesn't leave fingerprints because he *can't* leave fingerprints. He writes in some sort of magic ink that even the chemists can't analyze. He covers more ground and travels faster than would be possible for a human being.

JERRY (*In disgust*): Ah, you're crazy. There isn't such a thing as a goblin.

JASPER: There is too. I looked it up in the dictionary and it says that a goblin is a mischievous elf or sprite.

JOE: But there's no such thing as an elf or a sprite.

KAREN: If it's in the dictionary, it's real.

BETSY: Maybe Jasper is right. But how could you prove it?

JERRY: Yeah, how could you prove that it's a goblin?

JOE: It's like the old recipe for rabbit stew, first catch your rabbit.

KAREN: You mean set a goblin trap?

JOE: Say, there's an idea!

JERRY: What would we use for bait?

JASPER: Hold everything, kids! Are you really game to try to catch the goblin?

ALL: Sure.

JOE: What do you have in mind?

JASPER: Bait. The perfect bait. Wait here for two minutes. (*Exits*)

BETSY: A real goblin? I wonder if he could be right.

JOE: Of course not. There's no such thing as a goblin.

KAREN: Golly! I feel sort of scared! Creepy-Crawlies are going up and down my spine.

BETSY: Mine too.

JERRY: Aw, girls are all alike; always crack up in a crisis. (*Enter* JASPER *with a pumpkin pie and serving knife.*)

JASPER: Now here's the bait—a fresh-baked pumpkin pie!

ALL (*Sniffing*): Ummm! Doesn't it smell good?

JOE: This is a real museum piece.

BETSY: Where did you get it?

JASPER: Mom made it for our refreshments.

JERRY: That was swell. I can hardly wait to get a piece.

JASPER: But it's not for us any longer. It's for the goblin. Bait—remember? Betsy, you rummage in that table drawer and see if you can find a spool of black silk thread. Joe, you and Jerry raid the desk and see how many flashlights you can scare up. Dad always has three or four pocket flashlights in there. (*Children follow directions.* JASPER *places pie on tabouret or small stand in center stage; then arranges four chairs to form a hollow square with table in centre.*)

BETSY: Here's the thread, Jasper.

JASPER: You and Karen wind the thread from one chair

to the other as if you were making a silk thread fence. How are you coming with the flashlights, Joe?

JOE: There are four here and I have one of my own, so that's one apiece.

JASPER: Good.

BETSY: Is this all right, Jasper?

JASPER (*Inspecting the thread*): Sure, that's fine. Take another turn around the chairs and we'll call it a day. This should make the perfect booby trap for old Mr. Goblin. (*As girls finish with thread,* JOE *and* JERRY *distribute the flashlights.*)

JASPER: Now, we're all set.

KAREN: Set for the goblin?

JASPER: Right.

KAREN: Golly, I'm scared.

JASPER: There's no time to be scared now. Each of you take cover behind a piece of furniture. Keep perfectly still until you hear a crash, then focus your flashlights directly on the goblin trap! Got it?

BOYS: Check.

JASPER: Now scram and I'll turn out the lights.

GIRLS: Turn out the lights?

JASPER: Sure. Now go on, get behind a chair or something. (*Children take cover,* JASPER *turns out lights and squats down behind a desk or chair. There is silence for several minutes . . . then a loud crash.*)

ALL: We've got him! We've got him! (*Flashlights are turned on the goblin trap, revealing upset chairs and a figure flat on its stomach on the floor, clutching the pie.*)

JOE: Quick, Jasper, turn on the lights! (*Stage lights up*)

JASPER (*Approaching figure*): So there you are! Caught at last!

JERRY (*Advancing with flashlight raised as a weapon*):

Get up. On your feet, Bum! (GOBLIN *scrambles to his feet.*)

JOE: And give me that pie. (*Takes pie and sets it on table.*)

JASPER: Well, say something. Can't you talk?

GOBLIN: Sure I can talk.

JASPER: That's good! 'Cause you've got an awful lot of explaining to do.

GOBLIN: Where?

KAREN: Where do you think? Down at police headquarters, of course.

BETSY: Jasper, you'd better phone your dad.

GOBLIN: What for?

KAREN: Why, to arrest you, of course. Jasper's father is a city detective. (GOBLIN *laughs heartily.*)

JASPER: Don't you laugh at my father, you, you greedy goblin, you!

GOBLIN: I'm not laughing at your father, boy. I'm laughing at you! You actually think your father will come and arrest me and take me to police headquarters, don't you?

JASPER: He sure will. You just wait till I phone him.

GOBLIN: Go ahead and call him. I'll wait.

JOE: What makes you so sure you won't be arrested? You're guilty, aren't you?

GOBLIN: Guilty of what?

JERRY: Of stealing all the pumpkin pies in Canton City.

GOBLIN: Oh sure. Sure, I did that.

KAREN: You sound as if you aren't even sorry. What made you do such a dreadful thing?

GOBLIN: Curiosity. Every Halloween I hear you human beings raving about pumpkin pie, so I made up my mind I wanted to taste one.

BETSY: One! But you've stolen thousands. Surely you can't eat all of them.

GOBLIN: Of course not. I'm saving them for tomorrow night when I intend to throw the biggest Halloween party in Goblin Land. Now what are you going to do with me?

JASPER: We told you. We're calling my dad and having you locked up.

GOBLIN: Don't make me laugh.

JASPER: What's so funny, Mr. Goblin?

GOBLIN: You are! Don't you know that grown-ups can't see goblins. If you call your father and he comes tearing out here, he won't be able to see a thing. In fact, he'll be mad as a hornet. I wouldn't risk it if I were in your shoes.

KAREN: You mean no grown-ups can see you at all?

GOBLIN: How do you think I managed to steal all those pies without being seen? I was very careful to take the pies when there were no children around, and I was safe enough from all grown-ups. They don't believe in goblins so they can never see them.

JASPER: Just the same, I'm calling my dad.

GOBLIN: O.K. If you get into serious trouble, don't blame me. I gave you fair warning. (*Enter* MRS. WHITMAN *carrying a tray of paper plates, napkins, forks and a cinnamon shaker.*)

MRS. WHITMAN: Jasper, you forgot the plates for the pie. Dear me, why are you all standing around with flashlights? Are you playing some sort of game?

JASPER: Mother, don't you see anything strange in the room?

MRS. WHITMAN: Strange? Well, no. Nothing except the

strange way you're all acting. What's the matter with you?

JASPER: But Mother, we've caught the goblin!

MRS. WHITMAN: Caught the goblin, have you? Well, that's fine! Jasper, this goblin business is getting on your nerves. Oh, well, it's no wonder. I suppose you've made up a game about it. Here are your plates and napkins. I hope you enjoy the pie, my dears, and if I were you, I'd stop playing silly goblin games, and eat it, before somebody steals it right out from under your noses. (*Exits.*)

GOBLIN: You see! What did I tell you?

KAREN: She looked right at you!

GOBLIN: And never saw me. That's just what your father and the policemen will do, Jasper, if you call them. And will you catch it, if you call your dad home on a fool's errand!

JERRY: Maybe he's right, Jasper. Maybe your father would be sore.

JASPER: But what are we going to do with him? If all the rest of the goblins get a taste for pumpkin pie, we'll never have any.

KAREN: Oh, dear! Don't you realize how wicked it is to steal?

GOBLIN: It's wicked for *you* to steal because you're children and supposed to be *good*. I'm a goblin. I'm supposed to be *bad*. Even the dictionary calls me a "malicious, evil sprite." I have to live up to my reputation and besides I want all my goblin friends to taste this pumpkin pie concoction! I hope they like it.

JOE: If they like it as much as you do, it will be just too bad for us!

GOBLIN: To be quite honest, I haven't tasted any myself yet.

JERRY: You mean you've stolen all those pies and haven't tasted a single one.

GOBLIN: Of course not! That wouldn't be polite. I'll wait for my friends!

BETSY: You mean you don't even know if you like pumpkin pie?

GOBLIN: Oh, I'm sure I will. The rest of the world raves about it. Besides, it has a delicious odor.

JASPER: Say, gang, that gives me an idea. Let's give him a taste of this one.

JOE: Are you crazy? Then we won't even have that one for ourselves.

JASPER: It's a chance. Maybe he won't like it. Maybe he'll hate the taste of pumpkin! It's worth trying. Betsy, you cut the pie and we'll give him a piece.

GOBLIN: I must say this is very generous of you.

BETSY (*Cutting pie and putting piece on paper plate*): I'll just give him a small piece as a sample. There! That should be big enough. (*Hands pie to* GOBLIN *who picks up fork*)

JOE: Keep your fingers crossed, kids, that he doesn't like it.

KAREN: Oh wait! Wait! (*Picks up shaker and dusts the* GOBLIN'S *piece of pie heavily with cinnamon*) Don't forget the cinnamon.

GOBLIN (*Screaming, throws his piece of pie on floor and dances madly about*): Cinnamon! Cinnamon! Get it out of here! Get it away from me! Help! Help! Don't come near me with that cinnamon shaker.

JERRY: What's the matter with him? He's having a fit!

KAREN: But all pumpkin pies need cinnamon. Mrs. Whitman must have forgotten it.

BETSY: So she gave us the shaker so we could put some on top.

GOBLIN: But cinnamon is poison to goblins! It dries up our blood! It withers the flesh on our bones! Our hair falls out! Horrors! That stuff you call cinnamon is deadly goblin dust! It's worse than arsenic.

JASPER: Then you and your friends have had a narrow escape, old boy. There would have been mass murder in Goblin Land if you and your friends had eaten those pies.

GOBLIN: Let me out of here! Let me go!

JERRY: Not so fast, you rascal! We're not finished with you yet. Betsy, give me that shaker.

GOBLIN: No! No! Help! Help!

JOE: Now we have him at our mercy! Here's our chance to get rid of him once and for all. There won't be a trace of him. Sprinkle him well, Jerry, and watch him shrivel up!

GOBLIN: No! No! Save me! Save me! Help! Help!

JOE: Now's your chance to get a confession, Jasper.

JASPER: Why did you leave all those notes at the scene of the robberies, Mr. Goblin?

GOBLIN: Because I didn't want anyone else to be blamed for what I did. Not even a goblin would be that mean.

JASPER: Very nice of you, I must say. Now what did you use for ink? Our crime lab has not been able to analyze it.

GOBLIN: Firefly juice. I doubt if the chemical formula is known.

JASPER: Do you have any of it with you?

GOBLIN: Sure, I always carry a goose feather that is well soaked with it. (*Gets feather out of pocket*)

JASPER: Then write as I dictate. Shove him up to a table, Joe. Jerry, you keep that cinnamon shaker suspended over his head. Betsy, you'll find a piece of paper in the desk. (*They get* GOBLIN *ready for writing.*)

JASPER: I hereby confess to the robberies of all the pumpkin pies in Canton City which I solemnly promise . . .

GOBLIN: How do you spell *solemnly?*

KAREN: S-O-L-E-M-N-L-Y.

GOBLIN: . . . "which I solemnly promise—"

JASPER: To restore to their owners before daybreak.

JERRY: Do you know how to keep a promise, Mr. Goblin?

GOBLIN: Yes, yes, I promise. I wouldn't want a grain of cinnamon in my house! Oh, dear! If only my wife and children have not eaten any of those pies! Cinnamon! Brrr! It makes me shiver.

JASPER: Sit still and keep on writing. And I furthermore solemnly promise . . .

GOBLIN: "And I furthermore solemnly promise . . ."

JASPER: That I will never again steal a pumpkin pie from any human being on earth, so help me Beelzebub!

GOBLIN: There! It's finished!

JASPER: Now sign it! The Greedy Goblin!

GOBLIN: It's signed. Now will you let me go?

JASPER: Will you promise to make copies of this confession and leave one with every batch of pies you return?

GOBLIN: Yes, yes. I promise. Now, please let me go!

JASPER: O.K., Jerry. You can stop covering him with the cinnamon shaker.

GOBLIN: And one more favor, if you please.

JASPER: Make it snappy.

GOBLIN: Will you please turn out the lights so I can make a proper exit?

JASPER: O.K. Get moving. I'll keep them turned off until I count ten. (*Douses lights and counts ten slowly. Stage lights up.* GOBLIN *is gone.*)

KAREN: He's gone!

JASPER: And good riddance!

JERRY: Gee, I would have liked to shake that cinnamon on him to see what would happen.

JOE: I'm glad you didn't waste any of it on him. We'll need it for our pie. How about it, Jasper? I'm hungry.

JASPER: Sure. Betsy, will you cut us each a piece? (*They turn toward table where pie was located only to find it has disappeared. There is a note on the table.*)

BETSY: Why, it's gone!

JERRY: That dirty, double-crossing goblin! I should have given him the works with that cinnamon.

KAREN: Look, there's a note. Read it, Jasper.

JASPER: Dear Friends: This was my only chance to taste a pumpkin pie that I knew was free from cinnamon! Believe me, I'll never take a chance on another. Please forgive me! Signed . . . The Greedy Goblin.

JOE: Of all the nerve!

JERRY (*Laughing*): The poor little guy surely worked hard for a piece of pumpkin pie!

KAREN: I can't help hoping he enjoys it.

BETSY: Heavens, Jasper! Do you think that pie had any cinnamon inside of it?

JASPER: How should I know? (*Enter* MRS. WHITMAN.)

MRS. WHITMAN: Well, children, how did you enjoy your pie? I see it's all gone! You know, I completely forgot to put any cinnamon in. That's why I brought you the shaker. I hope it tasted all right.

BOYS: It was swell, Mrs. Whitman.

GIRLS: It was marvelous.

JASPER: Mother, you'll never know what a wonderful pie that really was. How about it, kids? Wasn't that a knock-out? (*Curtains close.*)

THE END

A School for Scaring

Characters

Miss Goblin, *teacher of Scare 'em School*
Professor Owl, *reading expert*
Beulah Banshee
Danny Demon
Fanny Phantom
Gregory Ghost
Gracie Ghost
Gloria Ghoulie
Harry Haunt
Helen Hobgoblin
Johnny Jack-o-Lantern
Winifred Witch
Wilfred Witch
Winona Witch
Walter Witch
Sammy Scarecrow
Solomon Spook

Time: *The present.*
Setting: Miss Goblin's *classroom at Scare 'em School.*
At Rise: *The* Pupils *are in their places, and* Miss Goblin *is standing behind her desk.*

MISS GOBLIN (*Looking over her glasses at the audience*): Have you ever wondered how a little witch learns to ride a broomstick, or how a ghost finds out about vanishing, or how a scarecrow learns his business? Well, it's really very simple. They all go to school—*my* school here on Haunted Hill. My name is Miss Goblin, and you'll meet the pupils just as soon as they sing their Good Morning Song.

ALL (*Singing traditional Good Morning Song*):
Good morning, good morning, good morning to you!
Good morning, Miss Goblin,
We're here to scare you! (*Add a very loud*) BOO!

MISS GOBLIN: Very good! Very good! I will now call the roll. (*As* MISS GOBLIN *calls the roll, each pupil responds by saying "Boo!" The "Boo's" should be varied in tone and inflection according to character.*) Beulah Banshee, Danny Demon, Fanny Phantom, Gregory Ghost, Gracie Ghost, Gloria Ghoulie, Harry Haunt, Helen Hobgoblin, Johnny Jack-o-Lantern, Winifred Witch, Wilfred Witch, Winona Witch, Walter Witch, Sammy Scarecrow, Solomon Spook.

ALL (*As* SOLOMON SPOOK'S *name is called*): Absent!

MISS GOBLIN: Not again! That makes the third time this month that Solomon Spook has been absent. Does anyone know what's wrong with him?

BEULAH BANSHEE: I saw him haunting the cemetery yesterday, and he seemed all right.

DANNY DEMON: He was at the demons' picnic last week.

HARRY HAUNT: I don't think he likes to go to school.

MISS GOBLIN: Don't be silly, Harry. Every little ghost and goblin likes to go to school, don't you, my little monsters?

ALL (*With false enthusiasm*): Yes, Miss Goblin.

MISS GOBLIN: I'm sure something has happened to Solomon Spook, and if he isn't here by recess time, I'll call his mother. But now it's time for our Broomstick Riding Lesson. Winifred, Wilfred, Winona, and Walter, take your places at the front of the room with your broomsticks. (*The witches obey.*)

WILFRED WITCH: I'm sorry, Miss Goblin, I forgot my broomstick. I left it at home.

MISS GOBLIN: The very idea! Didn't you know we were having our broomstick riding class today?

WILFRED WITCH: Yes, ma'am, but I forgot.

MISS GOBLIN: That's the trouble with you *boy* witches. You're always so careless. But no matter. We have some extras in the broom closet. You may get one.

WILFRED WITCH: Thank you, Miss Goblin. (WILFRED *gets broom and joins the others.*)

MISS GOBLIN (*To* WITCHES): Now form a straight line, and face left. We will fly around the room three times, going higher and higher, until our broomsticks hit the ceiling. Dear me, Winona Witch! What's wrong with your broomstick?

WINONA WITCH: I think it's broken. The last time I was out flying I got caught in a tree.

MISS GOBLIN: Never mind. It looks strong enough for an indoor flight. Now remember, you must be off the ground by the time I count three. Ready, get set . . .

WALTER WITCH: Please, Miss Goblin, *must* we fly these broomsticks?

MISS GOBLIN: Of course, Walter. Every witch rides a broomstick.

WALTER WITCH: Not any more, Miss Goblin. Lots of the modern witches use flying saucers.

MISS GOBLIN (*Angrily*): Walter Witch, you get on that broomstick right away and let's hear no more nonsense about flying saucers. A broomstick was good enough for your Daddy, and it's good enough for you! (*To class*) Now, the rest of the class will sing our flying song while we go on our practice flight. Be careful of the windows and watch out for the light fixtures! Ready! Get set! Go! (*The little witches on their broomsticks drill, as their classmates sing the following words to the tune of "One Little, Two Little, Three Little Indians."*)

Fly away, fly away, fly away, witches,
Fly over hedges, fly over ditches,
Fly through the night without any hitches,
Fly away, fly away, fly!

MISS GOBLIN: The witches may now be seated and we'll have our class in chain clanking. First, let me hear you clank your chains all together. (*Every pupil produces a chain from his desk and clanks it.*) Now, if Harry Haunt and Fanny Phantom come to the front of the room, we will have a little experiment with thunder and lightning. (HARRY *and* FANNY *go to front of room and hold up a large piece of sheet metal or aluminum.*)

HARRY HAUNT: This is a good way to produce the sound of thunder.

FANNY PHANTOM (*As they shake the metal*): You can make it crackle or crash depending on how you shake it.

MISS GOBLIN: Now clank your chains as the thunder rolls. (*Much clanking of chains and crashing of thunder.* MISS GOBLIN *holds up her hand for silence.*) Enough! Enough! I have some important questions to ask the class. (HARRY *and* FANNY *take their seats.*) Gloria Ghoulie, what sort of night would you choose for chain clanking?

GLORIA GHOULIE: A dark and gloomy night, Miss Goblin.

MISS GOBLIN: And what sort of house would you choose, Gregory Ghost?

GREGORY GHOST: A haunted house, Miss Goblin, or an empty house.

GRACIE GHOST: I don't think it would be good to clank your chains in an empty house, Miss Goblin, because then you wouldn't scare anybody.

MISS GOBLIN: Good for you, Gracie! We must always remember a monster's first duty is to scare folks. Suppose we have our school yell, just to refresh our memories. Beulah Banshee may lead the cheers.

ALL: Scare 'em, Scare 'em, Rah, Rah, Rah!
Dare 'em, Dare 'em, Ha, Ha, Ha!
Haunt 'em, Haunt 'em,
Doom and Daunt 'em,
Halloween! Halloween! Halloween!
(*Applause*)

MISS GOBLIN: That showed the true Halloween spirit, and I know I'm going to be proud of my pupils on Halloween Night. Dear me! What's the matter with Johnny Jack-o-Lantern?

JOHNNY JACK-O-LANTERN (*Crying*): Danny Demon hurt my feelings! He called me names!

MISS GOBLIN: Danny Demon, I'm ashamed of you! Even a demon doesn't call his friend names. And Johnny *is* your friend, isn't he?

DANNY DEMON: Sure, he's my friend.

MISS GOBLIN: Then, why did you call him a name?

DANNY DEMON: I didn't.

JOHNNY JACK-O-LANTERN: He did too!

MISS GOBLIN: Well, what did he call you? Was it so terrible?

JOHNNY JACK-O-LANTERN: Yes. He called me a "pumpkin head!"

MISS GOBLIN: Now, now, Johnny! Danny didn't mean anything bad by that. That's what you really are—a dear little pumpkin head, and we all love you very much, don't we, little monsters?

ALL: Sure we do!

MISS GOBLIN: If you weren't a little pumpkin head, you wouldn't be able to grin and show all your lovely, crooked teeth.

JOHNNY JACK-O-LANTERN: But he says there's nothing in my head. He says it's hollow.

MISS GOBLIN: It's hollow, all right, but there *is* something inside.

JOHNNY JACK-O-LANTERN: What? What's inside?

MISS GOBLIN: Danny knows. Danny, what's inside Johnny's head?

DANNY DEMON: A light, a big, shining light.

MISS GOBLIN: That's right. Johnny is the only one of all you Halloween creatures who can light up when it gets dark. Let's sing the special song we wrote in honor of Johnny Jack-o-Lantern.

ALL (*Singing to the tune of "Lavender's Blue"*):

Light up and grin, Jack-o-Lantern,
Let's see you smile.
Both day and night, Jack-o-Lantern,
Smile all the while.
Grin when you're gay, Jack-o-Lantern,

Smile when you're blue.
When we watch you, Jack-o-Lantern,
We're smiling, too!

PROFESSOR OWL (*Entering at close of song*): Very nice, very nice, indeed. Johnny Jack-o-Lantern, you should be proud to have such a song written in your honor.

JOHNNY JACK-O-LANTERN: I'm very proud and very happy, sir, and I'm not cross at Danny Demon any more.

PROFESSOR OWL: Good! I'm glad to hear that.

MISS GOBLIN: Dear me! The time has passed so quickly I didn't realize it was time for Professor Owl to take charge of your reading lesson.

PROFESSOR OWL: I'm sure we're all ready to begin, Miss Goblin. (*Pupils get books.*) I think we'll start with the ghost family this morning. Gregory Ghost, you may begin.

GREGORY GHOST (*Reading from book*):
A ghost must learn to disappear,
And vanish in a trice.
First you're there, then you're here.
It's really very nice.

PROFESSOR OWL (*Marking in record book*): That means a good mark for you, Gregory. Now, Gracie, you may continue.

GRACIE GHOST: A ghost must always quiet be,
As still as any mouse.
Unless he's busy clanking chains
Within a haunted house.

PROFESSOR OWL: Very good, Gracie. Next, Gloria Ghoulie.

GLORIA GHOULIE: A ghost is always dressed in white,
As clean as driven snow,
With good-sized holes cut in the face
For eyes and mouth to show.

PROFESSOR OWL: Gloria, you're improving every day. Now let's hear from Solomon Spook.

ALL: He's absent.

PROFESSOR OWL: Poor Solomon will be way behind with his lessons. Sammy Scarecrow, even though you aren't exactly a ghost, we'll let you finish the ghost lesson for today.

SAMMY SCARECROW: A ghost must always be polite,
When he is spoken to,
And learn to speak in ghostly tones,
With a loud and scary BOO!

PROFESSOR OWL: If you practice hard enough, Sammy, we might put you in the ghost class next year. Now we'll hear Winona Witch recite.

WINONA WITCH: A witch must ride a broomstick,
And learn to cast a spell,
And that is why we go to school,
To learn these lessons well.

PROFESSOR OWL: And Miss Goblin tells me you're doing very nicely. Now, Johnny Jack-o-Lantern, it's your turn.

JOHNNY JACK-O-LANTERN:
A Jack-o-Lantern still must grin,
When he is feeling blue.
He never lets his light grow dim
Till Halloween is through.

PROFESSOR OWL: Be sure you remember that, Johnny. Danny Demon, have you learned your lesson for today?

DANNY DEMON: A demon's duty is to play
All sorts of naughty tricks.
He must take care he isn't caught,
Or he'd be in a fix!

PROFESSOR OWL: Right! Beulah Banshee, what is your assignment?

BEULAH BANSHEE: A Banshee first must learn to wail,
And howl, and cry, and moan.
No one would want a Banshee
In any modern home.
But off in Emerald Ireland,
With castles by the score,
They're calling for us Banshees
More and more and more.

PROFESSOR OWL: Yes, my child. Every old Irish castle must have its special Banshee to scare the wits out of the tourists. I'm sure you'll get a good job there someday. Gracious sakes alive! (*Jumping up and pointing off-stage*) What's this? What's this?

ALL (*Looking around*): Where? Where?

PROFESSOR OWL: Right there—coming up the walk!

MISS GOBLIN (*Terrified*): It's a boy! It's a boy! A real sure-enough boy! Quick! Quick! We must hide. Duck down under your desks.

HELEN HOBGOBLIN: What will he do to us?

PROFESSOR OWL: There's no telling what he may do.

HELEN HOBGOBLIN (*Crying*): I'm afraid. I want to go home!

MISS GOBLIN: You'd never make it. I know these boys! They're terrible creatures at Halloween, even worse than we are! They play all sorts of tricks. Now hide behind your desks and be very quiet.

HELEN HOBGOBLIN: Is he coming in?

PROFESSOR OWL: Yes, I'm afraid he is. But keep very quiet and maybe he'll go away.

SOLOMON SPOOK (*Enters with a moaning sound. He looks all around in bewilderment*): Whooo! Whooo! Hey! Where is everybody? Miss Goblin, where are you?

ALL (*Coming out from behind desks*): It's Solomon Spook!

MISS GOBLIN: Solomon Spook! The very idea! What do you mean scaring us half to death?

PROFESSOR OWL: What are you doing here in those awful clothes? Don't you know they belong to a human being?

MISS GOBLIN: I'm going to report you to Officer Dragon!

SOLOMON SPOOK: Oh, please, don't do that, Miss Goblin. I didn't mean any harm.

PROFESSOR OWL: Then explain what you're doing here in these clothes.

SOLOMON SPOOK: I was chasing some children through the park last night. Somehow, I slipped and fell into a mud puddle. My sheet was simply ruined. Mother had to send it to the Witches' Washerette, and I had nothing else to wear!

MISS GOBLIN: But these dreadful clothes! Where did you get them?

SOLOMON SPOOK: From a clothesline. I only borrowed them so I wouldn't miss school. They're just my size, too.

MISS GOBLIN: Well, you did give us quite a scare. Don't ever do a thing like this again.

SOLOMON SPOOK: I won't. I won't.

PROFESSOR OWL: See that you don't, or you'll have to stay in after school and not go out haunting on Halloween night.

SOLOMON SPOOK: That would be the worst thing that could ever happen to a ghost, wouldn't it?

ALL: I'll say it would! (*Bell rings*) It's time for recess! Hooray! Hooray!

PROFESSOR OWL (*Rapping for order*): Quiet! We will dismiss in an orderly fashion. Everyone, please be seated.

Miss Goblin (*As pupils sit down*): Before we dismiss for recess, I want you to show Professor Owl how beautifully you can sing your Scare 'em School Song.

All (*Stand and sing to the tune of School Days*):

School days, school days,
Ghostly, ghastly school days!
Learning to do every magic trick,
Taught how to fly on a witch's stick.
We are the spirits foul and fair
Flying about in the midnight air,
If you know what is good, you had best beware,
When *You* meet a couple of SPOOKS! (*Curtain*)

THE END

The Mystery of Turkey-Lurkey

Characters

ALICE GORDON
FRED GORDON, *her brother*
BETSY GORDON, *her sister*
MIKE BROWN, *their friend*
POLICEMAN
TURKEY-LURKEY
DUCKS, GEESE, CHICKENS, EXTRA TURKEYS
CHORUS
SPEAKER

TIME: *One morning, a few days before Thanksgiving.*

SETTING: *The barnyard. Downstage left is an empty cardboard coop bearing a sign,* TURKEY-LURKEY. *Downstage right is a long cardboard cage marked* MARKET HOUSE, *large enough for eight children, and cut so that each child can stick his head out of a hole in the cardboard. Further right is a stepladder camouflaged as a cardboard tree. The ducks, geese, chickens, and turkeys wear paper-bag masks.*

AT RISE: *The* CHORUS, *seated in low primary chairs at center stage, is reciting; at least half the children have rhythm instruments.* TURKEY-LURKEY *hides, invisible to everyone, on stepladder behind tree foliage.*

CHORUS: "When the frost is on the punkin, and the fodder's in the shock,"
You can tell Thanksgiving's coming without looking at the clock;
'Cause all the leaves are turning brown, and many trees are bare,
And there's a sort of spicy smell afloating through the air.
And long about this time of year, we dream a lot of turkey,
And that's our story for today, THE TALE OF TURKEY-LURKEY.

(*Half the* CHORUS *sings "Over the River and Through the Woods"; the other half accompanies with rhythm instruments.*)

SPEAKER (*From* CHORUS): Yes, Thanksgiving Day is almost here. Thanksgiving is a happy time for most families, but it is a sad time for a family we know. Their name is Gordon. (*As* SPEAKER *names each member of the family, that child enters and takes his place beside* TURKEY-LURKEY'S *coop.*) First, there is Alice Gordon. Next, her brother—Fred Gordon, and third, her sister, Betsy Gordon. The children are sad today because they have a problem.

ALICE: Are you sure the coop is empty?

FRED (*Looking*): Not even a feather! Turkey-Lurkey is gone!

BETSY: Maybe he's hiding in his cage.

FRED: There's no place to hide.

ALICE: Maybe he ran away.

FRED: Here comes Mike Brown. Maybe he has seen Turkey-Lurkey.

MIKE: Hello. What's the trouble? Where is your turkey? His coop is empty.

FRED: Yes, he's gone. We can't find him. Have you seen him?

MIKE: No, I haven't seen him. This is a great mystery, the mystery of the missing turkey. It's our job to solve it.

ALICE: But we don't know how to solve mysteries.

MIKE: It's not hard. Everybody can do it on radio and television.

BETSY: What do we do first?

MIKE: First we get out a description of the missing turkey.

OTHERS: A description?

MIKE: Yes. How big was he? What did he look like? How could you identify him?

ALICE: Well, he was a great big fellow. He weighed over twenty pounds.

FRED: And he had an enormous tail, as big as a fan.

BETSY: And a real loud gobble that you could hear for blocks.

CHORUS (*Reciting*): Look sharp! Watch out! And spread the word!

We're looking for a missing bird.
He's big and fat! Weighs twenty pounds!
Please help us find him! Make the rounds!
He has a tail that spreads out wide.
He has a gobble deep inside.
And when he gobbles, never fear,
That gobble you will plainly hear.
If you should see a bird like that,

Don't even stop to get your hat,
But hurry, please, show us the way
To get him back Thanksgiving Day.

MIKE: Now that we have a description of him, the rest should be easy.

FRED: It doesn't seem very easy to me. What are we supposed to do?

MIKE: Ask a lot of questions. Ask everyone you meet. Maybe someone has seen him.

CHORUS: So Alice and Fred, and Betsy and Mike,
Set out upon their turkey hike.
Their hearts were sad, the day was murky,
As they were hunting Turkey-Lurkey!

CHILDREN (*Calling*): Here, Turkey-Lurkey! Here, Turkey-Lurkey! Here, Turkey-Lurkey! Where are you? Where are you? Where are you?

MIKE: We will never find him this way. We should each go in a different direction.

ALICE: I'll go search in the market house. Maybe he was homesick for the other Thanksgiving birds—the ducks, geese, chickens, and turkeys like himself.

FRED: I will go out into the forest. Maybe he went there to live with the wild turkeys.

BETSY: I'll go ask a policeman. Policemen always know where to look for lost dogs and lost children. Maybe they will know where to find a lost turkey.

MIKE: I'll look around the neighborhood. Maybe he has stayed close to home. (FRED, BETSY, *and* MIKE *exit.* ALICE *approaches the coop labeled* MARKET HOUSE. *The fowls stick their heads out of the cardboard crate and shout.*)

DUCKS, GEESE, CHICKENS, TURKEYS:
Gobble, Gobble, Gobble!

Quack! Quack! Quack!
Hiss! Hiss! Hiss!
Cluck! Cluck! Cluck!
Go away, girl! Go away, girl!

ALICE: I can't go away until I find Turkey-Lurkey. He has run away.

TURKEYS: Gobble! Gobble! Gobble! Good for him! Good for him! Good for him!

DUCKS: Quack! Quack! Quack! He'll never come back! He'll never come back!

GEESE: Hiss! Hiss! Hiss! You'll not find him like this!

CHICKENS: Cluck! Cluck! Cluck! You'll not have any luck.

ALICE: I believe you don't want us to find him. (*The fowls answer with a babble of gobbles, quacks, hisses and clucks.*) Oh dear! I can't make any sense out of your chatter. I'll have to look somewhere else. (*As she turns to exit, she meets* FRED, *entering.*)

FRED: Hello, Alice. Any luck?

ALICE: No, he is not in the market house. Did you find any trace of him in the forest?

FRED: No, but I saw something very wonderful.

ALICE: What did you see?

FRED: I saw the animals celebrating their Thanksgiving.

ALICE: What did they do?

FRED: All of the animals gathered in a circle under a great Oak. When everything was quiet, they began to talk. At first, I could not understand what they were saying, but as I listened their words became plain to me.

CHORUS (*Reciting. If desired, piano may play musical background: "Father We Thank Thee."*):

We're simple little forest folk,
Who live from day to day

Within the shelter of Thy love
And all Thy laws obey.

We thank Thee for the sunny skies
And water fresh and clear,
We thank Thee for the lofty trees
That spread their branches here.

We thank Thee for these forest glades
Where we are safe and free,
And for the shelter of our homes
In bush and briar and tree.

We thank Thee for the grain and fruit,
For berries, nuts, and seeds,
And all the good things Thou hast sent
To satisfy our needs.

ALICE: Oh, Fred, do you think I could see, too?

FRED: Perhaps, if you are very quiet. Come along.

ALICE: We'll look for Turkey-Lurkey on the way. (FRED *and* ALICE *exit right as* BETSY *enters left.*)

BETSY: Oh, Turkey-Lurkey, come to me,
Oh, turkey dear, where can you be?
Where are you, Turkey-Lurkey?
It's just no use! I can't find him any place. Oh good! Here comes a policeman. I'll ask him. (POLICEMAN *enters.*)

BETSY: Oh, have you seen our turkey pet?
I've searched but I've not found him yet,
And turkey birds are hard to get!
Have you seen Turkey-Lurkey?

POLICEMAN: I have not seen your turkey bird,
But this to me has just occurred,

If he is near, you should have heard
His gobble, gobble, gobble!

BETSY: Oh, thank you, sir, I guess you're right,
That turkey bird is not in sight,
And we are in a sorry plight
Without our Turkey-Lurkey.

POLICEMAN: Well, come along. I'll join the search.
We'll find that missing turkey's perch!
He cannot leave you in the lurch!
That naughty Turkey-Lurkey!
(POLICEMAN *and* BETSY *exit left as* MIKE *enters right.*)

CHORUS (*As* MIKE *walks slowly around stage, tired*):
Here comes Mike!
From his turkey hike.
Look at him! He's tired and weary!
See his face and hands are smeary!
Mercy! What a sight!

MIKE (*Mopping his face with handkerchief*):
How tired I am!
I've looked in the park! I've looked at the school!
I've looked in the alleys, I've looked by the pool!
I've looked in the graveyard, I've searched every street.
But that Turkey-Lurkey I never did meet!
I give up!

CHORUS (*Shaking all their rhythm instruments*):
Oh don't give up, oh don't give up!
Just say this magic word:
"I *know* I can! I *know* I can!"
And you will catch your bird!

MIKE: Well, maybe I should give it another try. (*Looking at ground*) Why, look here! What's this? It looks like a feather. (*Stoops, picks up feather and looks at it.*) Why, it *is* a feather! And here's another! And another! They look like Turkey-Lurkey's feathers. He must have passed this way. (MIKE *follows feather trail to tree.*) I think I'm getting closer. He must be very near.

TURKEY-LURKEY (*Poking his head up above the tree, from where he sits on the ladder*): Squawk! Squawk! Squawk!

MIKE: What was that? (*Looking up*) What was that?

TURKEY-LURKEY: Squawk! Squawk!

MIKE (*Spotting* TURKEY-LURKEY): Why, there you are, you rascal! What are you doing up there in that tree, Turkey-Lurkey?

TURKEY-LURKEY: Squawk! Squawk!

MIKE: I can't hear you. You'll have to come down. (TURKEY-LURKEY *gives an agitated series of squawks.* MIKE, *coaxing.*) Come on down. I won't hurt you. Come on. (*Slowly, as* MIKE *continues to coax,* TURKEY-LURKEY *comes down the ladder.* MIKE, *petting him*) There you are, Turkey-Lurkey! There you are, safe and sound. You're not lost any more. (TURKEY-LURKEY *squawks piteously.*) What's the matter, Turkey-Lurkey? Can't you talk? (TURKEY-LURKEY *shakes his head and utters more squawks.*) Maybe there's some corn stuck in your throat. Let me help you. (*Rubs* TURKEY-LURKEY'S *neck, then pounds him on the back.* TURKEY-LURKEY *coughs.*) That's right. Try to cough and clear your throat. That's good. (*More coughs*) That's fine. You look better already. Let's walk back to your coop where you can get a drink of fresh water. (TURKEY-LURKEY *and* MIKE *cross to coop.* MIKE *sets a dish of water in front of* TURKEY-LURKEY *who pretends to drink it with much gargling, and tossing of head.*) That water should do the trick. Take a nice long drink. Maybe that will put your gobble back where it belongs. (*As* TURKEY-LURKEY *is drinking,* ALICE, FRED, BETSY, *and* POLICEMAN *return.*)

ALL: Look! Look! There's Turkey-Lurkey! You've found him! You've found him!

POLICEMAN: So there's the missing bird. Where did you find him?

MIKE: I found him up in that tree. (*Pointing*) I don't think he feels very well.

ALICE (*As children fuss around him*): Why, Turkey-Lurkey, are you sick?

BETSY: What happened? Are you hurt?

FRED: He looks all right to me. He's just thirsty.

MIKE: Don't crowd around him. Give him plenty of air. I think he's lost his gobble!

ALL: Lost his gobble!

POLICEMAN: I never heard of such a thing.

MIKE: Sh! I think he can talk a little bit now. (*Gently*) How do you feel, Turkey-Lurkey? (TURKEY-LURKEY *emits a few faint gobbles.*) That's fine. Your voice is getting stronger. Maybe you can tell us what happened.

TURKEY-LURKEY (*Between gobbles*): I went for a walk (*Gobble gobble*) and on the way (*Gobble gobble*) I passed a corn patch. The farmer was away. (*Gobble gobble*). There was no one in the field. So I ate (*Gobble gobble*) and I ate (*Gobble gobble*) and I ate! Faster, and faster and faster!

MIKE: You mean you really gobbled your food?

TURKEY-LURKEY: Yes. I was afraid the farmer would come back and chase me. So I ate as much as I could eat as fast as I could eat it. Suddenly I found I had eaten too much! My gobble was gone!

CHILDREN: How awful! Imagine a turkey without his gobble!

MIKE: Then what did you do?

TURKEY-LURKEY: I knew everyone would laugh at me, so

I flew up into that big tree to hide. I was so ashamed. I thought I could never gobble again.

MIKE: Well, I'm glad I found you and got your gobble back in good working order again.

CHILDREN: So am I! So am I!

TURKEY-LURKEY: Gobble, gobble, gobble! So am I! So am I! So am I!

ALICE: When you gobble your food, you get indigestion.

BETSY: Turkey-Lurkey, I'm afraid you were a greedy gobbler.

FRED: That's right. He ate so much he couldn't even gobble.

ALICE: One time my Daddy ate so much Thanksgiving dinner, he had to walk around the block before he could eat his mince pie.

FRED: Maybe it's all right to be greedy on Thanksgiving Day.

CHORUS: That's where you're wrong! That's where you're wrong! That's where you're wrong!

MIKE: I don't agree with you, Fred. A greedy person wants to gobble everything up for himself. Thanksgiving is a day for sharing.

ALICE: Don't be greedy, help the needy.
Learn to give and learn to share.

BETSY: Share with others, live like brothers,
Give a neighbor love and care.

FRED: Count each blessing you're possessing,
Food you eat and clothes you wear.

MIKE: You are living true Thanksgiving
When you share and share and share.

TURKEY-LURKEY: Gobble, gobble, gobble! That's what I say! That's what I say!

CHORUS: "When the frost is on the punkin and the fodder's in the shock,"
You can tell Thanksgiving's coming without looking at the clock.
So when the Great Day spins around, remember, without fail,
This little lesson you have learned from Turkey-Lurkey's tale.
And when you see your heaping plate, don't let your promise wobble!
Remember you've made up your mind that you will never gobble!
For here's a day that means much more than all the food we bring,
So let your heart be filled with thanks and grateful praises sing!

(*Curtains close as children on stage sing any appropriate Thanksgiving song.*)

THE END

Strictly Puritan

Characters

JUDY CHALMERS
BARBARA BRISTOW
FERN DWYER
VERA JACKSON
SARA BLANCHARD
DEBBY COOPER
GRIFF JONES
TOBY TANNER
OFFICER KERR
MISS STEVENS
MRS. CHALMERS
SABINA RYNKIEWYCZ

TIME: *The week before Thanksgiving.*

SETTING: *The recreation room of the Chalmers home.*

AT RISE: *At the fireplace,* JUDY *is patiently turning an improvised spit. Kneeling at the hearth,* FERN *is attempting to pound kernels of dried corn.* BARBARA, *a chairman of the Menu Committee, is seated at a long table at center, arguing with* VERA. SARA *sits beside* BARBARA.

VERA: Who ever heard of a Thanksgiving party without pumpkin pie?

BARBARA: And how many times must I tell you this is a Puritan party? We're serving a strictly Puritan menu and Puritans didn't have pumpkin pie.

VERA: How do you know? Pumpkin pie is a traditional old-fashioned American dish. The recipe says so.

BARBARA: And the recipe also says *two cups of milk!* The Puritans didn't have milk! There were no cows in Plymouth until 1624. So there!

VERA: Well, I don't see why we have to be so fussy! My mother makes delicious pumpkin pies and she's promised to bake all we want.

BARBARA (*Shaking her head in despair*): Vera, you just don't try to understand! Your mother would bake those pies in an electric oven. She'd use milk and eggs and sugar and spices and all sorts of things the Puritans couldn't possibly have had. Imagine the Puritans cooking with Crisco or Spry or any of our prepared shortenings! Don't you remember how Miss Stevens impressed on us that they had to make everything themselves? And that's what we're going to do! That's the whole point of the Puritan Party!

FERN (*Pounding corn*): Ouch! Now I've pounded my finger! I don't see how the Puritans ever got their corn pounded into meal. I've hammered at this till my arm aches, and I'm getting no place fast! I give up.

SARA: Oh, you can't do that, Fern. Wait till Griff and Toby come. They're good at pounding. After all, we simply have to have corn meal.

FERN: Then let's buy it at market. We'll never get enough at this rate. And by the way, have you found a recipe for cornbread that doesn't call for eggs and milk?

SARA: (*Searching among books on table*): Yes. I found one in an old Colonial cookbook. It sounds easy. "Scald one pint of Indian meal (that's corn meal) with enough boiling water to make a stiff batter (about three cups). Add one teaspoon of salt. Drop on hot greased tin and bake in hot oven thirty minutes."

VERA: Oven? Where are we getting an oven? I thought everything was to be cooked over an open fire.

BARBARA: The boys are going to rig up an oven sort of like a barbecue grill. They know just how to do it.

JUDY: Well, I hope it works better than this spit Toby invented. I've been turning it for hours and this chicken leg isn't even brown.

SARA: It's too soon for anything to happen. It takes a good long time.

JUDY: I'll say it does. It's a good thing Mother gave us a chicken leg to practice on before we start on a whole turkey. (DEBBY *enters, her arms full of groceries.*)

DEBBY: Sorry I'm late, but Mother had a time parking at the Super-Market! She sure loaded me up with a lot of things.

VERA: I hope they pass inspection. Barbara here is as mean as can be! She ruled out my pumpkin pie just because the Puritans didn't have cows!

DEBBY: Oh well, mince pie is ever so much more old-fashioned! Look—I have two cans.

BARBARA (*Horrified*): Canned mince meat! Are you out of your mind? We can't use any canned goods at our party. That would spoil the whole idea. We must make everything ourselves, starting from scratch!

DEBBY: But we can't make mince meat! That takes simply ages!

JUDY: Anyhow, the Puritans wouldn't have had raisins and currants and spices and things!

BARBARA: Judy's right. No mince pie! What else do you have there?

DEBBY: Some nice celery and lettuce for salad.

ALL: Celery and lettuce!

FERN: Where would the Puritans get celery and lettuce?

BARBARA: You certainly couldn't have paid very much attention to our unit on Colonial Living this fall, Debby Cooper. What would Miss Stevens say? Celery and lettuce at a Puritan Thanksgiving Feast!

DEBBY: I did so pay attention to our unit! Anyhow I was on the handicraft committee! Didn't I spin and weave a whole napkin all by myself?

FERN: Well, we can't eat a handwoven napkin! Food is our main problem.

VERA: If Barbara keeps on censoring stuff, we won't have anything but water.

BARBARA: Don't be silly. (*Consulting book*) It says here: "Wild turkeys, geese, ducks and water fowl, fish, especially cod and shell fish; barley loaves, cornbread, and vegetables no doubt furnished the chief viands at their feast, not to speak of the five deer, brought in as an offering by the Indians."

DEBBY: And where do you think you'll get deer meat? At the Acme or the A. & P.?

BARBARA: Don't be so sarcastic! It so happens that Toby Tanner's father goes deer hunting every season, and Mrs. Tanner has some venison steak in the deep freeze.

DEBBY: Is that strictly Puritan . . . a deep freeze?

BARBARA: Oh, don't be so technical! We've got to make *some* allowances!

DEBBY: Then why can't you allow my lettuce and celery and mince pie?

SARA: We've gone into that a dozen times, Debby! Have you forgotten how enthused we all were when we started the Colonial Club in our history class? Now we're doing this special project all on our own to surprise Miss Stevens! She's even bringing a guest from the State University!

DEBBY: I still think it would be better to give them something decent to eat! But I won't argue! Here are some cranberries—raw—not in cans. We can grind them up and mix them with sugar and oranges . . .

SARA: No oranges, Debby. Oranges at that time came from Spain, and were considered great luxuries!

BARBARA (*Doubtfully*): And I really don't know about the cranberries! Remind me to look up when the cultivation of cranberries started! In the meantime, we'll let it go. I guess you're right; we can't be too technical.

FERN: I wonder how the boys are getting on with their fishing. It's pretty cold, you know. The water may be frozen.

JUDY: That doesn't stop the Eskimos. They just cut holes in the ice.

FERN: Yes, but we're not Eskimos, and besides, there's the little matter of the fish and game laws. I still don't understand how Toby and Griff expect to get a wild turkey.

BARBARA: That's their secret. They've been scouting around for days and this morning they said they're ready for the hunt.

JUDY: I hope they come back with something.

FERN: I do wish we were making some other arrangements. It all seems so uncertain.

BARBARA: What's uncertain about it?

JUDY: For one thing, the cooking. If I can't roast this one chicken leg, how are we going to do a whole turkey, complete with feathers?

SARA: I know what you mean. That worries me too.

BARBARA: I never saw such a bunch of worry-warts. What do you think we have all these books for? Here, Sara, read this.

SARA: (*Taking book and reading*): "To Pluck a Bird. Hold the bird in the left hand and commence to pull off the feathers from under the wing. Having plucked one side, take the other wing and proceed in the same manner until all the feathers are removed. Another way is to plunge the bird into hot but not boiling water for one minute and then pull out the feathers."

BARBARA: See. It's really quite simple, isn't it?

SARA: I don't know yet. I'll tell you after we've tried it. (*Perusing the book*) Heavens! There's a lot more to it. There's a whole chapter about singeing the bird, drawing it and trussing it. It sounds dreadful. I don't think I could ever eat it.

BARBARA: Thank goodness our Puritan ancestors had stronger stomachs. (MRS. CHALMERS *enters*.)

MRS. CHALMERS: Hello, girls. How are you getting along?

JUDY: It's hard to tell, Mother. We're still at the planning stage.

MRS. CHALMERS: Well, there's a little girl up here from your room at school. She's a rather shy little thing with some sort of odd name.

JUDY: Oh dear! That's Sabina Rynkiewycz! What does she want?

MRS. CHALMERS: She wants to help with the party. Shall I send her down?

ALL: No.

MRS. CHALMERS: But why? She seems such a nice little girl.

JUDY: She's nice enough, but my goodness! You ought to see her school lunches! She brings all sorts of funny things to eat. Tell her . . . oh, dear! I don't know what you should tell her.

MRS. CHALMERS: I think I'll tell her to come down. You can at least talk to her.

JUDY: But Mother, she'll want to bring some crazy kind of food to the party.

MRS. CHALMERS: Nevertheless, I'm sending her down and you girls be nice to her. (*Exit*)

FERN: Now we're in for it.

VERA: Not necessarily. Barbara censored the rest of us; she can just rule out whatever it is Sabina wants to bring. (SABINA *enters, carrying a small covered basket.*)

JUDY: Hello, Sabina.

SABINA: Hello, girls. I hear our room at school, it is having a party . . . no?

BARBARA: Well, not exactly *everybody* in the room, Sabina. Just the Colonial Club.

SABINA: But it is for Miss Stevens, and she belongs to everybody in the room. So I thought I would bring something for the feast.

JUDY: Well, that was very nice of you, Sabina, but . . .

SABINA: In Poland, my mother she is wonderful cook. Every holiday she makes such surprises. So I bring you, how you say? Some tastes. You like the tastes, I bring you more the day of the feast. (*Opening basket*) Here . . . here I have Polish pancakes! Ummm. So good! So light! Also, I have the "Bigos" . . . That is sauerkraut with meat and apples! Umm! I know you will like when you taste. And if you want, my mother will make her very special salt cucumber soup for the party!

FERN: Oh dear! I never heard of salt cucumber soup.

SABINA: Is very good. Also I could maybe bring partridges in vine leaves, but that is very, very special indeed.

BARBARA: It's awfully good of you, Sabina, but I'm afraid you don't understand.

SABINA: You mean you don't want my good things for your feast?

BARBARA: It's not that, Sabina. It's just that we're not having anything that the Puritans didn't have at their first Thanksgiving feast. That's the surprise for Miss Stevens. She knows we are having a Thanksgiving party for her, but she doesn't know what kind. We want it to be just like our unit in school on Colonial Living.

SABINA: But I love Miss Stevens. I would like so much to help. And I am so thankful that I have her for my teacher. So good she has been to me, helping and explaining American ways. Please, can't I too make part of the feasting?

DEBBY: Oh, dear! This is getting all mixed up.

SABINA: No, no! I will not mix up. I will do just like you say.

SARA: But this is a Puritan party . . . not a Polish party!

SABINA (*Angrily*): Oh, now I understand. You don't want I should come because I am Polish! Very well. I go home. I not come again!

JUDY: No, please, Sabina, it's not that way at all. Really and truly it isn't.

SABINA (*In tears*): I thought you girls were my friends. Miss Stevens, she say, we like one family in our room. Now I know different. I am Polish, so I am not in your family, not even for Thanksgiving.

BARBARA: Please, Sabina, you have it all wrong. You are quite mistaken.

MRS. CHALMERS (*Entering in a state of excitement*): Girls! Girls! Something dreadful must have happened. There is a policeman here with two boys and Miss Stevens. They're coming right down. (*Turning and calling*) Right this way, Officer.

ALL: A policeman! Miss Stevens! What in the world is the matter?

SABINA: I hope this policeman will arrest all of you! Every single one! (*Enter* MISS STEVENS, OFFICER KERR, GRIFF *and* TOBY. GRIFF *carries fishing equipment and* TOBY *carries a large gunny sack. All are excited.*)

MISS STEVENS: I'm sure I can explain everything, officer, if you just let me talk to the children.

OFFICER: I hope so, Miss, but you'll have to talk fast.

JUDY: What's the matter, Miss Stevens?

MISS STEVENS: That's the question I'd like to ask you girls. What's going on here?

TOBY: We told the officer about the party when he arrested us but he wouldn't believe us.

BARBARA: Arrested you? What for?

OFFICER: It's plain enough, young lady. I got this one (*Pointing to* GRIFF) for fishing out of season, and this one (*Pointing to* TOBY) for illegal trespassing and stealing!

ALL: Stealing!

MRS. CHALMERS: Oh, Toby! What will your mother say?

GRIFF: Miss Stevens can explain everything. She knows Toby wouldn't steal anything, especially not a turkey.

MISS STEVENS: Of course, Officer. The boy is right. Both of these youngsters are in my class at Hudson School and they are perfectly honest and law abiding. Whatever they've done, they've had good reason.

OFFICER: They said you'd vouch for them, Miss. That's why I took them to your house before I ran them in. I hate to see boys get into serious trouble if it can be avoided.

MISS STEVENS: I'm sure there's nothing serious here, Officer, if I may just ask a few questions. Now, boys, please tell me why you got into such a mess!

BARBARA: It's for the party, Miss Stevens, the Thanksgiving party.

OFFICER: First time I ever heard of fishing and turkey stealing mixed up with Thanksgiving.

TOBY: I tell you I didn't steal that turkey. It was a wild turkey just running around in that little woods, wild as could be, so I nabbed him with my slingshot. At least give me credit for not using a gun. I knew it was against the law to carry a gun.

OFFICER: Well, at least you know that much.

MISS STEVENS: But if you children wanted turkey and fish for your feast, why didn't you buy them? I have no doubt your parents would have donated them.

MRS. CHALMERS: We certainly would, Miss Stevens. We always try to cooperate with the children.

BARBARA: But don't you see, Miss Stevens, it was to be a Puritan Party. We wanted to do everything just the way the Puritans did. The Puritans couldn't go out to market and buy a turkey. They had to hunt their own.

TOBY: And that's what Griff and I were doing. We spotted this little woods out at the edge of town and yesterday I saw a couple of turkeys out there. So this morning . . .

OFFICER: Young man, that "little woods" you keep talking about happens to be a piece of private property belonging to The American Poultry Company. It's well posted with *No Trespassing* signs too.

GRIFF: Gee whiz, Officer, we didn't see 'em. Honest!

JUDY: We wanted it to be a strictly Puritan Party, Miss Stevens, like the first Thanksgiving we studied about in our unit on colonial life.

SARA: We thought we could do everything just like the Puritans, only, I must say we've had a pretty hard time.

OFFICER (*Sniffing*): I smell smoke. Something's on fire!

JUDY: Oh dear me! That's our chicken leg! (*Rushing to fireplace*) It's burned to a crisp!

OFFICER *and* MISS STEVENS: Chicken leg!

OFFICER: Is that stolen too?

MRS. CHALMERS: Indeed not! I gave Judy the chicken leg. She told me she wanted to try an experiment in cooking.

MISS STEVENS: Well, from the looks of it, it didn't turn out too well.

VERA: I guess we'd have had even more trouble with a whole turkey.

OFFICER: Bless my stars! Don't tell me you were going to cook a whole turkey in that fireplace!

VERA: All but the feathers. We were going to remove them.

MISS STEVENS (*Laughing*): Well, I must say you've made a noble effort and in a good cause too. Officer, I really think these boys and girls had the very best of intentions. They just didn't realize how modern laws would interfere with good old American customs. Can't you dismiss the charges this time, if I vouch for the fact that there will be no further trouble?

OFFICER (*Doubtfully*): Well, I'd like to, Miss, even though the whole thing sounds sort of screw-ballish to me! But there's still the matter of that turkey.

BARBARA: Couldn't we all pitch in and help pay for it?

ALL: I'd be willing to pay my share.

OFFICER: Tell you what I'll do. I'll take the matter up with Mr. Stern from the Poultry Company and see what he says. In the meantime, I guess it will be safe to leave these two sportsmen right here.

MRS. CHALMERS: Oh, yes, Officer. Yes indeed.

OFFICER: And one thing more. You kids find some other way to celebrate Thanksgiving. Don't get your dates mixed. This is 1958, not 1492!

BARBARA: Now you've got your dates mixed, Officer! The Pilgrims didn't come to America till 1620.

OFFICER: Well, history never was my long suit, but I think you get what I mean just the same. You boys and girls have a safe and sane modern Thanksgiving and forget about the Puritans. Goodbye, Miss, and thank you. As for you, (*Pointing to boys*) don't let me catch you trespassing again . . . or fishing out of season either.

BOYS: No sir! (*Exit* OFFICER KERR)

MISS STEVENS: Well! What an afternoon! I was never more surprised in my life than when that policeman showed up at my house with you two boys.

TOBY: We thought you'd talk up for us, Miss Stevens, if we could get him to see you.

GRIFF: Thanks a lot. I thought sure we were in for trouble.

BARBARA: I think he is a dreadful policeman. I don't even believe he's a real American.

MISS STEVENS: Why, Barbara! What a thing to say!

BARBARA: Well, did you hear what he said? "Forget about the Puritans!" No good American would forget about the Puritans at Thanksgiving time.

MISS STEVENS: He didn't mean it that way, Barbara. He just meant that each generation must celebrate Thanksgiving in its own way and according to its own customs!

But I do think it was lovely of you to plan a whole Puritan Party. Did everybody in the room help?

SABINA: No. No, Miss Stevens. Not everybody. I wanted to help! Oh, so badly I want to help. But they say "No" . . . because I am Polish.

MISS STEVENS: Oh dear! That doesn't sound like anyone in our room!

JUDY: No, Miss Stevens. Sabina doesn't understand. We were serving only Puritan foods, and so when she offered to bring some Polish dishes, Barbara, who's chairman of the Menu Committee, said "No.'

BARBARA: I wouldn't let Vera bring her pumpkin pie either.

DEBBY: And I couldn't use my mince meat, or my celery or the nice lettuce Mother bought at the supermarket.

BARBARA: You see it was to be strictly Puritan . . . just the way you taught us in school.

MISS STEVENS: Maybe I didn't teach you everything in school. Maybe we forgot one thing when we had our Colonial unit and the story of the first Thanksgiving. Actually you children can still have your Puritan feast if you want it.

DEBBY: How can we? It's all spoiled now.

MISS STEVENS: Oh, no, it isn't. You see, boys and girls, it isn't the food that makes a Puritan Thanksgiving. It's the spirit in which the food is eaten. You see, the Puritans used the very best foods they had for their feast. You can do the same. Use the very best foods you can obtain. And another thing! The Puritans invited *everybody* in their community, all their neighbors, all their friends, even the strangers, the Indians who didn't understand their customs.

TOBY: I told you we should have invited all the kids, not just the Colonial Club.

MISS STEVENS: If you plan to go ahead with your party, I think that would be a very good idea. And as for Sabina's Polish treat, I'll tell you a little secret. There's nothing I like better in the world than Polish pancakes!

SABINA: Really and truly?

MISS STEVENS: Really and truly! When I was a little girl, our nextdoor neighbor used to bake them and invite me over for supper just to see me stuff myself!

SABINA: My mother will let you stuff yourself anytime you'd like to come.

MISS STEVENS: Thank you, dear. And one thing more about those Puritans, boys and girls. They were never afraid to try something new, especially if it was something to eat. Remember, they would never have tasted corn or discovered it was good to eat if they hadn't received it as a gift from the Indians. The Indians also showed them lots of other good things they had never tasted. Does that give you any ideas?

BARBARA: It sure does, Miss Stevens, and if you'll still come to our Thanksgiving party next week, we'll have those Polish pancakes. That is, if Sabina will bring them.

SABINA: Oh, I will, I will. Now I can be strictly Puritan too.

THE END

Thanks to Butter-Fingers

Characters

MRS. UPTON, *a collector of antiques*
DEAN, *her teen-age son*
CHARLOTTE, *her ten-year-old daughter*
BETSY, *her ten-year-old niece*
DR. RINEHART, *an antique expert*

TIME: *Thanksgiving Day.*
SETTING: *The dining room of the Upton home.*
AT RISE: MRS. UPTON *and* CHARLOTTE *are arranging the centerpiece of fruit and autumn leaves on the table.* DEAN *is repairing an electric coffeepot at a side table. There is a brief pause, followed by a terrific crash that sounds as if an atom bomb had struck the kitchen.*

MRS. UPTON: Good heavens! What has she broken now?
CHARLOTTE: Sounds as if she knocked every plate out of the cupboard. If she stays much longer, we won't have a dish left.
MRS. UPTON: Charlotte! What a thing to say about your cousin! Remember she's our guest! But I must admit I never saw such a child. She's a regular butter-fingers! Drops everything she touches.

DEAN: Why are you two always picking on Betsy, Mom? She seems like a good kid!

MRS. UPTON: We're *not* picking on her, Dean. And she *is* a lovely child, in her way. If only she'd learn to keep her hands off things.

DEAN: But, Mom, you know how kids are. She wants to help. And with Aunt Frances and Uncle Buck in Europe I guess she feels pretty homesick right now. (*Enter* BETSY *with a stack of plates.*)

BETSY (*Cheerfully*): Did you hear the crash, Aunt Martha? I just dropped the dishpan and knocked the meat grinder off the kitchen table.

MRS. UPTON: So that's what it was! Heavens, child, put down those plates before you drop them.

CHARLOTTE: You should know better than to carry so many at a time. After all, they're Mommy's best china.

BETSY: Well, I didn't drop a single one, so there! (*Trips slightly but lands the plates safely on the table.*) What can I do now, Aunt Martha?

MRS. UPTON (*With a shudder*): Why don't you start peeling the potatoes while Charlotte and I finish the table?

BETSY: But, Aunt Martha, I hate to peel potatoes, and these dishes are so beautiful. Please let me help. I promise to be careful.

DEAN: Have a heart, Mom.

MRS. UPTON: All right. I guess you could lay the silver. It's in the kitchen. You can bring in the tray of glassware, Charlotte. But do be careful. (*Two girls start for kitchen.*)

CHARLOTTE: But, Mommy, I'm always careful. You say yourself I *never* break anything. (*Exit* CHARLOTTE *and* BETSY)

DEAN: Isn't that Charlotte getting a little on the prissy side, Mom? (*Mocking his sister*) "I *never* break anything." That's the kind of talk that makes you feel like breaking her little neck.

MRS. UPTON: Don't even use the word *breaking*, Dean. That little Betsy breaks enough stuff for the whole family. Oh, well, she goes back to school tomorrow. I only hope she and Charlotte can manage to stay friends that long. They've fought like cats and dogs ever since they were little.

DEAN: I guess they're just jealous of each other, Mom.

MRS. UPTON: Jealous? What on earth would they have to be jealous of?

DEAN: Don't ask me. But you know how girls are. (*Enter* CHARLOTTE *and* BETSY, *each with a tray.*)

BETSY: Here we are, Aunt Martha, and I didn't so much as drop a single spoon.

MRS. UPTON (*To* CHARLOTTE): Careful with the tray, dear. I wouldn't want anything to happen to those glasses. (*Both girls set down trays.*)

BETSY: You have such beautiful dishes, Aunt Martha. They must be terribly expensive.

MRS. UPTON: I'm glad you like them, dear. You see, these are not only *good* dishes, Betsy, they're also very *old* dishes. They're antiques and they can't be replaced.

DEAN: Then why are we using them, Mom? These "anticues" of yours always make me nervous.

MRS. UPTON: We're using them because Dr. Rinehart is coming for dinner, dear. Now I really must look at the turkey. (*Exit* MRS. UPTON)

BETSY: Who's Dr. Rinehart?

DEAN: Oh, he's some sort of "anti-cue" bug that knows all about cracked sugar bowls and teapots.

CHARLOTTE: Don't be silly, Dean. Dr. Rinehart writes articles for magazines and takes colored pictures of beautiful table settings. Mommy's just dying to have him take some pictures of our dishes. And besides, she thinks he might want to feature the bride sugar bowl in his exhibit.

BETSY (*With great interest*): The bride sugar bowl! What in the world is that?

DEAN: Just an old sugar bowl that looks like a cross between a wash bowl and a coffeepot.

CHARLOTTE: Dean, you're terrible. Don't believe a thing he says, Betsy. The bride sugar bowl is over two hundred years old. It was brought over from England by the first Upton family who came to America.

BETSY: But why is it called the bride sugar bowl?

CHARLOTTE: Because it's always been handed down to the first bride in the family.

BETSY: Isn't that romantic! Where is it? I'm dying to see it.

CHARLOTTE: It's in the china closet . . . way in the back. (*As* BETSY *runs toward closet*) You'll see it later. Nobody's allowed to touch it but Mommy.

DEAN: You might as well tell her the rest of the story, Sis —all about the poor little Southern bride who disappeared during the Civil War.

CHARLOTTE: That was Great-grandmother's youngest sister, Delia Upton. Their plantation was burned by the soldiers. She escaped with the sugar bowl, but while she was running in the darkness, she fell over a big boulder and was killed. The sugar bowl wasn't even nicked.

BETSY: You mean the sugar bowl was the only thing she saved out of the whole house?

DEAN: That's all. Everything else was destroyed. But

there's the old sugar bowl safe and sound in the china closet this very minute. After an adventure like that, no wonder it's a museum piece.

BETSY: It all sounds sort of corny to me.

CHARLOTTE: Corny? What do you mean by corny?

BETSY: Well, don't you think it was sort of dumb of your ancestor to save a silly thing like a sugar bowl?

DEAN: Careful, Betsy, my girl, she's *your* ancestor too, you know.

BETSY: She is?

DEAN: Of course. We're both Uptons, aren't we? Grandpa Upton had two sons, your dad and ours.

BETSY: Well, what do you know? You mean I'm part owner of the sugar bowl?

CHARLOTTE: Of course not. It belongs to Mommy.

DEAN: Actually, Sis, it belongs to Dad. Grandma got the sugar bowl when she was a bride, and since she had no daughters, she gave it to the first son who brought home a bride and that was Dad.

CHARLOTTE: And Dad will give it to me when I am a bride.

BETSY: How do you know? If the *first* bride in the family gets the sugar bowl, how do you know it won't be *me?*

DEAN (*Laughing*): Now, there's a point we never figured on, did we, Sis?

CHARLOTTE: But you *couldn't* get the sugar bowl. You couldn't! It belongs to me. Mommy always said it would be mine when I get married. How dare you say it will be yours?

DEAN: Oh, for Pete's sake! Two kids not even twelve years old, fighting about who will be the first bride.

CHARLOTTE: But she won't be the first bride. She won't! She won't!

DEAN: O.K., so she won't. I'm going down to the cellar for an extension cord. You two can fight it out and may the best woman win. (*Exit*)

BETSY: Just what makes you so sure I couldn't be a bride as quick as you, Charlotte Upton? I'm quicker at everything else. I can jump rope faster and I can swim faster. You're nothing but an old slowpoke.

CHARLOTTE: Is that so? Well, that just goes to show how much you know about getting a husband. It has nothing to do with jumping or swimming. You have to be beautiful.

BETSY: Beautiful! You think *you're* beautiful. Ha! I wouldn't have those sissy blonde curls on a bet. Boys don't like curls either, except to pull them.

CHARLOTTE: I suppose you think boys are crazy about pigtails? Well, you'll find out! Besides, a bride's got to be good at housework, and you're nothing but an old butter-fingers. You drop everything you touch.

BETSY: I do not! And who said I was a butter-fingers?

CHARLOTTE: My own mother said so!

BETSY: I don't believe you. Aunt Martha likes having me here. She told Mother she did.

CHARLOTE: Well, she doesn't like to have you break all our dishes.

BETSY: I never broke a single dish—just a lamp and two flower vases. And I don't believe Aunt Martha ever said that.

CHARLOTTE: She did too.

BETSY (*Doubling up her fist and starting toward* CHARLOTTE): Charlotte Upton, if you're making this up . . . I'll . . .

CHARLOTTE (*Picks up glass off table*): Don't you dare

touch me, don't you dare! (*Glass slips out of her hands and breaks*)

BETSY (*Triumphantly*): There! See what you did? You *threw* that glass at me.

CHARLOTTE (*Almost in tears*): I did *not* throw it. It slipped. It was an accident. Oh dear! It's one of Mother's real crystals. (*Enter* MRS. UPTON.)

MRS. UPTON: Well, how are you two getting along? Is the table ready? (*Sees the broken glass*) Oh, Betsy, how on earth did you manage to break this? I distinctly told you to lay the silver and keep your hands off the glass and china.

BETSY: But Aunt Martha, I . . .

MRS. UPTON: You're a regular little butter-fingers! Charlotte, go get the dustpan and broom and help me sweep this up. Betsy, you might as well go to your room and stay there till it's time for dinner. And while you're there, change your dress and comb your hair. We're having guests for dinner, remember? (CHARLOTTE *exits*)

BETSY: Yes, Aunt Martha, I remember.

MRS. UPTON: And try not to touch anything breakable in the bedroom. I bet your mother is grateful for the invention of plastics. (*Calling*) Charlotte, hurry up with that broom and dustpan. Oh well, I'd better get them myself. (*Exit*)

BETSY (*Bursting into tears*): I didn't break that hateful old glass! And I am *not* a butter-fingers. I'll show them! They'll be sorry they ever called me *butter-fingers!* (*Rushes out of room in a storm of tears.* MRS. UPTON *and* CHARLOTTE *enter and begin to sweep up glass.*)

MRS. UPTON: This just makes me sick. Now my set is broken.

CHARLOTTE (*Slowly with much swallowing between*

words): Mommy, I don't think you should blame Betsy for breaking the glass. It was . . . well . . . it was an accident.

MRS. UPTON: Of course, dear. They're all accidents. I realize she doesn't go around breaking things on purpose. But that doesn't make me feel any better about my glass.

CHARLOTTE (*Glumly*): No, I suppose not.

MRS. UPTON (*Sweeping glass into dustpan that* CHARLOTTE *is holding*): There! I guess we got it all. Now please dump it in the rubbish, and then come back and finish the table. I have to go pick up Dr. Rinehart and his equipment. Please, dear, try to do a good job with the table and help keep Betsy from any more accidents till I get back.

CHARLOTTE (*Meekly*): I'll try, Mommy. (MRS. UPTON *and* CHARLOTTE *exit at opposite sides of the stage. There is a brief pause and* DEAN *enters, carrying a long narrow piece of plywood and an extension cord.*)

DEAN: Well, gals, have you finally decided who's gonna be the first Upton bride? (*Shrugs his shoulders as he sees the room is empty.*) Hum! They must have gone to slug it out with boxing gloves. Oh well, I have my own troubles with this extension cord and Mom's antique table that wobbles. Maybe this board will fix that. (*Puts plywood board on chair and crawls under table with the extension cord where he is almost completely out of sight*) Now why do the electric outlets always have to be at such impossible places? (*He is barely out of sight when* BETSY *enters with a large cold cream jar.*)

BETSY: *Butter-fingers,* am I? Well, I'll soon show them who's a *butter-fingers.* (*Goes to table and starts putting plates and glasses around at place settings. Stands back and surveys her work.*) Umm! Very nice, if I do say so myself! And Miss Butter-Fingers didn't drop a single glass or plate! (DEAN *has crawled partly out from under the table and watches this scene in amazement.* BETSY *opens the cold cream jar and starts greasing the bottom of each plate and glass*) I think this cocoa butter will do the trick. (*Giggles*) I can hardly wait till they start passing their plates up to Uncle Harry. (*On this speech she bursts into chuckles.* DEAN *emerges from under table and grabs her.*)

DEAN: So you can't wait, can't you? Well, here's something I just can't wait to do for you. (*Drags her to chair and picks up his piece of plywood which he brandishes as a paddle*) It's high time you learn what happens to a little girl who deliberately plays a dirty trick on Thanksgiving Day.

BETSY (*Yelling*) Please, Dean. That isn't fair. Give me a chance.

DEAN (*Putting down the paddle*): O.K. But talk fast. What was the big idea of greasing all those dishes?

BETSY: So the rest of this family would know how it feels to be a butter-fingers.

DEAN: And break all of Mom's good dishes, just like you broke the other stuff, is that it?

BETSY: But I didn't break it all, Dean. Not the glass.

DEAN: What glass?

BETSY: The glass that Charlotte broke and blamed on me.

DEAN: Charlotte did a trick like that?

BETSY: Well, she didn't exactly *say* I broke it, but she didn't say *she* did, so naturally Aunt Martha thought it was Butter-fingers again.

DEAN (*Grimly*): I see. I think I'll have a double use for

this paddle. Just where is my darling little sister at this minute?

BETSY (*Starting to cry*): I don't know. I didn't mean to tell on her, honest I didn't. Oh dear, Charlotte hates me, and Aunt Martha says I'm a butter-fingers and now you hate me, too!

DEAN: No, I don't, Betsy. And what's more I think I know *why* you're a butter-fingers.

BETSY (*Through her tears*): Why? Just because I'm a wicked, careless girl?

DEAN (*Laughing*): Not at all. Just because you happen to need a pair of specs, just like mine. When I was a kid about your age, Betsy, the fellows on our block all called me *lunk-head* because I could never hit a ball. But the trouble wasn't my head. It was my eyes. I think that's your trouble too. You'll find the answer to your problem not in your fingers but in your peepers.

BETSY: Oh, Dean, do you really think so?

DEAN: Sure I do. And as soon as your Mother and Dad come back, you talk it over with them.

BETSY: Oh, I will! I will! And I'm sorry about the plates. I'll wipe them off again real quick and nobody will ever know. (*Enter* CHARLOTTE. *She sees* DEAN *and* BETSY *and stops short*)

CHARLOTTE (*To* BETSY): I thought you were supposed to be in your room.

DEAN: She's right where she's supposed to be at this minute, Charlotte, and if you know what's good for you, you'll sit down in the other chair before I start using this paddle.

CHARLOTTE: Why, Dean Upton, what are you talking about?

DEAN: I'm talking about administering justice to a certain sister of mine who would let her cousin take the blame for a glass she broke.

CHARLOTTE (*Turning on* BETSY): Why, you little tattle-tale!

DEAN (*Seizing her arm and pushing her into a chair*): Quiet! We've had enough name calling in this house. Now we're going to have justice here and fast. Ever since you two girls were knee-high to grasshoppers you've fought every time you've been together. You fought over dolls, over dresses, over games and today you even fought over husbands. Now this is the end. Thanksgiving is for families and families should like each other, be grateful for each other.

CHARLOTTE: Well, I'm not grateful for her! She's spoiled my whole Thanksgiving and made me break one of Mother's glasses.

BETSY: I'm not grateful for you either. You said I was ugly and would never get married first and called me a butter-fingers.

DEAN: Well, here's news for you. I'm giving you exactly five minutes to think of five good reasons why you're thankful for each other. So start thinking.

CHARLOTTE: I couldn't think of five reasons to be thankful for *her* in five months.

BETSY: It would take me five years.

DEAN: That's very bad. Because if you don't come across with those reasons in five minutes, I'm going to turn each one of you across my knee and wallop you five times with this paddle. Take your choice.

CHARLOTTE: Dean Upton, I'll tell Mother on you.

DEAN: She won't be home till it's too late.

BETSY: Golly, Charlotte, I think he means it. We'd better get started.

CHARLOTTE (*In a wail*): But I can't think of any reason to be grateful for you.

BETSY: Well, I'm gonna try. (*Squeezes her eyes shut as if thinking hard, then opens them*) How much time have we?

DEAN (*With watch in hand*): Not too much. Make it snappy.

BETSY: O.K. I'm ready. I'm thankful I have a cousin with such beautiful blue eyes and golden curls.

CHARLOTTE: That's no fair. That doesn't count. You told me just this afternoon you hated my curls.

BETSY (*Shyly*): I know. But I never really hated them, Charlotte. I guess I *said* I hated them because I wanted them myself instead of these ugly pigtails.

CHARLOTTE: Do you really mean that?

BETSY (*Earnestly*): Yes, I do.

CHARLOTTE: Well, then, I guess I've found something to be thankful for. I'm thankful I have a cousin who is so good at games and always comes in first at all the races.

BETSY: But I thought you hated games. You always said they weren't ladylike.

CHARLOTTE: I said that because I couldn't do them. I'm the slowest runner in the whole school and you know it.

BETSY: Golly, this isn't so hard after all. I'm thankful I have a cousin who is always so neat and clever around the house. I'm never allowed to do anything at home except nasty things like making beds and peeling potatoes.

CHARLOTTE: I'm thankful I have a cousin who isn't afraid to climb trees and doesn't mind getting dirty or tearing her dresses. I think she must lead an exciting life.

BETSY: Not very exciting. Just messy, I'm afraid. I'm thankful I have a cousin to come to visit on Thanksgiving Day when my parents are away from home.

CHARLOTTE: Why, this is really beginning to be fun. I'm thankful I have a cousin who visits me on Thanksgiving Day because we can do things together. It's almost like having a sister.

BETSY: How are we doing, Dean?

DEAN: Fine and dandy. But keep it up. You have two more to go.

BETSY: O.K. I'm thankful I have a cousin who is sweet and pretty enough to be the first bride of the Upton family.

CHARLOTTE: And I'm glad I have a cousin who's smart and clever enough to give me a good race.

DEAN (*Laughing*): Hey, this is going a bit too far.

BETSY: No it isn't. For number five, I'm thankful I have a cousin who has a brother who threatened to beat some sense into us if we didn't start appreciating each other.

CHARLOTTE: And I'm thankful I have a cousin who is such a good sport about everything including her butter-fingers!

DEAN: Charlotte!

BETSY (*Laughing*): I don't care, Dean. That name doesn't make me mad any more now that Charlotte and I are friends as well as cousins.

CHARLOTTE: Now put down that awful paddle. It makes me nervous.

DEAN: I'm going to put it right where it belongs, under the table legs to stop that wobbling. Now you two get busy and wipe that cocoa butter off those plates. (*Crawls under table with paddle.*)

CHARLOTTE: Cocoa butter? I don't understand.

BETSY: I was trying to make butter-fingers of all of you, Charlotte, by greasing the plates with Aunt Martha's cocoa butter. Come on and help me wipe it off before she arrives with Dr. Rinehart.

CHARLOTTE: I'll get a cloth. (*Exit*)

BETSY (*To* DEAN *under the table*): I'll never forget this Thanksgiving, Dean, even if I live to see my granddaughter get the bride sugar bowl. (CHARLOTTE *enters with two dishcloths. Girls wipe the plates and glasses quickly.*) Doesn't the table look pretty?

CHARLOTTE: Beautiful. I do hope Dr. Rinehart will take some pictures.

DEAN (*Emerging from under table*): Well, if he does, he'll find the table is perfectly level. (*Enter* MRS. UPTON *with* DR. RINEHART *who carries a flash camera.*)

MRS. UPTON (*Removing wraps and taking* DR. RINEHART'S *coat*): Here we are, Dr. Rinehart. Dean, will you take our wraps upstairs, please? My son, Dr. Rinehart. (*They acknowledge introductions and* DEAN *exits with coats*) And this is my little niece, Betsy, whose parents are abroad this winter.

BETSY: Good afternoon, Dr. Rinehart.

DR. RINEHART: Hello, Betsy.

MRS. UPTON: And, of course, you already know my daughter, Charlotte.

DR. RINEHART: Happy Thanksgiving, Charlotte. Did you help set this gorgeous table?

CHARLOTTE: Betsy helped me, Dr. Rinehart. (MRS. UPTON *looks at* CHARLOTTE *in surprise.*)

DR. RINEHART: And do you like antique dishes, Betsy?

BETSY: I think they're beautiful, sir, but I don't know very much about them. I never even heard of the bride sugar bowl until today. (*Reenter* DEAN)

DR. RINEHART: Ah, yes, the bride sugar bowl. That is the piece I've been hoping to borrow and photograph for our Early American Exhibit, Mrs. Upton. I'm so anxious to see it.

MRS. UPTON: It's right here in the china closet. (*To* DEAN) Will you get it down, please, dear?

DEAN: Oh gosh! Why pick on me? Suppose I drop it?

MRS. UPTON: You won't, and you're tall enough to reach it. (DEAN *gets sugar bowl from closet and hands it to* DR. RINEHART *who inspects it carefully.*)

DR. RINEHART: Beautiful! Beautiful! In fact I may say exquisite! As perfect a piece as I have ever seen, Mrs. Upton. You realize, of course, that this piece is worth quite a sum?

MRS. UPTON: Oh, yes, but we'd never dream of letting it go out of the family. You see, the tradition is that it always goes to the first Upton bride. Since we have only two girls in the family, it will go either to Charlotte or Betsy here.

DR. RINEHART: Well, I must say they're a bit young to be thinking of that right now. But since you are the heiresses apparent, how would you like to be photographed holding the precious bowl?

CHARLOTTE: But I'm never allowed to touch it.

BETSY: I'd be frightened to death to as much as breathe on it.

MRS. UPTON: Nonsense, girls. If Dr. Rinehart wants to take a picture, it will be all right.

CHARLOTTE: Well, it *would* be dreadful to break it now, after all it's been through.

BETSY: I still can't see why that little Southern bride would have let the whole house burn down and save nothing but a sugar bowl.

MRS. UPTON: Heirlooms are always precious, my dear.

DR. RINEHART (*Posing girls*): Now you little ladies stand right here in front of the table, holding the bowl like this. (*Gives bowl to* CHARLOTTE)

BETSY (*Picking up the lid by the knob*): Maybe I could be looking inside like this . . . (*Drops lid. Everyone screams.*)

MRS. UPTON (*Clutching a chair, her eyes closed*): I can't bear to look.

DR. RINEHART (*Scrambling around on the floor*): I regret to say, Mrs. Upton, the knob and lid are now two pieces.

MRS. UPTON: Ruined! That beautiful piece is absolutely ruined! Betsy! Betsy! How could you?

CHARLOTTE (*Setting bowl on table and putting her arms around* BETSY): It wasn't Betsy's fault, Mother. She barely lifted the lid and the knob came off.

DEAN (*Also on floor*): Let me see those pieces. (*Picks up knob and lid.*)

BETSY (*Running to* DEAN *who is studying the lid and knob*): Oh, Dean, I *am* a butter-fingers. It wasn't my eyes this time. It just fell out of my hand.

DEAN: I know it did, Betsy. And do you know why? Because this piece had been broken long before you ever touched it. Look, you can see little pieces of gritty cement around the edges.

DR. RINEHART: Nonsense! I am an expert. I would have detected it. That was a perfect piece.

DEAN: Sorry to disagree, but that sugar bowl lid had been mended ages ago. The cement or glue or whatever was used had dried out and when Betsy picked it up, the weight of the lid made the lid and the knob part company. (*Leaning over suddenly and picking something up off the floor*) And if you don't believe me, here's proof.

ALL (*Crowding round*): What? What is it?

CHARLOTTE: Why it's a diamond ring.

MRS. UPTON: Where did it come from?

DR. RINEHART (*Examining the ring*): Why bless me! It's a fabulous antique setting. To whom does this belong?

MRS. UPTON: I have no idea.

DEAN: I have. It must have belonged to the little bride who saved the sugar bowl from the great fire. She wasn't saving the sugar bowl. She was saving her ring from the marauding soldiers.

DR. RINEHART: Young man, you really have something there. She doubtless concealed her most valuable and cherished possession from the enemy by sealing it between the knob and the lid of the sugar bowl.

BETSY: And because she was killed, no one ever knew it was there.

CHARLOTTE: And we wouldn't know it yet if it hadn't been for Betsy.

DR. RINEHART: If this ring is worth what I think it is, a vote of thanks is highly in order.

MRS. UPTON: Betsy, dear, you gave us a bad scare, but we're certainly thankful for your discovery.

CHARLOTTE: Now we have a family heirloom that's really worth inheriting.

DEAN: But remember, it still goes to the first Upton bride, girls. So the race is still on.

DR. RINEHART: What a story this will make in my magazine.

DEAN: What a story this has already made! Can't you get

on with that picture-taking, Dr. Rinehart? I'm beginning to feel every symptom of starvation.

MRS. UPTON: Yes, it is getting late. Mr. Upton and the boys will come charging in here any minute ready to declare war on that turkey.

DR. RINEHART: It will take only a second, Mrs. Upton. Which of the girls will display the ring?

CHARLOTTE: Let Betsy wear it, Mother. After all, we owe it all to her.

MRS. UPTON: That's a fine idea, Charlotte. (*Putting ring on* BETSY'S *finger*) Here, dear, here's your first chance to wear the family heirloom. Maybe some day you can wear it for keeps.

BETSY: Oh, thank you, Aunt Martha. I never knew I'd live to see the day I'd be thankful for being a butter-fingers. But I really am.

MRS. UPTON: Thanks to those butter-fingers we've solved our little mystery of the sugar bowl and found a valuable jewel.

CHARLOTTE: And thanks to butter-fingers, and to Dean, Betsy and I have discovered that the best part of a family Thanksgiving is being thankful for each other.

THE END

Mr. Snow White's Thanksgiving

Characters

TINKER FOSTER } *owners of Mr. Snow White*
HONEY FOSTER }
MR. FOSTER, *a farmer*
MRS. FOSTER, *his wife*
MARY ROBERTS, *a neighbor*
MR. BLODGET, *a guest*
MRS. BLODGET, *a guest*

TIME: *The day before Thanksgiving.*
SETTING: *Living room of the Foster farmhouse.*
AT RISE: MRS. FOSTER *is seated at a small desk or table left stage, laboriously typing the last few words of a letter. She then removes the original and three carbons with a sigh of relief.*

MRS. FOSTER: There! I'm glad that's done. I'd rather cook three meals a day than type three letters a month. (*Calling*) Hiram! Hiram! Your letters are ready to be signed.

MR. FOSTER (*Entering. He wears jeans, a short heavy coat, a cap, scarf, and gloves.*): I just got in from the barn.

Mighty cold outside. Looks like snow too. I bet we'll have a white Thanksgiving this year.

MRS. FOSTER: We'll really have a lot to be thankful for, if we sell the house on the hill and the wood lot.

MR. FOSTER: I hate to part with my grandfather's old home, but we can't run both places. We can put something aside for the children's education if we get our price.

MRS. FOSTER: I thought sure the Blodgets would take it. They liked the idea of having all that land around them.

MR. FOSTER (*Shaking his head*): I wonder what they plan to do with the land.

MRS. FOSTER: Maybe they just want to look at it—*if* they want to buy the place. But we haven't heard a word from them. I did think they'd answer my note asking them here for Thanksgiving, even if they weren't interested in the house.

MR. FOSTER: Now, Sarah, don't be so impatient. You know how slow the mails are.

MRS. FOSTER: That's so, and if you want these ads to go in the papers by Monday, you'd better sign them. We can send Tinker down to the mailbox at the crossroads.

MR. FOSTER: Consarn it! My pen's upstairs. I'll sign them later. (*Inspecting letters*) These look very nice. Folks will think I have a real secretary when they see these neat letters.

MRS. FOSTER: I'm afraid I'm a better cook than a typist. You'll have to wait for Tinker and Honey to grow up and do your office work.

MR. FOSTER: By the way, where is that pair? I haven't see them since breakfast.

MRS. FOSTER: It wouldn't be hard to guess where they are.

They spend every minute hanging over that turkey coop, mooning over Mr. Snow White!

MR. FOSTER (*Snorting*): Mr. Snow White! Did you ever hear a sillier name for a turkey gobbler?

MRS. FOSTER: Oh, Hiram, what are you going to do about him?

MR. FOSTER (*Grimly*): Do about him? What do we usually do about a turkey at Thanksgiving time?

MRS. FOSTER: Yes, but . . . oh, Hiram, none of us will be able to eat a bite. After all, it isn't every year the children raise a prize-winning turkey.

MR. FOSTER: It beats all, doesn't it, that our whole turkey crop should have been a failure, all except this one I gave the children. But that's the way it is!

MRS. FOSTER: I never dreamed he'd win the blue ribbon at the Farm Show!

MR. FOSTER: Neither did I. But blue ribbon or no blue ribbon, we have to have Thanksgiving dinner.

MRS. FOSTER: But, Hiram, don't you think. . . .

MR. FOSTER: Now, Sarah, don't *you* start! The children are giving me a bad time as it is!

MRS. FOSTER: Oh dear! Well, I suppose they'll get over it! When . . . when are you counting on . . . well, you know? When are you counting on doing it?

MR. FOSTER (*Laughing*): Sarah, you sound as if I were planning to commit a crime, instead of killing a turkey for our own table. I haven't thought that much about it. Sometime this morning, probably.

MRS. FOSTER (*Rising*): Well, I'll have to get the children out of the way. (*Phone*) Oh dear! Maybe that's a call from the Blodgets. (*At phone*) Hello! Oh, hello, Betsy. Oh my! That's too bad. Why, of course, I'll come right away. In the meantime, you call Dr. Phelps. Now don't try to move her, dear, and I'll be there as fast as I can. (*Hangs up*)

MR. FOSTER: Now what?

MRS. FOSTER: That was Betsy King. Her mother just fell down the cellar stairs, and seems to have broken her ankle. I'll have to go right over there.

MR. FOSTER: Golly! That's tough luck. And the day before Thanksgiving too.

MRS. FOSTER: Be sure to tell the children where I've gone. I'll be back as soon as I can. (*Takes coat and scarf from clothes tree*)

MR. FOSTER (*As* MRS. FOSTER *exits*): I'd better go back to the barn. I didn't like the look of old Ben's left front foot this morning. (*As he is about to exit,* TINKER *and* HONEY *enter. They also wear outside clothing which they remove and hang on clothes tree.*)

TINKER: Hello, Dad. Where's Mom?

MR. FOSTER: Betsy King called. Her mother fell down the cellar steps, and your mother's gone over there to help out!

HONEY: Oh, dear! I hope Mrs. King isn't hurt.

MR. FOSTER: Sounds as if she broke her ankle or something. Your mother will stay till the doctor comes.

HONEY: Gracious! Five children! And Betsy isn't old enough to get a Thanksgiving dinner.

MR. FOSTER (*Clearing his throat*): Now that reminds me. We have something to settle about our own Thanksgiving dinner.

HONEY: Oh, Father, please . . . please! You know how we feel about Mr. Snow White.

TINKER: Mr. Snow White isn't just an ordinary turkey . . . he . . . he's a champion . . . a blue ribbon turkey.

MR. FOSTER: Nevertheless, he's the only turkey we happen to have on the whole place.

HONEY: But we have chickens!

MR. FOSTER: I've told you a dozen times, Honey, we can't spare the hens, and the roosters are tough as shoe leather. We can't ask the Blodgets to sit down to roasted shoeleather, now, can we?

HONEY: Oh, the Blodgets! Why can't they eat their Thanksgiving dinner at home?

MR. FOSTER: Because they are lonely people and your mother thought they would enjoy spending Thanksgiving weekend with us. We haven't heard from them as yet, but we're expecting them to arrive sometime today. Now I must get moving. (*Starts to exit*)

TINKER: But, Dad, you're not going to . . . you're not going to . . .

MR. FOSTER: No, I'm not going to put an end to Mr. Snow White right now. I'm just going to take a look at old Ben's foot.

TINKER: Promise me, Dad, we'll at least talk it over one more time before—before you do it!

HONEY: Promise?

MR. FOSTER (*Smiling*): I promise. But I'm warning you . . . my mind's made up. (*Exit* MR. FOSTER)

HONEY: Tinker, what are we going to do? We just can't let him kill Mr. Snow White.

TINKER: How are we going to stop him?

HONEY: I don't know, but we'll think of something. We have to. Mr. Snow White trusts us.

TINKER: And look at all he's done for us. Gee, we're practically famous, all on account of Mr. Snow White. (*Opens box on table*) Just look—(*Holds up blue ribbon*) a blue ribbon, (*Holds up newspaper clippings*) all these newspaper stories, (*Holds up medal on a ribbon*) a medal from the Turkey-Growers' Association! We just can't let anything happen to him. (*Doorbell*)

HONEY: I'll get it. (*Runs to door*)

TINKER: Never you mind, Mr. Snow White. We'll think of something.

HONEY (*Returns with* MARY ROBERTS): It's Mary Roberts, Tink, and she has something for us.

MARY: Yes, I was supposed to have it ready for you yesterday in school, but Mother didn't get to town. (*Hands* TINK *and* HONEY *a gift-wrapped package*) Miss Gailey thought it would be nice for the whole class to give you something for bringing such honor to our school, so we decided to get a book.

HONEY: Oh, that was nice. Open it, Tink. Hurry up.

TINKER (*Opening book*): The whole class really took an interest in Mr. Snow White and Miss Gailey showed us how to write to the Farm Bureau for suggestions. (*Holding up book*) Say, this is great.

HONEY: What's the name of it?

TINKER: *Turkey Tales.*

MARY: That was Miss Gailey's idea. She read about it in the Sunday paper. It has all sorts of stories about turkeys, how to raise them, interesting facts about them, and stories different authors have written about turkeys. It even tells how some people think the wild turkey should be our national emblem instead of the bald eagle.

HONEY: It looks terribly exciting, Mary. Thanks a million. We'll write the class a note and a special note to Miss Gailey. If we write today, she should get the letter before she comes back to school.

MARY: Oh, she didn't go home for Thanksgiving.

HONEY: But I thought . . .

MARY: Yes, we thought so too, and so did she, but her car broke down and it's in the garage.

HONEY: You mean she's staying here over the Thanksgiving holidays?

MARY: Yes, she'll be at the Bradford Inn.

HONEY: How awful not to go home for the holiday.

TINKER: Maybe we could ask her here for Thanksgiving dinner, Honey.

MARY: That would be nice, but . . . well, maybe she'd be better off at the Inn.

HONEY: Why, Mary, what a thing to say! My mother's a wonderful cook!

MARY: Yes, but . . . gee, what I meant was . . . well, Miss Gailey *did* take an interest in Mr. Snow White, and well, I bet she'd hate to eat him just as much as I would. I don't see how you and Tink could eat a bite.

TINKER: Now look here, Mary Roberts, we're not going to eat Mr. Snow White.

HONEY: I should say we're not. He's not going to be killed.

MARY: Did your father say so?

TINKER: Well, no . . . not exactly . . . but he's promised not to do anything till we talk it over again.

MARY: You're just wasting your time, and I know. Because *my* father said that your father said times are plenty hard this year, and much as he hates to make you kids feel bad, Mr. Snow White goes into the oven tomorrow morning.

HONEY: Well, he's not, he's not, he's not!

TINKER: We won't *let* him kill Mr. Snow White.

MARY: Well, my goodness, don't get so excited! I only

told you what my father said your father said, and my mother says that your mother told her that. . . .

HONEY: I don't want to hear any more. I won't listen.

MARY: Well, I have to go anyhow. Goodbye. Hope you enjoy your book . . . and hope you enjoy your dinner tomorrow. (*Exit* MARY)

HONEY (*Almost in tears*): That hateful Mary Roberts! I wish she had stayed at home.

TINKER: Never mind her, Honey. Don't pay any attention to what she says. Say, this is an interesting book.

HONEY: How can you stand there and read a book at a time like this? Tink, we have to do something. Maybe, we could take Mr. Snow White some place and hide him till after Thanksgiving.

TINKER: Don't be silly. We'll have to think of something more practical.

HONEY: Like what, for instance?

TINKER: Well, like . . . say, Honey! Listen to this. (*Reads from book*) "A turkey played a very important part in Christmas at the White House in 1863. Tad Lincoln saved the life of his pet turkey, Jack, by obtaining from the President a . . . (*Spelling*) r-e-p-r-i-e-v-e.

HONEY: Reprieve! That means a pardon.

TINKER: A reprieve which spared the pet from the axe of the . . . the . . . (*Spells again*) e-x-e-c-u-t-i-o-n-e-r.

HONEY: Executioner! Oh, golly, Tink, I wish Father were more like Mr. Lincoln.

TINKER: Well, let's try him, Honey. Don't you see? There's our idea. We'll get him to sign one of those things for Mr. Snow White.

HONEY: But what good would that do?

TINKER: You've heard Father say a hundred times he

never goes back on anything he's signed. "A man's word is his bond."

HONEY: But he'd never sign it.

TINKER: Let's draw one up anyhow. Now you sit down at the typewriter and I'll tell you what to write.

HONEY: O.K., if you think it's worth trying. (*Going to typewriter*)

TINKER: We'll make it legal. Now here goes. (*Dictating very slowly*) I, comma, the undersigned, comma, do solemnly promise . . .

HONEY (*Pecking away*): Wait, wait, not so fast. How do you spell solemnly?

TINKER (*Spells word and continues*): Do solemnly promise to spare the life of Mr. Snow White for Thanksgiving and to serve chicken for our family dinner. Got that?

HONEY (*Pounding away on typewriter keys*): I—I think so.

TINKER: Read it back to me. (HONEY *reads letter.*) That's fine. Now type the word *signed* and leave space for his name at the bottom. (*Watching as she finishes his instructions*) There! Now it's all over but the signing.

HONEY: And do you have any ideas on that subject? How do we get him to sign on the dotted line?

TINKER (*Looking at letters typed by* MRS. FOSTER): He hasn't signed these yet. What do you say we stick our letter in with the rest? Maybe he'll sign it without bothering to read it.

HONEY: But that wouldn't be legal.

TINKER: Oh, yes, it would. Dad says himself you should never sign anything without reading it first. Look out . . . here he comes. (MR. FOSTER *enters in a hurry as the children dart away from the table.*)

MR. FOSTER: Oh, there you are! I'm glad I caught you before you got out of sight. I want to sign some letters so you can take them down to the mailbox at the crossroads. They'll be picked up quicker there. Honey, will you please run upstairs and get my pen?

TINKER (*Quickly*): Here's mine, Dad. (*Whips out pen and hands it to his father who signs all of the papers, as he talks and without looking.*)

MR. FOSTER: These are letters to the newspapers with ads for your great-grandfather's house. We've been trying all year to sell it privately, but now I'm going to advertise. Well, I thought your mother made only three carbons, but I seem to have an extra here. Now where are the envelopes? (*Searching in desk*)

TINKER *and* HONEY (*Exchanging looks of delight.* TINKER *grabs paper*): You signed it! You signed it! Now you'll have to keep your word.

HONEY: You will, won't you, Father? Even though you signed it without reading it?

MR. FOSTER: What is all this? What are you talking about?

TINKER: This. (*Shows him the letter*) We got the idea from a story about President Lincoln. He signed a reprieve for his little boy's pet turkey.

HONEY: And we figured you were just as good a father as Mr. Lincoln.

MR. FOSTER (*Reading the words of the letter aloud*): Well, bless my soul! So you've tricked me into signing a pardon for your prize turkey? Pretty slick, but not exactly cricket!

TINKER: But it's binding, isn't it? You said yourself you should never sign anything without reading it and if you do, you're bound by the terms.

MR. FOSTER: I'm glad to hear you've paid such close attention to my words of wisdom, son. However, it's high time you learn that two can play at this sort of game. It's true, I signed your paper without reading it, and I'm prepared to abide by it. But I'll carry out the terms as you've laid them down. Fair enough?

TINKER *and* HONEY: Absolutely.

MR. FOSTER: Very well, then. Your paper reads that we serve chicken for our *family* Thanksgiving dinner. To this I agree, but you have failed to mention *company dinner*. Therefore in the event that we have company, the Blodgets, for instance, or any other company, your paper is worthless. Company in this house demands a turkey dinner and the only turkey on this place, unfortunately, is your Mr. Snow White. Understand?

TINKER: Golly, Dad, we're right back where we started.

MR. FOSTER (*Smiling*): It takes a pretty smart lawyer, son, to draw up an agreement without any loopholes, just remember that. (*Handing him the signed paper*) Now here's your document, (*Putting letters in envelope*) and here are my letters.

TINKER: I'll take them down to the box for you.

MR. FOSTER: On second thought, I'll take the car and stop at the Kings'. Maybe your mother is ready to come home. It will be a sorry Thanksgiving for those children if their mother's laid up in bed. (*Reaching in his pocket, he pulls out two pure white turkey feathers.*) Here, (*Handing a feather to each child*) I picked these up this morning. I thought you might like to have them.

HONEY: Oh, dear! They're from Mr. Snow White.

MR. FOSTER: I (*Clearing his throat*) I-er . . . I want you to know that I understand about Mr. Snow White. I understand how you feel, but well, it's a part of growing up to learn to face unpleasantness with a stiff upper lip. Sometimes it takes courage. (*Exit* MR. FOSTER)

TINKER (*Looking at feather*): Golly, Honey, I don't feel so good.

HONEY: Neither do I. But, Tink, maybe we can save Mr. Snow White yet. Father said if there's no company . . .

TINKER: Sure, but there's bound to be company . . . the Blodgets, remember?

HONEY: Yes, I remember . . . and not only the Blodgets.

TINKER: Who else?

HONEY: Well, I've been thinking about those King children, and Mr. King. It . . . it would be sort of nice to have them here for dinner.

TINKER: Yeah, and Miss Gailey. She's been so nice to us. I don't think I'd like to eat my Thanksgiving dinner at the Bradford Inn.

HONEY: If . . . if it weren't for Mr. Snow White, we could . . . well, we could ask them.

TINKER: Yes, I know, but, well, Mr. Snow White's counting on us. We can't let him down. (*Sound of automobile horn outside*)

HONEY: Someone's coming. Let's look. (*Children run to door right stage*) Oh dear! Tink, it's the Blodgets. I know their car.

TINKER: What'll we do?

HONEY: If they ring the bell, let's not answer it. Maybe they'll go away.

TINKER: Mr. Blodget's getting out of the car. He's coming up on the porch. (*Doorbell*)

HONEY (*In stage whisper*): Let's keep real quiet.

TINKER (*As doorbell rings again*): Dad will be furious, if we don't let them in.

HONEY: I don't care. This is a matter of life and death. (*Doorbell*)

TINKER: I wish he'd quit ringing that bell. Can you see him now?

HONEY: Yes, I think he's leaving. Yep. He's going down the steps.

TINKER: Boy oh boy! That was a close one. Have they gone?

HONEY: He's getting into the car. Yes, now . . . there they go. Oh, Tinker, they've gone! They've gone! Mr. Snow White is safe.

TINKER: I just hope Mr. Snow White knows the price we're going to pay for his life when Dad finds out what we did!

HONEY: I don't care. I don't care about anything except that Mr. Snow White is safe. We're rid of the company. Tinker, I do believe you're scared.

TINKER (*Picking up feather and looking at it*): Maybe I am, Honey.

HONEY: But my goodness, Father can't put us on bread and water! He'll be mad, of course, and maybe, well, maybe we'll have a bad time for awhile . . . but . . . well, we'll just have to be brave.

TINKER: That's what bothers me, Honey. About being brave, I mean.

HONEY: Why, you're always brave, Tink. There's not a boy in school any braver than you are. And you're not scared of snakes, or bugs, or staying out in the dark or any of those things.

TINKER: But I'm scared just the same, and so are you, Honey. Maybe, maybe it's this white feather started me thinking.

HONEY: A white feather? Why, that's one of Mr. Snow White's feathers.

TINKER: I know, but remember, getting a white feather is always the sign of a coward.

HONEY: Don't be silly.

TINKER: I'm not being silly, Honey. I just keep wondering if that's what Dad had in mind. He looked so serious when he handed us these feathers.

HONEY: Oh, Tink, you're making all that up. He just gave us the feathers to . . . to remember Mr. Snow White.

TINKER: And maybe he wanted us to remember what cowards we've been.

HONEY: Cowards? We were brave enough to keep the Blodgets from coming in!

TINKER: Was that so brave? After all, we were hiding, weren't we? And we've been afraid to face up to losing Mr. Snow White!

HONEY: We love Mr. Snow White. He's ours.

TINKER: I know. But we're also afraid. I . . . I'm thinking we've both shown the white feather, Honey. Somehow or other, I—I feel ashamed.

HONEY: You mean if we were really brave, we'd have a proper Thanksgiving and let Mr. Snow White go?

TINKER: That's right, Honey. We both feel we should have the Kings and Miss Gailey, and we know perfectly well Mother and Dad have invited the Blodgets . . . and yet . . .

HONEY: Tinker Foster, you have me all mixed up. I . . . I don't want to show the white feather.

TINKER: Neither do I. I always, well, sort of boasted about being brave.

HONEY: I guess it would take more courage to lose Mr. Snow White than to stand up to Father and save him.

TINKER: You're catching on, Honey.

HONEY: Oh, Tink, do you suppose we could catch the Blodgets?

TINKER: They're miles away by now. (*Enter* MR. *and* MRS. FOSTER)

MR. FOSTER: It's a good thing I took the car. I met your mother coming down the hill and it's snowing in earnest now.

MRS. FOSTER: Poor Mrs. King. She'll be in bed for a week or two. Her ankle is broken and her knee is badly sprained.

HONEY (*Rushing to her mother*): Oh, Mother, Mother, let's have the children and Mr. King over here for dinner tomorrow.

TINKER: And we could send Mrs. King some . . . (*Swallowing hard*) turkey.

MR. FOSTER: Did you say *turkey?*

HONEY: We can't let the Kings miss out on Thanksgiving, not even for Mr. Snow White.

MRS. FOSTER: That's a wonderful way to feel, Honey.

TINKER: And Miss Gailey too.

MRS. FOSTER: We might as well invite her for dinner. Her car broke down and she's stuck at the Bradford Inn.

MR. FOSTER (*Clearing his throat*): I must say I'm proud of you both. I realize this was a hard decision for you to make. I didn't think you'd have the courage.

HONEY: Don't talk so nice to us, Father, not till you know the horrible thing we did. We have something to tell you.

TINKER: Yes, and you're going to be plenty angry. (*Doorbell*)

MR. FOSTER: Well, I can't be so angry till I find out who's at the door. Your story will have to keep. (*Goes to door, sounds of greeting.* MR. *and* MRS. BLODGET *enter.*) Well, this *is* a surprise. How nice that you could come.

MR. BLODGET: Didn't you get our letter?

MRS. FOSTER: Letter? Oh dear! The mails are so slow in this corner of the world.

MRS. BLODGET: I told Leonard we'd probably arrive ahead of the letter. I do hope we're not inconveniencing you.

MRS. FOSTER: Oh, not a bit. Mr. Foster and I just came in. We've been . . .

MRS. BLODGET: Yes, I know you were out. We stopped here awhile ago and couldn't get in.

MR. FOSTER (*With a look at the children*): Couldn't get in?

HONEY: Father, we tried to tell you!

MRS. BLODGET: We figured you had just gone out on an errand, so we drove up the hill to the big house for a final look.

MRS. FOSTER: A final look?

MR. BLODGET: Yes, a final look before we buy. You see, we've really made up our minds at last. We're going to take the house, Foster, and I'm ready to meet your terms.

MR. FOSTER: Good! Good! I'm glad to hear it. How much land will you want?

MR. BLODGET: Well, we're going to take the wood lot and we want enough land for our turkey run.

MR. FOSTER *and all:* Your turkey run?

MR. BLODGET: Yes, we're going to try our luck with turkeys.

MRS. BLODGET: You know that's what I've always wanted to do . . . raise turkeys. We've had pretty good luck on our small place with just a few, but I've always wanted to branch out and go in for it in a big way.

MR. BLODGET: I understand you have a couple of turkey raisers right here in your own family, Foster. Read about it in the paper. (*To children*) Congratulations, you two.

TINKER *and* HONEY: Thank you, Mr. Blodget.

MRS. BLODGET: Leonard, will you please go out to the car and bring in that big roaster? We've brought one of our turkeys along so you could sample the flavor and let us know if you think it could be improved.

TINKER *and* HONEY: You mean you've brought your own Thanksgiving turkey?

MRS. FOSTER: You certainly didn't have to do that, Mrs. Blodget.

MRS. BLODGET: Indeed yes, we appreciate being invited here so much. Thanksgiving is a day for families and ours is pretty small, you know. Besides, we want you experts to taste one of our turkeys.

MR. BLODGET: When we start our new place we'd like to experiment with raising white turkeys. Maybe we could strike a deal with you youngsters to buy Mr. Snow White for our flock. What would you say to that?

TINKER: Gee, Mr. Blodget, that would be swell.

HONEY: Oh, Mr. Blodget, we'd love to let you have Mr. Snow White.

MRS. BLODGET: We were afraid you might not want to part with him.

HONEY: It was the fun of raising him that mattered most, Mrs. Blodget. We'll never forget him, will we, Tink?

TINKER: I should say not! And we'll always have these feathers (*Holds up the two feathers*) to remind us of Mr. Snow White and his Thanksgiving.

THE END

Mary's Invitation

Characters

MARY
RUTH
JESSICA
TIM
JOE NELSON
MRS. COOK
MRS. BARRY
MR. LESKOV
MISS HAMILTON
CHORUS

TIME: *The present.*
SETTING: *A small park or square in the midst of a business area.*
AT RISE: MARY *enters with her friends,* RUTH *and* JESSICA. *Each girl carries an envelope. As they approach center stage,* JESSICA *drops hers.*

SCENE 1

RUTH: Be careful, Jessica. You dropped your invitation.
JESSICA (*Picking it up and brushing it off*): No harm done! It's as good as new.

MARY: You certainly wouldn't want to lose it. Miss Hamilton wants every single one to be delivered.

RUTH: My mother already knows about Open House. I've been talking about it for a week.

JESSICA: My whole family's coming whether they get an invitation or not. You couldn't keep them away if you tried.

MARY: Oh, dear! I'm so worried.

RUTH: Why are you worried? You already know your song for American Education Week.

MARY: It's not that. It's my invitation.

JESSICA: What's wrong with it? Miss Hamilton corrected all our invitations before we put them in the envelopes.

MARY: There's nothing wrong with it. My mother can't come to visit school in the afternoon. She works, and of course Daddy does, too, so there's no one to give it to.

JESSICA: How about an aunt or uncle, or even a cousin?

MARY: We don't have any relatives here.

RUTH: Then give it to a neighbor.

MARY: You don't know our neighborhood. Our neighbors aren't interested in the schools.

RUTH: They're taxpayers, aren't they?

MARY: I guess so.

JESSICA: Then the schools really belong to them. They should look after their interests.

RUTH: Miss Hamilton says everybody should visit the schools.

MARY: I know, but it sounded better when *she* said it. More convincing, somehow.

RUTH: Well, you can at least try.

JESSICA: You've written the invitation and it shouldn't be wasted.

RUTH: Miss Hamilton says our room could win the attendance banner, if every pupil brings at least one guest.

MARY: I wouldn't want our room to lose the banner on account of me.

JESSICA: Don't worry, Mary. You'll find someone to accept your invitation. (*Looks at watch*) I must hurry. Mother doesn't like me to be late. Bye—see you tomorrow. Are you coming my way, Ruth?

RUTH: Yes, I have to stop at the library. So long, Mary. And stop worrying about that invitation. All you have to do is find one person in your block who cares about the schools. (*Starts to exit, then returns*) Say, I have an idea. My dad is a salesman, and every time he starts out to sell something, he makes a list of prospects.

MARY: What are prospects?

RUTH: Prospects are people who are most likely to buy.

MARY: But I'm not selling anything.

RUTH: It's the same thing, in a way. Just sit down and make a list of the people in your neighborhood most likely to accept your invitation. Try it anyhow. There's nothing to lose. (*Calling after* JESSICA) Wait for me, Jessica. I'm coming.

MARY (*Sitting down on bench*): A list of prospects. That's not a bad idea. (*Gets out notebook and pencil from her pile of school books*) Now, let me see. There's no good listing the Bentons, the Clarks, the Snyders or the Grays because they all have children of their own who will be delivering invitations for American Education Week. There's Mrs. Bennet. She might come. And there's little Miss O'Malley who lives all alone in the big house on the corner, but she hardly ever goes any place. I *might* ask Mrs. Graham, but she's always going to parties in the afternoons. Oh dear; I can't seem to think of anybody. (TIM *enters with a bag of newspapers. He crosses behind* MARY'S *bench and pulls a lock of her hair as he passes.*)

MARY (*Startled*): Goodness gracious, Tim Mullens. You almost scared the life out of me.

TIM (*Leaning over back of bench*): What are you doing anyhow? I never saw you sitting on a park bench before.

MARY: I'm making out my list—my list of prospects.

TIM: What prospects?

MARY: I'm trying to find someone who will accept my invitation to come to our Open House, so I'm listing all the possibilities.

TIM: How many do you have?

MARY: Hardly any.

TIM (*Looking at her list over her shoulder*): That's because you have too many women. You should try the men.

MARY: Who, for instance?

TIM (*Pondering*): Well, you might try Joe, the barber. He should be interested in kids. He cuts most of the hair in this neighborhood.

MARY: That's not a bad idea, Tim. Mr. Nelson is a very friendly man.

TIM: Sure, he is. That's why most people call him "Joe" instead of "Mr. Nelson." He'll be coming out of his shop most any minute now. Maybe you can catch him on the run.

MARY: Thanks, Tim. I'll try. He should be able to make it because his shop is closed Thursday afternoons. That was a good idea, Tim.

TIM: No charge for an idea, Mary. Glad to help out. Maybe I'll stop on my way back from the paper route to see how you're doing. Lots of people come through this park on their way home from work. You should be able to nab quite a number. Here comes Joe now. (MR. NELSON *enters.*) Try your luck on him and I'll keep my fingers crossed. (TIM *exits, holding up a paper and calling.*) Evening Paper! Get today's news today! Latest Edition!

MARY (*Rising and approaching* MR. NELSON): Hello, Joe. Aren't you leaving a bit early?

JOE: Hello, Mary. Yes, it is early, but the shop is open this evening and I want to grab a bite of supper and get back.

MARY (*Nervously*): Joe, I have something to ask you—something terribly important.

JOE: Now, Mary! If it's tickets, you're just wasting your time. Every youngster in town comes into the barber shop with tickets.

MARY: It's not tickets this time, Joe. In fact, I'm not selling anything. I'm *giving* you something.

JOE: What's the catch?

MARY: There's no catch, Joe. It's an invitation. This is American Education Week and I'm inviting you to visit our school on Thursday afternoon. We're having our Open House for parents and friends. Here is the invitation. You can read it for yourself. (*Hands him invitation which he opens and reads*)

JOE (*Reading*): "Dear Mother and Dad." Say, this isn't for me. I have no children.

MARY (*Pointing to letter*): Look, Joe, it says down below, "Dear Friend." You are a friend, *aren't* you? At least, you're *my* friend, and I am the one who's inviting you.

JOE: Now, Mary, this is very nice of you to extend this invitation, but—well—I—I'm afraid I can't make it.

MARY: But, Joe, your shop is always closed on Thursday afternoons.

JOE: Yes, yes, I know it is. But what would I do in school all afternoon? I'd be like a fish out of water.

MARY: Joe, we're having a special program. I'm going to sing a song.

JOE: That's great, Mary. Good luck to you.

MARY: Wouldn't you like to hear it, Joe? (*Angling him toward bench*) Here. Sit down a minute. I'll sing it for you. It will only take a minute.

JOE: O.K., Mary. Let's hear it.

MARY (*Singing to tune of "Oh, Dear, What Can the Matter Be"*):

Oh, dear, what can the matter be? Dear, dear, what can the matter be?
Oh, dear, what can the matter be? Parents don't visit the schools.
They visit the circus, they visit the neighbors,
They visit the show to see clashing of sabres,
They visit their clubs and they talk of their labors,
But why don't they visit the schools?

(*Second Verse*)

They care for their houses, they care for their money,
They buy television and think that it's funny,
They go out for golf if it's rainy or sunny,
But why don't they visit the schools?

JOE (*Applauding*): That's a cute song, Mary, and I guess you've really put the sixty-four thousand dollar question to music.

MARY (*Running to him*): Then you'll come, Joe?

JOE (*Shrugging his shoulders*): Mary, this sort of thing isn't for me. The schools aren't any of my business. I don't have any kids.

MARY (*Drooping*): Oh, dear, I'm so disappointed.

JOE (*Rising and patting her on the shoulder*): Cheer up, Mary. It isn't the end of the world. Some other day maybe I can come. That's it. Ask me some other time, and maybe I can arrange it.

MARY (*Looking at invitation*): But, Joe, my invitation . . .

JOE: You won't have any trouble with that invitation, Mary. Lots of people would be delighted to accept.

MARY: Name one.

JOE (*Looking around blankly and then spotting two women who enter*): Let me see . . . there's . . . How about Mrs. Cook or Mrs. Barry? Here they come now. You can ask them right away. (*Edging off stage*) And thanks, Mary. It was nice of you to think of me. (*Exits*)

MARY (*Approaching* MRS. COOK *and* MRS. BARRY *who are laden with packages. One is pushing a grocery cart.*): Hello, Mrs. Cook. Good evening, Mrs. Barry. Looks as if you two have been shopping.

MRS. COOK: All afternoon, dearie, and my feet are killing me.

MRS. BARRY: Are you just going home from school, Mary?

MARY: Yes. I've been working on our Open House for American Education Week.

MRS. COOK: The schools do such interesting things these days.

MRS. BARRY: Much nicer than when I went to school.

MARY: I'm so glad to hear you're interested in our schools.

MRS. COOK: Naturally we're interested in the schools. We help pay for them, don't we?

MRS. BARRY: The way taxes are going up is something scandalous.

MARY: I wouldn't know about that, but I do know we're

having an Open House at our school on Thursday afternoon, and I would like to ask you ladies to come.

MRS. COOK: Thursday afternoon? Why, I'd love to come, dearie, but I have a standing appointment at the hairdresser's every Thursday afternoon.

MARY: How about you, Mrs. Barry?

MRS. BARRY: It's sweet of you to ask me, Mary, but that's the day for my bridge club. Some other time, maybe.

MARY (*Sadly*): I'm so sorry. I do so want someone from our block to be there.

MRS. BARRY: Well, how about Mrs. Martin. Did you ask her?

MRS. COOK: Oh, she couldn't come, dear. That's her day for the sewing circle.

MRS. BARRY: Thanks for asking us, Mary. Try us again sometime when your school has something going on.

MRS. COOK: Yes, indeed. We'll be glad to come—some other time. (*Exit* MRS. COOK *and* MRS. BARRY.)

MARY (*Angrily*): Some other time! Some other time! I'm sick of hearing it. (*Flopping on bench*) I might just as well tear up this invitation and be done with it. Not a soul on our block cares about the schools.

TIM (*Entering from direction in which he previously made his exit*): Well, how's tricks? How are you doing? Did you get rid of your invitation?

MARY: I'm getting rid of it all right. I'm going to tear it up.

TIM: You can't do that! We all promised Miss Hamilton we'd deliver our invitations.

MARY: How can I deliver mine if no one will take it?

TIM: Didn't my suggestion about Joe the Barber work out?

MARY: Nothing works out. Nobody wants to come. They just don't care about our school.

TIM: Sure they do. Lots of people care. You just happened to hit the wrong ones. Say, have you tried Mr. Leskov?

MARY: Who?

TIM: Mr. Leskov—you know, the little man who has the Oriental rug shop.

MARY: Now why would I try Mr. Leskov? He hasn't been in this country long enough to know anything about our schools. He wouldn't be interested.

TIM: Look. Here he comes. Why don't you try him? (MR. LESKOV *enters. He carries a rolled-up rug under one arm.*)

MR. LESKOV: Hello, Mary. Hello, Tim. How goes your world today?

TIM: Fine, Mr. Leskov. Just fine.

MR. LESKOV: But look at our little Mary's face. There is no smile. (*Peering at* MARY *closely*) Is your world out of order, child?

TIM: She has troubles, Mr. Leskov.

MR. LESKOV: Troubles! But you are far too young to have troubles. Troubles are only for us older people.

MARY: My trouble is I can't get anyone to come to visit our school on Thursday.

MR. LESKOV: Why do you want someone to visit your school?

MARY: Because it is American Education Week, the week set aside for visiting schools. See, I have an invitation to deliver, but everyone in our block is too busy to come.

MR. LESKOV: What about me? My rug shop is in your block, and I live over the rug shop.

MARY: Oh, Mr. Leskov. Would you come? Would you really come?

MR. LESKOV: Sure I come. I like to see what goes on in school.

TIM: What did I tell you, Mary? You've got yourself a customer.

MARY: That's wonderful, Mr. Leskov. Simply wonderful.

MR. LESKOV: I think so too. I too old to be scholar, so I be visitor, O.K.?

MARY: O.K. and double O.K. Our teacher wants to show people what a fine school we have.

MR. LESKOV: Good idea. Fine idea. School good place—wonderful place. Everybody in town should go see.

MARY: I wish everybody felt the way you do, Mr. Leskov. What makes you so different?

TIM: Mary was afraid you had been in this country too short a time to care about our schools.

MR. LESKOV: I care. I care very much. You see, my parents come from country where education was very expensive or entirely forbidden. My mother often told stories of how children learned to read behind closed and locked doors and drawn shades.

TIM: Why weren't they allowed to learn to read, Mr. Leskov?

MR. LESKOV: Very simple. Children learn to read, they read books about other countries. They learn new ways of life. They learn about freedom in other lands. Pretty soon they grow wise. When they grow up, they throw off chains. They make revolution.

MARY: I scc.

MR. LESKOV: But when I come to this country, I see children of my homeland getting free education here. I see whole families go to school, learn many things; get good jobs, make money, live in free world—all because of education. You bet I go to school with you on Thursday.

MARY: It's a date, Mr. Leskov. I think you're the greatest.

TIM: That goes for me too, Mr. Leskov.

MARY: My goodness! I wish you were on our committee.

MR. LESKOV: Committee?

TIM: She means the publicity committee that boosts Education Week throughout the town.

MARY: They put up posters and make speeches and urge people to visit the schools.

MR. LESKOV: I like that. I help to boost. I tell you what. You come over to my shop and help me make poster. We put it in rug shop window—great big letters. (*With elaborate gesture*) Come one! Come all!

MARY: Celebrate American Education Week in the American Way!

TIM: Visit your schools.

ALL (*Pointing fingers toward audience*): *You'll like what you see!*

CURTAIN

* * *

SCENE 2 *

TIME: *The afternoon of the Open House.*

SETTING: *The school classroom.*

AT RISE: MISS HAMILTON, *the teacher, leads the class in a*

* Scene 2 is included for the convenience of the Teacher who may wish to present a classroom demonstration. The play may end with Scene 1, if desired.

song, to be sung to the tune of "How do you do, everybody, how do you do."

ALL: How do you do, everybody, how do you do.
Is there anything that we can do for you?
You can watch us read and write,
And for you we will recite.
How do you do, everybody, how do you do.

How do you do to our parents, how do you do.
You will soon see what is what and who is who.
You will meet our teachers, and
You will shake them by the hand!
How do you do to our parents, how do you do.

How do you do, friends and neighbors, how do you do.
Oh, we know how much our school is costing you,
So be right up on your toes,
See where all your money goes,
How do you do, friends and neighbors, how do you do.

RUTH: We're glad to see you here today,
And hope that you'll remember
You're welcome all the year around
As well as in November.

JESSICA: We children try to learn to be
Good citizens like you,
And keep our country strong and free,
As you have taught us to.

TIM: These schools of ours are training grounds,
For leaders yet to come,
For workers who will do the work
That always must be done.

ALL: So you boost us, and we'll boost you,
And work and plan together,
Until we have the best of schools
And best of nations ever.*

MISS HAMILTON: It's a wonderful thing to have so many of our parents and friends visiting us today. This is one of the best-attended programs we have ever presented, and I think that high attendance is due to the efforts of some of our own pupils and their friends. We wish to say a special word of thanks to our good friend, Mr. Leskov, who helped to advertise our Open House. Mr. Leskov, would you say a few words?

MR. LESKOV (*Coming to stage from audience*): Since I come to America, I celebrate many weeks. Iced Tea Week, Straw Hat Week, Bow-Tie Week, and many other really wonderful weeks. But best of all I like this week, American Education Week, and I tell you why. This week, we all get together, the pupils, the teachers, the principals, the superintendents, the boards of directors, the friends, the neighbors, the relatives, the aunts, the uncles, the cousins . . . the fathers . . . the mothers . . . and we all learn and understand what goes on in our schools. That makes us very happy. It makes

* At this point the real teacher of the class introduces any demonstration the class may have prepared for this occasion. If there is no demonstration of classwork, or after the demonstration is completed, the play continues.

us happy because we work together on something that is important to all of us . . . our boys and girls. It's like the song I hear these children singing on the playground . . . The More We Get Together, the Happier We Are.

ALL (*Singing to the tune of "Did You Ever See A Lassie?"*):

The more we get together, together, together,
The more we get together, the happier we'll be.
For our school is your school, and your school is our school,
The more we get together the happier we'll be.

THE END

Turning the Tables

Characters

MISS WARREN, *head librarian*

		ROBIN HOOD	
BRADY		TINY TIM	
BARBIE		ICHABOD CRANE	
RALPH		DR. DOLITTLE	
EDITH-JO		HEIDI	
MARILYN		SENSIBLE KATE	
WEB	*children*	DRISS	*book characters*
HENRY		JIM HAWKINS	
MARCIA		NICK	
TOM		PENNY	
SHIRLEY		CAPTAIN NEMO	
PHIL		BEST BELOVED	
		HEAD HOBGOBLIN	

SETTING: *The Children's Room of the Cardiff Public Library. Prominently displayed on a long central table is a collection of books with a large sign:* CHOOSE A PAL FOR BOOK WEEK.

AT RISE: MISS WARREN *is checking out books to a line of children awaiting their turns. A group of boys and girls seated at a corner table seems to be having a heated discussion, mostly in whispers.*

MISS WARREN (*To boy at desk*): There you are! (*Handing him a book*) Now try to bring this one in on time. (*As boy leaves*) Next! Well, Brady, how did you like this one? *Treasure at Bar X?* Did you find it exciting?

BRADY (*In a bored manner*): Oh, it was O.K. But I'm getting tired of westerns. I'd like something about the North.

MISS WARREN: Have you tried *Kudla and His Polar Bear* by Miriam McMillan?

BRADY: No, I haven't read it, but I don't care for books about animals.

MISS WARREN: Getting a little hard to please, aren't you, Brady? Well, take a look around. Maybe you'll find something you like. You might look at *Green Seas and White Ice* if you're really interested in the North. That's real adventure at its best.

BRADY: Thanks a lot, but I think, after all, I'd rather have a mystery. (*Moves on to bookshelves*)

MISS WARREN (*To girl next in line*): Hello, Barbie. How did you enjoy *Melody, Mutton Bone and Sam?* (*As she takes book* BARBIE *is returning*)

BARBIE: Oh, it was wonderful, Miss Warren. Do you have any more books by Lavinia Davis that I haven't read?

MISS WARREN: I think you've read most of hers. But why don't you try something else for a change? Dorothy Deming has a fine mystery based on nursing. It's called *Curious Calamity in Ward 8*. I believe it's in. Do you want it?

BARBIE: No, thanks, Miss Warren. It was nice of you to

suggest it, but you know me. I never read anything but horse stories.

MISS WARREN: But there are so many wonderful books in the world, my dear. It's like going on a diet of cornflakes, or eating nothing but cream puffs, to stick to one kind of book all the time. You'll get mental rickets or something.

BARBIE: Just the same, I think I'll look for another horse story, Miss Warren.

MISS WARREN: Suit yourself. After all, this *is* a public library. (*As children at table become noisy*) I'll have to ask you folks at that corner table to be more quiet.

RALPH: Sorry, Miss Warren! (*To boys and girls*) I told you we were making too much noise. First thing you know she'll put us out.

MISS WARREN (*With a smile*): Oh, I don't think I'd do that, Ralph, at least not until I find out what the trouble is. You've had quite a buzz session over there, ever since you came in. (*Rising and moving to table*) Anything I can do to help?

RALPH: Thanks for offering. I sure hope you can do something, because, I'll admit, I'm stuck!

MISS WARREN: What seems to be your trouble?

RALPH: It's not *my* trouble, Miss Warren. It's *their* (*Indicates group*) trouble. Miss Lucas—she's our teacher—wants everyone in our room to take a book out of the library for Book Week, and it's up to me to see that everyone in our reading circle finds a book to suit him.

MISS WARREN: That shouldn't be so hard. We certainly have plenty of books.

RALPH (*Wiping his forehead*): I know, but these kids . . . I-er-mean, these people are real characters. In the first place, they don't know what they want themselves. Now here's Edith-Jo. (*Points to first girl*) I bet she hasn't read a book since *Peter Rabbit.*

EDITH-JO: I have so, Miss Warren. You've seen me in here lots of times, haven't you?

MISS WARREN: Of course I have, Edith-Jo. Now let me see . . . Aren't you the girl who won't read anything but ghost stories?

EDITH-JO: That's right, Miss Warren, and the spookier the better.

MARILYN: I don't like a book unless it has lots of conversation. The minute I see long paragraphs of description, I know it's not for me.

WEB: I never have any trouble picking a book. I always go by the pictures.

HENRY: I look at the print. Nice big print, and not too many pages, that's what I like.

MARCIA: I always check on the names of the characters. If I can't pronounce all the names, I know the book wouldn't be interesting.

TOM: My trouble is there just aren't enough science fiction books.

SHIRLEY: I look for a book with a bright-colored jacket and a picture on the cover.

MISS WARREN: You boys and girls really have your problems, don't you?

RALPH: And they're all settling down on me. Miss Lucas says there's a Book Pal for everybody, but I can't seem to find any to suit these characters.

MISS WARREN: Have you looked at our special Book Week table? We think we have an unusually varied selection. (*All move to central table.*) Now here's a book you just can't help liking. (*Picks up book*) It's *The Story of Dr.*

Dolittle by Hugh Lofting. Marilyn, I bet you'd enjoy this one.

MARILYN: Not if it's about doctors, Miss Warren. I hate doctors.

MISS WARREN: But Dr. Dolittle is a very unusual doctor. He keeps his house so full of animals, he has no room for his patients.

MARILYN: Oh, an animal doctor!

MISS WARREN: In a way, but Dr. Dolittle is in a class by himself. You have to read him to get to know him. Why don't you give him a try?

MARILYN: No, thank you, Miss Warren, I just don't like his name. Dr. Dolittle—it sounds so funny to me.

MISS WARREN: But it's a funny book, Marilyn. (*With a sigh*) Oh, well, here is something quite different. Web, you should like this one. It's *The Lion's Paw* by Robb White. Plenty of adventure.

WEB: I don't think I'd like a circus story, Miss Warren.

MISS WARREN: A circus story? What makes you think *The Lion's Paw* is about a circus? *The Lion's Paw* happens to be the name of a boat, a sailboat that goes through the inland waterways of a Florida swamp.

WEB: Let me see it. I can tell if it's any good by the pictures. (BARBIE *and* BRADY *join the others at the table.*)

BARBIE: Brady and I haven't found anything on the shelves. May we look at these too?

MISS WARREN: Certainly. That's why they're here. Help yourselves.

MARCIA: Is there something you think I'd like, Miss Warren?

MISS WARREN: Now, let me see. Oh, yes. I think you'd enjoy *Sensible Kate* by Doris Gates. Kate is a little red-haired orphan who comes to a foster home in a strange town, and makes two new friends, Vic Corsatti and his big brother, Leo.

MARCIA: Corsatti! What a funny name! I don't like characters with odd names.

MISS WARREN: Really! You children are certainly difficult to please!

RALPH: You're telling me, Miss Warren? They're impossible!

MISS WARREN: Maybe we'll have better luck with some of the well-known children's classics. Now, Shirley, you're bound to like *Heidi* by Johanna Spyri.

SHIRLEY: Oh, I've seen that in the movies and on TV. Anyhow, there's no picture on the cover.

MISS WARREN: This copy happens to have been re-bound. The first cover wore out because so many children were reading it. That's one way to tell a popular book, you know.

SHIRLEY: But it looks so drab!

MISS WARREN: Tom, you claim you like science fiction. I think you're old enough to read this simplified version of *Twenty Thousand Leagues Under the Sea.*

TOM: I'll try it, Miss Warren, but I'm more interested in space ships.

PHIL: What do you have in sports?

MISS WARREN: You've read so many of the ordinary sport stories, Phil. Here's something different. *The Merry Adventures of Robin Hood.* Wait till you read of the trial of strength between Robin Hood and Little John, and the shooting match at Nottingham! And then, there's the greatest sport of all, Robin Hood outwitting the Sheriff.

PHIL: That's not the kind of sport I mean. I had baseball and football in mind.

MISS WARREN (*Slightly annoyed*): But can't you change your mind once in a while? That's what books are for—to give you a different point of view, to help you have new experiences.

HENRY: Excuse me, Miss Warren. What is this book about?

MISS WARREN: Oh, that's a delightful story, Henry—*Pepperfoot of Thursday Market*. Pepperfoot is a little donkey who belongs to Driss, a boy from one of the ancient Berber tribes, dating back to Bible times. Driss, Amoor, Omar and Pepperfoot have some great adventures together.

HENRY (*Examining the book*): Hmmm! The print's nice and big, but I don't like the title! *Pepperfoot of Thursday Market!* That's too long! I like 'em short and snappy.

BRADY (*Picking up book*): I've always thought I'd like to read this one, *Treasure Island*, but I don't like the way it begins.

MISS WARREN: But if you'd just read on a few chapters . . .

BARBIE: That's how I feel about this—Kipling's *Just So Stories*. I've tried it a couple of times, but I always brought it back after the first three pages.

EDITH-JO: Don't you have any new ghost stories for me, Miss Warren?

MISS WARREN: Why don't you try Dickens' *Christmas Carol?* That has ghosts in it. Or *The Legend of Sleepy Hollow?* That should be spooky enough.

EDITH-JO: They're not scary enough! I like to be frightened out of my wits!

MISS WARREN: That does it! That absolutely does it!

EDITH-JO: Does what, Miss Warren? I don't understand!

MISS WARREN: You'll understand soon enough! And remember—you asked for it!

EDITH-JO: Asked for what?

MISS WARREN: You asked to be frightened out of your wits! Well, now you better hang on to the few you have left, because in just a few seconds—*the tables will be turned!* (MISS WARREN *begins to speak in a slow, frightening tone, making fearsome gestures, as she recites the following*:)

Abracadabra!
Fee-Fie-Fo-Fum!
Open Sesame!
What's done is done!

Aladdin's Lamp,
And the fearful Genie,
Fairy godmothers—
Goody and Meany,
Ogres and Pixies,
Brownies and Sprites,
Help me extinguish
The library lights!

(*There is a complete blackout accompanied by clashes of metal and terrified screams. Then silence, during which* MISS WARREN *continues her incantation.*)

Bats and Banshees,
Witches and Elves,
Come clamber down
From your library shelves!
Spooks and Spirits of

Seven Gables,
Now is the time
For turning the tables!

(*When lights go up again, the tables are literally turned. Lined up in front of the central table which formerly bore the Book Week display are all of the* CHILDREN, *each wearing a name card around his neck. The* BOOK CHARACTERS, *released from their covers, are walking around the room.* MISS WARREN *is slumped at her desk, her head in her arms, as if completely exhausted. Standing beside her is a tall hooded figure in a long black gown. His name card reads:* HEAD HOBGOBLIN.)

HEAD HOBGOBLIN: Well, she did it! She finally did it! I never thought she'd have the nerve.

DR. DOLITTLE: You find courage in the strangest places, Sir Hobgoblin. Now, when I was in Africa, treating the monkeys, I . . .

HEIDI: Yes, yes, Dr. Dolittle, you've told us all that hundreds of times. But right now, we can't afford to waste a minute of our freedom. Oh, doesn't it feel good to walk about and stretch after being shut up in those books for so long?

JIM HAWKINS: Yes, indeed. It's almost as good as when I first stepped ashore after being cooped up so long on the Hispaniola.

HEAD HOBGOBLIN: Come, come, we must not waste our time with words. We've all had enough of words. Action is what we want now. Remember, you are all released for a purpose.

NICK: A purpose? What purpose?

HEAD HOBGOBLIN: Didn't you hear what Miss Warren said? She wanted us to turn the tables.

NICK: Well, they're turned, aren't they? Jim Hawkins and Robin Hood and I swung them around quite easily.

HEAD HOBGOBLIN: But that isn't enough. Now is our chance to turn the tables on these wretched children. For years and years and years, they've had the privilege of coming to the library and selecting books to take home with them. Now that the tables are turned, we can take *our* choice.

KATE: You mean we can actually select them, instead of having them select us?

HEAD HOBGOBLIN: Exactly. Now which one of these fine-looking, intelligent boys and girls will you choose to go home with? Step right up and take your choice. Dr. Dolittle, since you are our oldest member, we'll let you take first choice.

DR. DOLITTLE (*Rubbing his hands in glee*): Excellent! Excellent! Wait till I tell my friends in Puddleby about this. Well . . . it's a little hard to decide. (*Pausing in front of* MARILYN) This is a likely looking little girl, but I heard her say she doesn't care much for doctors. And then, there's her name. (*Adjusting his glasses and peering at name card.*) I can't quite make it out. M-A-R-I . . . That's a funny way to spell *Mary*.

HEAD HOBGOBLIN: It's not *Mary,* Doctor, it's Marilyn.

DR. DOLITTLE: Marilyn! Now what sort of a crazy name is that? I've heard of Marion and Marigold. But not Marilyn! No, I don't think I'd like to go home with anyone named Marilyn.

HEAD HOBGOBLIN: But Dr. Dolittle, she might be quite a nice child at that.

DR. DOLITTLE: Perhaps so. But I'm not going to take a chance on anyone named *Marilyn*. Besides, Chee-Chee, my pet monkey might not care for her.

NICK (*To* PENNY): Penny, how do you think you'd like to go home with this fellow? (*Stops in front of* WEB.)

PENNY (*Thoughtfully*): Ummm! I'm not so sure, Nick. Look at the way his hair grows along his forehead. I don't think he'd be very much fun!

NICK: I see what you mean.

PENNY: And then, there are his ears! Just see how small they are. Boys ought to have bigger ears to be really interesting.

NICK: You're right. And his eyes are too close together. All in all, I think we'd better forget about him. Anyhow, I doubt if he'd ever really believe I faced up to an alligator all by myself.

PENNY: Let's look at some of the girls. Maybe we'll have better luck.

HEIDI: I doubt it. I went home one time with that one (*Pointing to* EDITH-JO) and she left me out in the rain all night. I was soaked through. That's one of the reasons I had to be re-bound.

KATE: What about this one? (*Stopping in front of* BARBIE)

HEIDI: I don't really know much about her except that she's crazy about horse stories. How do you like her looks?

KATE: Not bad! But look at that jacket she's wearing. Did you ever see a more hideous color in all your life? It would certainly clash with my red hair.

HEIDI: Here's one that might do. (*Points to* MARCIA)

KATE: Never! Not if I stay on the shelves till doomsday! Did you hear what she said about names? Made a fuss about Vic's name, Corsatti. Said it was hard to pronounce! And what do you think *her* name is?

HEIDI: It says *Marcia* on her name card.

KATE: Yes, but Marcia what? (*Whispers to* HEIDI)

HEIDI (*In disbelief*): No! It can't be!

KATE: But it is! I saw it just as plain as day on Miss Warren's desk. I was right there when she was filling out her card, and there it was—*Marcia Mulligatawny,* as big as life.

HEIDI: Well, I don't blame you! I'd never go home with anyone with a name like that! Not if I could help it!

ROBIN HOOD: And this time we can help it! We're as free as if we were roaming the greenwood. Come, my merry men, let's make a choice and be done with it. Now here's a likely lad! I'll wager he would make a fair companion. (*Stops in front of* PHIL)

HEAD HOBGOBLIN: Take a good look before you decide, Friend Robin.

ROBIN HOOD: Ummm! Looks a bit nearsighted to me. I doubt if he'd be a good man with a bow and arrow.

HEAD HOBGOBLIN: He's a great sports fan, you know. No time for anything but baseball and football.

ROBIN HOOD: Perhaps I had best leave this one for you, Jim. (*To* JIM HAWKINS) Perhaps he'll strike your fancy.

JIM: I was rather thinking of *this* one. (*Indicating* BRADY) But he's the sort who doesn't see things through to a finish.

BEST BELOVED: Isn't it too bad, Jim? That's the way it is with this little girl. (*Pointing to* BARBIE) She said she's tried to read the *Just So Stories* that were written especially for me, but she gives up before she's really started. I feel so sorry for her. Just think, she'll never find out what the Crocodile had for dinner or how the Elephant's Child got his long trunk.

JIM: It *is* a great pity about readers like that; but aren't you glad we don't have to go home with them! Now,

Captain Nemo is looking them over. I wonder what his choice will be.

CAPTAIN NEMO (*Pointing to* TOM): I can tell you one thing—it won't be this fellow! Space ships indeed! I want to go home with someone who can appreciate adventure underneath the ocean. Something tells me that one of these young ladies might have the proper spirit for adventure in a submarine. How about this one? (*Stops at* SHIRLEY)

HEIDI: Oh dear me! Not that one, Captain Nemo. She's forever telling you how much better the stories are in the movies and on something they call "television.' She's really very dull company.

CAPTAIN NEMO: Thank you for warning me, little lady. Well, I'll play the gallant part and let the rest of you make your choice. Anything left over will do for me. Here, young man, you haven't had your turn.

DRISS (*Indicating* HENRY): Not that stupid fellow, Henry! Remember, he likes his titles short and snappy! *Pepperfoot at Thursday Market* doesn't suit him! Well, I'm sure Amroo and Omar wouldn't like his company any more than I would. And as for Pepperfoot, he always likes what I like, so there you are! I think, perhaps, we'd like to go home with this little girl. (*Indicates* EDITH-JO.)

TINY TIM: Remember, she's the ghost-fan. Maybe she wouldn't care for real, live characters like you and your friends. She thinks the ghosts in *A Christmas Carol* aren't scary enough for her.

ICHABOD CRANE: I could tell her some tales that would make her hair stand on end.

HEAD HOBGOBLIN: Very good. Then you are going to go home with this young lady?

KATE: Careful, boys. Beware of that one. She's dangerous.

TINY TIM: What do you mean?

ICHABOD CRANE: She doesn't look dangerous.

KATE: Oh, but she is! I know a book that went home with her one time and she turned all of his corners down!

ICHABOD *and* TINY TIM: No!

KATE: Yes, she did! And what's more, every time she'd stop reading, she'd just turn the book over flat on its face! And what's even worse, she wasn't even careful about her hands! I want to tell you that book was a mess when it came back on the shelves! All sticky, corners turned down, the backbone loosened!

TINY TIM: I've a good mind to throw my crutch at her!

PENNY: Mr. Hobgoblin, these children don't really care for books!

NICK: They don't appreciate the library one single bit!

HEIDI: They won't take the trouble to get to know us!

BEST BELOVED: They judge us by the jackets we wear.

DRISS: Or by our names . . .

JIM: Or by the size of our type . .

DRISS: The color of our binding!

NICK: Or the number of pages!

CAPTAIN NEMO: I suggest, Mr. Hobgoblin, now that we have them in our power, we destroy them once and for all!

HEAD HOBGOBLIN: That's a pretty drastic suggestion, Captain.

DRISS: Think how many of us have been destroyed by them—our pages torn out, our pictures ruined, our backs dislocated!

BEST BELOVED: Some of us have even been given up for lost!

ROBIN HOOD: Well, what do you say, my jolly Hobgoblin?

You know the magic words. Say the spell that will enable us to take them home with us. I can make short work of this puny Philip once I get him in Sherwood Forest. A stray arrow will do the trick.

HEIDI: A little push could send my friend Shirley tumbling over a cliff.

CAPTAIN NEMO: No one would ever think of looking for Tom on the ocean floor . . . twenty thousand leagues under!

BEST BELOVED: I think the Elephant's Child would enjoy spanking a little sense into Barbie with his good strong trunk!

JIM: Long John Silver would make short work of that Brady boy!

DRISS: Pepperfoot and I could take Henry on a panther hunt from which he would never return.

KATE: I'm not called *Sensible Kate* for nothing. I'd find a way to dispose of Marcia Mulligatawney!

DR. DOLITTLE: Terrible accidents happen to people in Africa. My animal patients could advise me how to get rid of Marilyn.

PENNY: Nick, how do you think Web would do for alligator bait?

NICK: Excellent. The alligators aren't particular at this season of the year.

TINY TIM: Go ahead, Mr. Hobgoblin! Cast your magic spell. My friend, Ichabod Crane, will turn this girl (*Points to* EDITH-JO) over to the Headless Horseman.

HEAD HOBGOBLIN: I see you are quite determined! Very well. I will oblige you.

Abracadabra
Fee Fie Fo Fum!

Clouds of deep midnight,
Darken the sun!

(MISS WARREN *stirs, stretches and yawns once or twice as stage darkens.*)

Spirit of darkness,
Lean from your tower!
Deliver these children
Into our power!

MISS WARREN (*Springing up*): No! No! What are you doing? Stop! Stop! What is the meaning of this?

HEAD HOBGOBLIN: We are getting rid of these creatures once and for all, Miss Warren. Surely you have seen enough of them here in your library to know that they don't really love our Book People.

MISS WARREN: Oh, but they do! They do! And they're really lovely children when you get to know them.

HEIDI: So are we, but those hateful creatures won't take the time to get acquainted.

MISS WARREN: You could share so much pleasure together, if you'd just have a little patience.

HEAD HOBGOBLIN: What do you want of us?

MISS WARREN: Give them another chance! That's all I ask.

HEAD HOBGOBLIN: After all the trouble they've given you, you still want them to have another chance?

MISS WARREN: Of course. Look! (*Pointing to* RALPH) Take Ralph for instance. He's always making friends with books! He's read at least one book from every shelf in this room. No matter how much he has to do, or how many activities there are, he's never so busy that he neglects his Book Friends. Please! Go back to your books! Let the children discover you in their own way and make friends with you.

HEAD HOBGOBLIN: Well, fellow characters, what do you say? (*Characters form a football huddle in center of stage.*)

CAPTAIN NEMO: We cast our vote for another chance.

DR. DOLITTLE: We'll go back to our shelves.

KATE: But we expect to see some changes around here or certain people will be sorry.

HEAD HOBGOBLIN: Quiet, Kate. Go ahead, Miss Warren. You know the magic words:

MISS WARREN:

Abracadabra!
Pixies and Elves
Help these good people
Return to their shelves!

(*There is a blackout during which* MISS WARREN *completes her rhyme.*)

Spirit of Stories,
Legends and Fables,
Come, do my bidding,
Turn back the tables!

(*A moment later, the lights go up again. The tables are back in position, the book display is in place and the children are grouped around it.* MISS WARREN *is at her desk.*)

RALPH: Well, have you made up your minds? It's getting near closing time.

BARBIE: Don't rush me, Ralph. I know what I want. I'm taking *Just So Stories* by Rudyard Kipling. I've had it before, but this time, I'm determined to finish it. It's high time I started reading something else besides horse stories. (*Going to desk*) Miss Warren, will you check this one out to me?

MISS WARREN: Certainly.

BRADY: I'm taking *Treasure Island*. I sort of feel that Jim Hawkins and I should get better acquainted. (*Crosses to desk*)

PHILIP: I feel the same way about Robin Hood. He'd be a good guy to have as a friend every week in the year. (*Crosses to desk*)

TOM: There's something about this Captain Nemo that sort of gets me. I want to read *Twenty Thousand Leagues Under the Sea*. (*Crosses to desk*)

SHIRLEY: Wasn't I the silly one to turn down *Heidi* all because of a faded cover? The cover doesn't hurt the story one single bit. (*Crosses to desk*)

MARILYN: This Dr. Dolittle was quite a character. He even learned to speak the language of the animals. I want to know him better. (*Crosses*)

MARCIA: *Sensible Kate* is the one for me. I have a feeling I'm going to enjoy her.

HENRY: I just peeked in the back of this book and found out that Pepperfoot was stolen. Now I can't put it down to see if he ever got back to his master. (*Crosses*)

WEB: I guess the only way I'll ever get on a boat is to make friends with Nick and Penny and join them on *The Lion's Paw*. (*Crosses*)

EDITH-JO: I can't decide between these two, so I'll take them both! Even if I'm not really scared, I should get a few shivers out of them. (*Crosses to desk*)

RALPH (*As* MISS WARREN *checks out books*): What do you suppose got into them, Miss Warren, that they made up their minds all of a sudden?

MISS WARREN: I'm not sure, Ralph! But there's a kind of magic in books, you know. When the right books and the right readers get together . . . well . . . they just sort of click, and before you know it—anything can happen! (*Curtain*)

THE END

The Miraculous Tea Party

Characters

MINTY, *a lonely little girl*
MRS. STEVENS, *her mother*
JANIE WEST
BETTY ROSS
RUTH HILL
JANET SIMMS
BILLY EVANS
TIM TRACY
BUD BILLINGS
THE SLEEPING BEAUTY
WALTER, THE LAZY MOUSE
PINOCCHIO
DICK WHITTINGTON
BARTHOLOMEW CUBBINS
MARY POPPINS

SETTING: *The front lawn of the Stevens home. There is a large umbrella table to the right of stage center, and six or seven small chairs standing near it. At downstage left, a few feet from edge of stage, is a picket fence. The boys and girls enter from left, from stage steps or from an entrance located in front of picket fence. Another exit at right leads into house.*

AT RISE: MRS. STEVENS *is seated at the umbrella table, sewing.* MINTY *is pushing her doll carriage across the stage. She is dressed up in her mother's hat, fur piece, and high-heeled shoes. Her own shoes stand under table.*

MINTY (*To her doll*): Suzabelle, you were a good baby! You never cried once while I was in the store. Dear me! We'll have to go back again. I've forgotten the eggs, and we must have eggs for supper. (*Moves in opposite direction*) But if I go back to the store for the eggs, I won't get home in time for supper, and then what will we do? (*Reverses doll cart*) Oh, well, I guess I'll just go home without them, and we'll have tea and toast.

MOTHER (*Looking up from her sewing*): It's a good thing you're not cooking for Daddy. He would want more than tea and toast.

MINTY (*Laughing*): Yes, he would! He'd want fried chicken and ice cream and chocolate cake. But I don't have any of those things.

MOTHER: I guess you and Suzabelle will just have to go back to the shopping center.

MINTY (*Coming to her mother*): No, it's too late! And anyhow I'm tired of playing grownups. (*Sits down and takes off shoes*) Besides, my feet hurt! (*Slips into her own shoes. Takes off hat and fur piece.*)

MOTHER: Those shoes always hurt my feet too.

MINTY: What shall I play now, Mother?

MOTHER: Why don't you cut out some paper dolls?

MINTY: I'm tired of paper dolls.

MOTHER: You could play with your blocks.

MINTY: I'm tired of blocks.

MOTHER: You could play with your modeling clay.

MINTY (*Crossly*): I'm tired of modeling clay.

MOTHER: Dear me! You're tired of everything.

MINTY: I'm tired of playing by myself. I want someone to play with me. Why don't I have anyone to play with, Mother?

MOTHER: Because we just moved to this town. We don't know any people yet. But don't worry. You'll make friends.

MINTY: How?

MOTHER: Oh, I'm sure there are some nice children in this neighborhood. When you see some of them, ask them to come in and play with you. (*Phone rings off-stage.*) Oh dear! There's the telephone. I must answer it. (*Puts down sewing and exits*)

MINTY: Mother made it sound so easy. (*Walks to edge of stage and looks up and down.*) I wish someone would come along right now. (*Closes her eyes and clenches her fists tightly*) I wish a wish, I make a bow, (*Makes a bow*), I wish somebody would come right now. (*As* MINTY *opens her eyes,* BILLY EVANS *enters, whistling, and carrying a ball and glove.*) Here comes a boy! Maybe he'll come in and play with me. (*To* BILLY) Hello, Boy. I'm Minty Stevens. What's your name?

BILLY: Billy Evans. I've never seen you before.

MINTY: That's because we just moved here. Would you like to come in and play with me?

BILLY: Sorry, but I've got to play ball.

MINTY: I have a ball. I'll play with you.

BILLY: I mean real ball—the kind only boys can play. Thanks anyhow. So long. (*Exit* BILLY.)

MINTY: Oh, dear! And he was such a nice boy. (*As* JANIE WEST *approaches with skipping rope*) But here's much better luck. Here comes a girl. (*As* JANIE *stops in front of her*) Hello! I'm Minty Stevens. We just moved here. What's your name?

JANIE: I'm Janie West. It's a nice day, isn't it?

MINTY: Would you like to come in and play with me, Janie?

JANIE: I'd like to, but I have to go to the store for my mother. See you sometime. (*Exits*)

MINTY: She might have asked me to go along! Oh well! I'll try again. (*Three girls enter together, laughing and talking.*) Hello, girls. I'm Minty Stevens. Wouldn't you like to come and play in my yard?

RUTH: We can't now. This is Betty Ross, and Janet and I are going over to her house to look at television. I'm Ruth Hill. I live across the street from you. We watched you move into your new house.

MINTY: I hope we can be friends.

JANET: Sure we can. We might even be in the same grade at school.

BETTY: I hope you're in our room. Miss Gray is the teacher and she's very nice. Now, come along, girls, or we'll miss the program. (*Girls exit.*)

MINTY: I'll try once more, and if I can't get anyone to play with me, I'm going to go in the house and stay there! (TIM TRACY *and* BUD BILLINGS *enter.*) Hi, boys. I'm your new neighbor, Minty Stevens.

TIM: Hi! This house has been vacant a long time. I'm glad somebody moved in. My name is Tim Tracy, and this is Bud Billings.

BUD: Hi!

MINTY: Don't you want to come in my yard and play for awhile? Maybe my mother will let us have some lemonade and cookies.

BUD: That sounds good. But we're in a hurry.

TIM: Maybe some other time.

MINTY: Yeah, maybe some other time.

BUD: We'll be seeing you.

MINTY: I hate the boys and girls in this town. I just hate them! They'll never be friends with me, never! I'm going to ask my daddy to move away from this horrible place. (MOTHER *enters carrying a big armload of books.* MINTY *runs to her, crying.*) Oh, Mother, Mother, let's move away from this town. Let's go back where we came from. Nobody will play with me! Not a single soul!

MOTHER (*As she puts books on a table beside her chair*): Now, now, Minty! Don't take it so hard. You might be lonely for a little while, but it won't be long. As soon as you meet some of the children in town, you'll make friends.

MINTY: But I did meet some. I met a whole lot and not one would come in and play with me. Everyone had something else to do or some place to go.

MOTHER: They didn't mean to be unfriendly or unkind. They're just busy with their own little plans. Now as soon as you get acquainted and discover you have a lot of things in common, you'll be running in and out of each other's houses just the way you did back in Park City. And in the meantime, aren't you forgetting about some of your old friends?

MINTY: All my old friends are back in Park City. They can't help me now.

MOTHER: I don't mean those friends, Minty. I mean some other old friends whom you've been neglecting lately.

MINTY (*Drying her eyes*): Who?

MOTHER (*Reaching for a book*): Well, here's *The Sleeping Beauty*. You haven't spent any time with her lately.

And here's another good friend of yours, *Dick Whittington*. And here's good old Bartholomew. Remember how you used to laugh at *The Five Hundred Hats of Bartholomew Cubbins?*

MINTY: Yes, I remember. And you even remembered to bring *Pinocchio* and dear little *Mary Poppins!* And my darling Walter, *Walter, the Lazy Mouse!* Mother, you've brought all my favorites.

MOTHER: In that case, why don't you have a tea party?

MINTY: A tea party! How could we have a tea party? After all, they're just books!

MOTHER: Sh! Don't say that! They might hear you! I'm going in the house and find some lemonade and cookies while you set the table.

MINTY: You mean I should really seat the books as if they were guests?

MOTHER: Why not? You might find them the liveliest guests you ever had. (*Rising*) I'll call you when the refreshments are ready. (*Exits*)

MINTY: It seems funny to me, but it's worth a try. If books are my only friends, I might as well entertain them. (*Arranges books around the table*) Now let me see, I'll put Pinocchio here, and Mary Poppins next. Mary's such a great talker, she'll keep Pinocchio entertained. Then next to Mary, I'll put Bartholomew Cubbins! Oh, dear! I wonder how many hats he'll be wearing! Next comes The Sleeping Beauty. Maybe she'll feel funny coming without the Prince, but there just isn't room. Oh, dear! Where can I put Walter? The ladies might object to sitting next to a mouse. And if Dick Whittington should have his cat with him! Gracious! Well, I'll just have to take the chance. (*Arranges chairs around table*) Dick Whittington goes next to The Sleeping Beauty and Walter next to Dick. As hostess, I'll sit between Walter and Pinocchio.

MOTHER (*From offstage*): Minty, the refreshments are ready.

MINTY: All right, Mother. I'm coming. (MINTY *exits after placing the last chair at the tea table. Almost immediately* THE SLEEPING BEAUTY *and* DICK WHITTINGTON *enter.*)

SLEEPING BEAUTY (*Yawning*): Oh, dear! I'm so sleepy, I can hardly keep my eyes open, but this must be the place. Where do we sit?

DICK: Here are our place cards. (*Indicating books on the table*) You sit right here and I am beside you.

SLEEPING BEAUTY: That's fine. I heard Minty talking about inviting a mouse and I should hate to sit beside him. (*They sit.*)

DICK: Yes, she's invited Walter. Poor Walter! He's a very nice mouse but so dreadfully lazy.

SLEEPING BEAUTY: I hope he's not too lazy to come to the party. (WALTER *enters.*)

WALTER: Maybe I'm not so lazy as you think, Mr. Dick Whittington. I hope you didn't bring that dreadful cat of yours!

DICK: No danger, Walter. You're perfectly safe. Sit down. I believe you know The Sleeping Beauty, don't you?

WALTER: I've never had that pleasure. Charmed, I'm sure. (*Sits*) And don't be nervous, Princess. I'll try not to frighten you.

SLEEPING BEAUTY: Thank you. You're very kind.

WALTER: Actually, it's because I'm so lazy. It takes a lot of effort to frighten people, so I don't even try.

DICK: Here come Bartholomew Cubbins and Pinocchio. Hello, you two!

BARTHOLOMEW: Good afternoon, my friends. This is a very happy occasion. (*Takes off his hat and bows. There is another hat underneath.*) You'll have to excuse my hats at the table. They just keep reappearing, you know. Is this my place?

SLEEPING BEAUTY: Right here beside me, Mr. Cubbins. Pinocchio, you're over there.

PINOCCHIO: There's an empty chair on either side of me. Who else is expected? (*Enter* MARY POPPINS)

MARY POPPINS: Here I am! I'm late, but you know I can never blow in without the east wind.

PINOCCHIO: Sit here by me, Mary, and tell me how you came this time.

SLEEPING BEAUTY: Did you blow in on the tail of a kite?

DICK: Or did you come on a rocket?

MARY POPPINS: Now—no questions. You know I never explain anything.

PINOCCHIO: That's right. She doesn't. Where's our hostess?

WALTER: I think she went inside for the refreshments. I hope she remembers to bring a bite of cheese for me. (MINTY *enters with a tray of refreshments.*)

MINTY: Oh, I'm so glad to see all of you! And to think every single one of you managed to come.

BARTHOLOMEW (*Doffing his hat under which there is another*): My dear Minty, we wouldn't have missed it.

PINOCCHIO: It isn't every day a puppet gets invited to a party.

DICK: As Lord Mayor of London, I had to cancel several meetings but here I am.

SLEEPING BEAUTY: The Prince and I are going to a great ball this evening, but I couldn't miss talking over old times with my little friend, Minty.

MINTY: Was the east wind blowing today, Mary Poppins? Or how did you manage to get here?

MARY POPPINS: Ask me no questions!

DICK: Remember, she never explains anything!

MINTY: And you, dear Walter, I'm so glad to see you.

WALTER: I know what you're thinking, but it isn't true. I am *not* too lazy to visit my friends.

MINTY: Oh, it's so good to hear that word *friend*. Since we've moved to this horrible town, I don't seem to have any friends at all . . . that is none except you loyal Book Friends.

BARTHOLOMEW: No friends? That's a sad state of affairs.

PINOCCHIO: It's making you unhappy!

DICK: As Lord Mayor of London, I could pass a law requiring that the children of this town make friends with you immediately.

SLEEPING BEAUTY: I could ask my Fairy Godmother to cast a spell on these children.

WALTER: If I weren't so lazy, maybe I could do something. I really am a clever mouse, you know.

MARY POPPINS: Don't brag, Walter. Maybe I can take things in hand here.

MINTY: Oh, could you, Mary? You always straightened out the Banks family, when they were in trouble.

MARY POPPINS: Quiet! Let me think. (*All are quiet while* MARY *thinks.* MINTY *passes lemonade and cookies. During this silence,* BILLY EVANS *returns from his ball game. He stops in amazement and stares at the tea party.*)

BILLY: Wow! Will you look at that?

JANIE (*Entering with basket of groceries*): What are you staring at, Billy? What's going on?

BILLY: Look at all those strange people. Who do you suppose they are? (RUTH, BETTY, *and* JANET *enter.*)

JANIE: I haven't the faintest idea. (*To girls*) Did you ever see anything like that?

RUTH: It looks like a tea party!

BETTY: But what strange-looking people.

JANET: One of them looks like a mouse! (TIM *and* BUD *enter.*)

TIM: What are you all gazing at? Is there a circus in town?

BILLY: It's that new girl. She's having a party.

BUD: A party! Just a little while ago she didn't know anybody! (*The children stare.* MARY POPPINS *pounds her fist on the table in glee and springs to her feet.*)

MARY POPPINS: I've got it! I've got it! We'll have a thunderstorm!

ALL: A thunderstorm!

MARY POPPINS: Right! And my friends and I will vanish with the third clap of thunder. Are you ready?

MINTY: You're not going to leave me, are you?

MARY POPPINS: Not really, Minty. You know your Book Friends are always as close as your library shelf. Don't worry, you'll be all right. Just wait and see. (*A rumble of thunder is heard from offstage.*)

JANIE: Listen, it's starting to thunder!

BETTY: There's going to be a storm! (*At the second clap of thunder, book characters rise.*)

JANET: I'm afraid of thunderstorms.

RUTHIE: I don't want to get wet. Maybe we could run for shelter under that umbrella. (*Points to umbrella table. At the third clap of thunder, the lights blink out for a second during which the book characters run offstage.*)

TIM: Come on, let's make a run for it. (*The children outside the fence run into* MINTY's *yard.*)

JANET: Excuse us for bursting in like this but I'm afraid

of storms and we thought we might find shelter under your umbrella.

MINTY: You're certainly welcome. But look, the sky seems to be clearing.

TIM (*Holding out his hand*): And not a drop of rain.

BILLY: You girls are silly to be scared of storms.

BUD: Where did all the people go?

MINTY: What people? Oh, you mean the guests at my tea party. They had to leave in a hurry.

JANIE: I thought you didn't know anyone in town.

MINTY: I don't.

RUTH: Then who were all those people?

MINTY: They were my friends.

ALL: Your friends?

MINTY: Yes, my Book Friends! Surely you must know some of them. (*Picking up book*) There was The Sleeping Beauty. You must know her from your fairy tale books.

JANIE (*Taking book from* MINTY): Oh, yes. I remember. I always loved her. This is a beautiful book (*Leafing through*) and it has a lot of stories I've never read.

MINTY: You may borrow it if you like.

JANIE: Oh, could I?

MINTY: Why not? Mother says the nicest part of owning books is sharing them with your friends.

JANIE: Oh, thank you. Maybe you'd like to come over to my house and borrow some of mine?

MINTY: I'd love to.

BILLY: Who was that one character who kept his hat on at the table? He didn't seem to have good manners.

MINTY: Oh, that was Bartholomew Cubbins, and you mustn't blame him for keeping his hat on. Every time he takes one off, another pops on in its place.

BILLY: That strikes me funny. I'd like to read that story.

MINTY: Here. Take this. I know you'll love it.

TIM: Give it to me next, will you, Billy? That is—if it's all right with Minty.

MINTY: Sure, I'll be glad to lend it to you.

BETTY: Who was that handsome young man who sat right here? (*Points to* DICK WHITTINGTON'S *chair.*)

MINTY: Oh, that was Dick Whittington.

BETTY: Didn't he have a cat or something in the story?

MINTY: He certainly did, and I'm so glad he didn't bring him to the party. Poor Walter would have been scared to death.

RUTH: Walter? Who's Walter?

MINTY (*Picking up the book*): This is *Walter, the Lazy Mouse* by Marjorie Flack. It's one of my favorites. Would you like to read it?

RUTH: Well . . . if you're sure he'll stay inside the book and not go running around.

MINTY: You don't need to worry about Walter. He's too lazy to come out of the book covers.

JANET: But he was here this afternoon. I saw him.

MINTY: Oh, that was different. He made a special effort because he knew I needed him. You see, Book Friends always come when you need them.

BUD: Say, I didn't have any idea you liked books as much as you do. Why, here's an old favorite of mine—Pinocchio.

MINTY: Isn't he wonderful?

BUD: Do you remember the time he . . .

BETTY: Now don't start that . . . do you remember this and do you remember that? I know how you are when you get talking about books.

BUD: What about yourself? You took up a whole class period in school telling about *Mary Poppins*!

MINTY: Oh, do you like *Mary Poppins,* too?

BETTY: I love her. Do you have *Mary Poppins Comes Back* and *Mary Poppins Opens the Door*?

MINTY: No, I've never read those.

BETTY: Then ask your mother if you can come along over to my house and I'll give them to you right away.

MINTY: I'd love to. But why don't we sit down at the table and finish the tea party—or rather, the lemonade party?

BILLY: Thanks. That would be great.

ALL: Thanks a lot.

MINTY: Just sit where you like, and make yourselves at home. (*All sit at table.*) Here comes Mother with an extra supply of cookies.

MOTHER: Why, Minty! I'm so glad to see you entertaining. You're having a real tea party now.

MINTY: Oh, Mother! These are all my new friends.

MOTHER: I'm certainly glad to meet all you boys and girls and I'm sure you and Minty will have a lot in common.

MINTY: Oh, we do already, Mother. We have the same Book Friends! (*A roll of thunder is heard from offstage.*)

MOTHER: Oh, dear! Don't tell me we're going to have a storm.

MINTY: That's not a storm, Mother! That's just Mary Poppins giving me the signal that everything is all right and that she and the rest of my Book Friends are always standing by. (*Curtain.*)

THE END

The Forgotten Hero

Characters

MISS MERRYWEATHER, *a teacher*
MR. CAUFIELD, *an elderly school janitor*
HARRY, TERRY, MIKE, PAT, HELEN, MARY, RUTH, SARAH } *pupils in Veterans' Day chorus*

TIME: *The morning of Veterans' Day, November 11.*
SETTING: *The stage of a school auditorium.*
AT RISE: *The students are rehearsing for the annual Veterans' Day Assembly.* MISS MERRYWEATHER *is directing a small chorus in "Keep the Home Fires Burning." At the close of the song, she steps back and surveys the group.*

MISS MERRYWEATHER: That was pretty good, boys and girls, but some of you in the back row weren't watching me.

HARRY (*From back row*): We can't see you back here, Miss Merryweather.

MISS MERRYWEATHER: I know, Harry. That makes it difficult. But you'll be able to see as soon as Mr. Caufield brings the risers up from the basement. Now let's try it once more from "There's a silver lining," and be sure to take the second ending. (*Repeat last bars of song*) That was much better. (*Consulting notes*) Now, Terry, that's where you step forward and introduce our guest of honor, Colonel Wilcox. We'd better try it just to make sure. That's what rehearsals are for.

TERRY (*Stepping forward from center of first row*): All during World War I the people of America *did* keep their home fires burning for the return of their soldier boys. One of those who returned to bring great honor to his home town was Colonel John B. Wilcox. Colonel Wilcox fought in all of the major battles of World War I and was decorated for bravery during the battle of the Argonne. For the past five years, Colonel Wilcox has been living in New York, but this year he happens to be home on a visit and we are fortunate enough to have him as our guest speaker. On this one day of the year when we pay tribute to the heroes of our great wars, it is a great pleasure to be able to present a man of such distinction and courage as Colonel John B. Wilcox, who will speak to us on the topic *Heroes and How They Are Made*. Colonel Wilcox.

MISS MERRYWEATHER: Now remain standing, Terry, until Colonel Wilcox takes his position and nods to you. (MR. CAUFIELD, *school janitor, who limps slightly, enters carrying small bench.*)

MR. CAUFIELD: I couldn't find the big platform, Miss Merryweather. They must have sent it to another building during the summer. Will this bench do for what you want?

MISS MERRYWEATHER: I think so, Mr. Caufield. We'll try it. Some of you boys, put the bench in place for Mr. Caufield. (*Boys put bench in back row and stand on it.*) They seem a little crowded back there, but I guess it will have to do. Thank you, Mr. Caufield.

MR. CAUFIELD (*Looking around*): You're welcome, Miss Merryweather. The stage looks nice. You've gone to a lot of trouble for this program.

MISS MERRYWEATHER: In my opinion this is one of the most important assemblies of the whole year, Mr. Caufield. More than anything else, our boys and girls should know and appreciate what others have sacrificed to ensure their rights and liberties as Americans. That's why we're all so thrilled to have a famous hero like Colonel Wilcox as our guest speaker.

MR. CAUFIELD: By cracky! I almost forgot. I have a message for you from the office. You're to call this number right away. (*Fishes note from his pocket and hands it to* MISS MERRYWEATHER.)

MISS MERRYWEATHER: You children go right on with your rehearsal. Pat, suppose you lead the pledge to the flag. (*As she starts to exit*) Now remember, make it good and loud. (*Exit*) I'll be back in a minute.

PAT (*Stepping forward to lead pledge*): We will pledge allegiance to the flag of the United States. (*He salutes and leads chorus in pledge to the American flag.* MR. CAUFIELD *watches carefully.*)

MR. CAUFIELD (*After pledge*): If you don't mind a bit of a suggestion, sonny, that salute could be a lot snappier. Like this. (*Demonstrates*) Nothing I hate worse than a sloppy salute.

PAT: Gee, that looks neat, Mr. Caufield. You know just how to do it.

MR. CAUFIELD: I should know, boy, I've had plenty of practice saluting. Now suppose you try it again. (PAT *starts the pledge to the flag several times until the salute is satisfactory.*)

MR. CAUFIELD: That's first rate, sonny. We used to have a young fellow in my company who could never get the proper snap into a salute. One day the sergeant called him out of line and . . .

PAT: Were you in the army, Mr. Caufield?

MR. CAUFIELD: Sure, sure, I was in the army. (*There is a crash in the back row of the chorus as the bench upsets, and pandemonium breaks loose. In the general commotion there are howls of pain.*)

RUTH: It's Mike. He was standing too near the edge and fell off.

MARY: The whole bench upset!

MR. CAUFIELD (*Hastening to untangle the heap*): Easy! Easy! What's the matter? Anybody hurt?

MIKE (*Hopping up and down on one foot*): Ouch! Ouch! My foot! My foot! It's broken! It's broken.

MR. CAUFIELD (*Supporting him*): Steady now. Steady. (*As others crowd around*) The rest of you stop pushing. This young fellow will live to see a lot more assembly programs, if I'm not mistaken.

HELEN: I'd better get Miss Merryweather.

MR. CAUFIELD: Not so fast. Miss Merryweather has enough on her mind. Let me have a look at this first. (*He eases* MIKE *into a chair. The rest crowd around.* MR. CAUFIELD *kneels in front of* MIKE *and takes off his shoe.*)

MIKE: Ouch! Ouch! It's broken, I tell you.

MR. CAUFIELD: I don't think so, Mike. (*Holding ankle*) Now let's see if you can move it.

MIKE (*Twisting foot about*): Yes, I can move it, but it hurts.

MR. CAUFIELD: Sure it hurts. You've got a slight sprain there, young fellow, but with a proper bandage, you'll be as right as rain.

MARY: The school nurse isn't here today. Maybe we'd better call a doctor.

MR. CAUFIELD: If you want me to, Mike, I'll bandage that foot for you in a jiffy.

MIKE: Gee, thanks, Mr. Caufield. I wish you would.

MR. CAUFIELD: I have a first-aid box down in my locker in the furnace room. If one of you girls would go down there and bring it up for me, I think we can get Mike patched up before Miss Merryweather even gets back.

HELEN: I'll go, Mr. Caufield.

MARY: Let me go with her, Mr. Caufield.

MR. CAUFIELD (*Laughing*): It always takes two to go on an errand in this school. Very well. You may both go. The first aid kit isn't marked. It's just in a black metal box like a cash box. You'll find it without any trouble. Here's my key. (*Exit* HELEN *and* MARY)

BOTH: We'll find it, Mr. Caufield.

SARAH: My goodness, Mr. Caufield. You know how to fix everything. You mended that broken desk in our room, you put the new pane of glass in the window and you fixed the clock in the office when it wouldn't run. Now you're fixing Mike's foot.

MR. CAUFIELD: Mike's foot won't be as hard to fix as the broken desk or the run-down clock, Sarah. It's just a bad twist.

MIKE: How do you know that, Mr. Caufield? Were you ever a doctor?

MR. CAUFIELD: No, sonny, I was never a doctor. But I had lots of experience with the wounded when I was in the war.

TERRY: What war were you in, Mr. Caufield?

MR. CAUFIELD: I was in World War I, Terry.

TERRY: Golly! That's the same war Colonel Wilcox was in.

MR. CAUFIELD: It was a pretty big war.

RUTH: Were you a colonel, Mr. Caufield?

MR. CAUFIELD: A colonel? No, indeed. I was just a company sergeant.

TERRY: Were you in any big battles?

MR. CAUFIELD: Well, now, it depends on what you call a big battle. What sounds like a little skirmish in the history books might be a pretty big battle to the men who were in it.

TERRY: I mean battles like the Argonne and the Marne?

MR. CAUFIELD: Yes, yes. I was in those.

RUTH: What were they like—the battles, I mean.

MR. CAUFIELD: It's mighty hard for a man to describe a battle, child. After you've been in one, the best thing you can do is try to forget it. I wonder what's keeping the girls who went for the first-aid box. (GIRLS *enter with box*)

HELEN: Is this it, Mr. Caufield?

MARY: It doesn't look very much like a first-aid kit.

MR. CAUFIELD (*Taking box and opening it*): I keep a little bit of everything in here . . . even some of my personal treasures. (*Draws out roll of bandage*) Now, here we are. I think I can fix you up in a hurry. (*Begins to bandage foot as others watch.*)

MIKE: I hope it will stop hurting when the bandage is on, so I can walk on the stage this afternoon without limping. Does *your* foot hurt when you walk, Mr. Caufield? Is that why you limp a little bit when you walk?

MR. CAUFIELD: No, Mike. My foot doesn't hurt—not any more. That stopped hurting a long time ago.

TERRY: How did you hurt your foot, Mr. Caufield? Did you fall the way Mike did?

MR. CAUFIELD: No, I didn't fall. I was wounded. There's a bit of shrapnel still in that leg just above the ankle.

ALL: You mean you were wounded in the war?

MR. CAUFIELD: Yep. In the war. (*Working with bandage*) Tell me if this is too tight.

MIKE: No, it's not too tight.

TERRY: Were you wounded in battle, Mr. Caufield? Tell us about it.

MR. CAUFIELD: There isn't much to tell, not really. One of my buddies had gone out to try to break up a machine-gun nest. He was crawling back to our trench when a sniper got him. He let out a yell, and I crawled out after him. Before I could get hold of him and drag him back to safety, the sniper got me too. But somehow I managed to get back to our lines with him.

HARRY: Golly, Mr. Caufield. You're a hero—a real hero.

MR. CAUFIELD: Nothing of the sort, sonny. Nothing of the sort.

SARAH: But you saved a man's life. . . .

HELEN: At the risk of your own. . . .

MARY: In the midst of a battle.

TERRY: You're a real hero, Mr. Caufield.

MR. CAUFIELD: Now, will you all stop staring at me as if you'd never seen me before and hand me the scissors. You look for 'em, Mary. They're somewhere in that box.

(*As* MARY *hunts for scissors*) How does that bandage feel now, Mike?

MIKE: It feels fine, Mr. Caufield. I think I can stand on it.

MR. CAUFIELD: Well, don't try it until I get it fastened properly. Didn't you find those scissors yet? (MARY *and* HELEN *are staring at a small case they have taken from box.*) Here! Here! What's that you have? (*As he reaches for the case, they drop it, and the case opens.* HELEN *picks up the medal.*)

HELEN: It's a medal.

TERRY: Let me see. Why, it's the Medal of Honor, the highest award you can get.

HARRY: Mr. Caufield, you've been holding out on us. You really *are* a hero.

MR. CAUFIELD: I'm just the same man you see every day picking up the paper and sweeping the floors.

MIKE: But you're a hero just the same. Nobody gets one of these unless he's performed some act of bravery beyond the call of duty. (MISS MERRYWEATHER *enters.*)

MISS MERRYWEATHER: My goodness! What's happened? Why aren't you going on with your rehearsal?

SARAH: It's Mike. He fell off the bench and hurt his foot.

MISS MERRYWEATHER: Oh, dear! How bad is it? Let me see.

MIKE: It's all right, Miss Merryweather. Mr. Caufield fixed me up fine.

MISS MERRYWEATHER: Thank goodness! It seems as if everything in the world has gone wrong with this program. We'll have to change the whole thing. Colonel Wilcox isn't coming.

ALL: Isn't coming!

MISS MERRYWEATHER: No, his plans were canceled at the

last minute. He won't be coming to town until next week.

RUTH: But what will we do?

SARAH: We *must* have a speaker.

MISS MERRYWEATHER: Maybe we could find another speaker, but I wanted the boys and girls to meet a man like Colonel Wilcox . . . a real hero.

MIKE: It's too bad Colonel Wilcox can't come, Miss Merryweather. But I know where we can get someone who is just as great a hero, if not greater.

MISS MERRYWEATHER: Oh, Mike, do you really? Where?

MIKE: Right here. Right here on this stage. (MISS MERRYWEATHER *looks around, puzzled.*)

ALL: Mr. Caufield!

MARY: Look, look, Miss Merryweather, Mr. Caufield was awarded the Congressional Medal of Honor.

TERRY: He was decorated for bravery under fire.

HARRY: He rescued his buddy at the risk of his own life.

SARAH: And now, everybody's forgotten about him.

MR. CAUFIELD: Don't say that, child. Don't say that.

PAT: But it's true, just the same. Here you are, working in our school every day, and we never even knew you were a war hero until just now.

MR. CAUFIELD: Well, what do you expect? When I first came home from the war, I had my share of parades. and speeches, and celebrations. But even a hero has to go back to work, you know. And we have to put our uniforms away in mothballs, and lay aside our medals, and forget about battles. If it's heroes you're looking for, there are lots of them in town. Old Doc Nelson, down at the drug store . . . he was one of the bravest men I've ever seen in action. Then, there's Ed Thomas, at the Thomas Garage, Dick Palmer who runs the News Service, Mr. Hogan, Editor of the *Morning Times*. All of them served in the war.

HARRY: Golly, Mr. Caufield. Are they all heroes?

MR. CAUFIELD: Every man who serves his country is a hero, boy.

HELEN: But people should *remember* that they are heroes. They should remember what you did.

MR. CAUFIELD: They do remember, my dear. That's the reason we have Veterans' Day on our calendar—a day for remembering—a day for honoring our heroes. And when we remember one, we remember all. When we honor one, we honor all. When the President places the wreath on the tomb of the Unknown Soldier at Arlington, Virginia, he honors the grave of every fallen hero of every war this country has ever had. No one is forgotten—neither the living nor the dead.

MISS MERRYWEATHER: Thank you for saying that, Mr. Caufield. That's just what I want the children to learn about Veterans' Day. Will you say it for us this afternoon in assembly?

ALL: Please, Mr. Caufield, please.

MR. CAUFIELD: Well, now, I'd like to help you out, Miss Merryweather, but I'm no speech-maker.

ALL: Come on, Mr. Caufield! We need you!

MR. CAUFIELD: What would I have to say?

MISS MERRYWEATHER: The topic is *Heroes and How They Are Made,* but you could talk about anything you like, just so you point out the true meaning of Veterans' Day.

MR. CAUFIELD: I think I like that topic—*Heroes and How They Are Made*. Because that's something I really understand. You see, heroes are made right here in this school, and in other schools like this all over the country.

ALL: Right here in our school?

MR. CAUFIELD: Certainly. I've seen lots of heroes that were made here. Remember, I've been working at this school for a long, long time. I've seen classes come and go. Down in my locker I have a whole scrapbook about men and women from this school, and plenty of them were heroes. Lots of men who went into battle in World War II and served in Korea went to school in this very building. I remember them as little tackers no bigger than you.

HARRY: How did they learn to be heroes here in school? Nobody teaches that subject.

MR. CAUFIELD: Nobody needs to teach it as a special subject. But every day you're learning to understand and love your country. You're learning what America stands for. You're learning about her ideals and the principles of democracy. You're learning to think for yourselves, to read the books of your own choice. You're learning what it means to grow up in a free country. When you do grow up, you'll place a high value on that freedom. You'll be ready to fight for it, die for it, if need be . . . and that's what it takes to be a hero, you know.

MISS MERRYWEATHER: And you have what it takes to be our speaker. We'd be proud to have you, Mr. Caufield.

MR. CAUFIELD: Well, Miss Merryweather, if that's the way you want it, I'll do the best I can.

MISS MERRYWEATHER: Just say what you've said here this morning, and we'll have the best Veterans' Day program ever.

MR. CAUFIELD (*Picking up his things to leave*): If I'm to be the guest of honor, I'll have to spruce up a bit. If there's nothing else you need here on the stage, I'll go put things to rights, so I can leave at noon and get back in time for the program.

MISS MERRYWEATHER: We have everything we need, Mr. Caufield, and thank you. (*Exit* MR. CAUFIELD)

RUTH: Is our rehearsal finished, Miss Merryweather?

MISS MERRYWEATHER: I think we'd better take Terry's closing speech and the final song. Please take your places. (*Chorus gets into place,* TERRY *steps forward.*)

TERRY: It has been a privilege to hear our Veterans' Day message from a man like Sergeant Caufield. As long as we have such men as our heroes, we know that America will hold her place among the nations of the world. These are the men we remember today, the men in all walks of life, the veterans who have sacrificed themselves for the peace and security of the land we love. (*The Chorus sings "God Bless America." Curtain.*)

THE END

Vicky Gets the Vote

Characters

VICKY DEANE, *Campaign Chairman*
BOB LIGHTNER, *Candidate for Junior Mayor*
JIM, *Campaign Manager*
UNCLE JOE, *State Senator*
MR. DEANE
MRS. DEANE
EDITH
CARL
ARCHY
GEORGE
THELMA
FRANK
MIMI

SETTING: *The Deane living room.*

AT RISE: VICKY DEANE *is holding a meeting of the Lightner Campaign Committee. Ten boys and girls are scattered around the room.*

VICKY: I think we have everything under control. The posters are up and you will distribute the tags tomorrow. I think they look very nice. Edith, will you please write a letter to Mr. Zinn and thank him for printing them for us?

EDITH: I never knew being secretary for a Campaign Committee could be so much work.

VICKY: That's because we're really doing this campaign up right.

BOB: I certainly want to thank every one on this committee for working so hard. If I win, I'll owe it all to this committee, and especially to Vicky. We're sure lucky to have the niece of a state senator as our Campaign Chairman.

VICKY: I don't know about that, Bob. But I've heard Uncle Joe say that one of the most important things about a campaign is to keep the candidate's name before the public as much as possible.

BOB: And that slogan—"Light the Way with Lightner!" That's really keen.

CARL: You're just lucky to have a name that was so easy to fit into a slogan.

THELMA: Yeah. Polly Douglas did the best she could with her slogan, but yours really means something.

ARCHY: "Golly! Vote for Polly!" She'll never win with that slogan.

VICKY: It takes more than a slogan to win an election. The most important part of our campaign is tomorrow's rally in assembly. That's why I called this special meeting, so we could have a practice.

GEORGE: We're really going to show that Junior High bunch we mean business.

FRANK: We'll make 'em sit up and take notice!

MIMI: Those Junior High School kids think we're just a bunch of babies! But we'll show them a thing or two.

VICKY: Our stunt will fall flat as a pancake unless we keep

it an absolute secret and pull it off as a big surprise. Now, let's run through it just the way we'll do it tomorrow. Mimi, you stand over there by the light switch and turn off the lights on cue. (MIMI *goes to switch*) Everybody set?

ALL: We're set.

VICKY: Then, here we go. Jim, as Bob's Campaign Manager, you'll make the first speech.

JIM (*Coming forward and addressing the audience*): Mr. Chairman, members of the faculty, and student body: As you all know, this is the first time in the history of Valley View School that the lower grades have participated in a school election. The Junior High School students have conducted elections for Mayor, Assistant Mayor, Community Clerk, Treasurer and Council Members ever since the school was established. But now for the first time the elementary classes are going to vote and elect a Junior Mayor, Junior Assistant Mayor, Junior Community Clerk, Junior Treasurer and a Junior Cabinet. This is a great step forward in making our school a democratic school, and we elementary pupils feel a keen responsibility. We have made every effort to secure the best possible candidates for every office. As Campaign Manager for the office of Junior Mayor, I am very proud of my candidate. In the six years that he has been enrolled in Valley View he has held a perfect attendance record. Last year he received a merit award as the pupil who had made the greatest progress in his class, and he also received the Junior Citizenship Award. My candidate is an outstanding student, he is active in sports, and is a member of the elementary school orchestra. Outside of school, he takes part in Boy Scout activities and is well liked and respected in his neighborhood. If you vote for my candidate, you will be doing yourself and your school a favor. I now present my candidate for Junior Mayor of Valley View—Robert Lightner. (*On signal from* VICKY, *the houselights go off and every child on stage turns on a flashlight which he waves in time to the music of "Tramp, Tramp, Tramp."*)

ALL (*Singing*): Light, light, light the way with Lightner!
Bob's the boy who's here to stay.
Vote for Lightner and you'll see
What a great school this will be!
Vote for Lightner on the big Election Day! (*During the song,* MRS. DEANE, MR. DEANE *and* UNCLE JOE *enter. When lights go on at end of song, they applaud.*)

UNCLE JOE: Very fine! Very fine, indeed!

MR. DEANE: What in the world are you youngsters doing here in the dark?

MRS. DEANE: Oh, dear, Vicky, I hope we haven't interrupted your meeting!

VICKY: Why, Uncle Joe! (*Running to him*) Where in the world did you come from?

UNCLE JOE: I'm just on my way to Philadelphia, and thought I'd drop in for a visit with my favorite niece. That was mighty nice singing. What's it all about?

VICKY: Oh, Uncle Joe! You came at just the right time. We're in the midst of an election!

MR. DEANE: Here we go again, Joe! That's all she talks about! She must have gotten her political ideas from you!

UNCLE JOE: What sort of election?

VICKY: For the first time in history, the elementary pupils at Valley View are taking part in the general elections, and we're allowed to have our own Junior Officers. Uncle Joe, I'd like you to meet our candidate for Junior Mayor, Bob Lightner. Bob, this is my Uncle Joe I'm always talking about, Senator Ames.

UNCLE JOE: Glad to meet you, young fellow.

BOB: Thank you, sir. I've never met a real senator before.

UNCLE JOE: Well, maybe I won't be a real senator any more after Election Day. I'm in the midst of my campaign right now, you know.

VICKY: We're betting on you, Uncle Joe.

UNCLE JOE: That's one thing about elections, Vicky, you can never be sure till the last vote is counted.

BOB: That's what I keep telling Vicky, but she's so dead sure we're going to win that she won't even listen.

UNCLE JOE: What was all that singing when I came in?

GEORGE: That was our campaign stunt for the rally tomorrow. Each candidate is allowed a two-minute speech by his Campaign Manager, a stunt of some kind and a two-minute speech of his own.

THELMA: Vicky made up the stunt and the song.

ARCHY: "Light the Way with Lightner!" That's Bob's slogan.

UNCLE JOE: Very good. Very good. And what about his speech? I think I'd like to hear it. As one campaigner to another, maybe I can give you some tips.

VICKY: Thanks, Uncle Joe. We were just getting to that part. After the Campaign Manager makes his speech, we have the stunt with flashlights, and then Bob speaks. Go ahead, Bob.

BOB: Mr. Chairman, members of the faculty and fellow students: You have all seen my posters on the bulletin boards and heard my campaign slogan: "Light the Way with Lightner." But there is one thing I would like to point out to you. In the stunt which you have just seen, one flashlight would not have been very effective. Each light is small and flickering by itself. But all the flashlights, working together, made a good, strong beam. And that's the way it is with this election. I cannot light the way to good school government by myself. It will take all of us, working together, to do that. If I am elected Junior Mayor, I promise I will do everything in my power to secure the cooperation of all grades and all classes, so that, together, we can light the way to a better, happier Valley View School. (*All applaud.*)

UNCLE JOE (*Clapping* BOB *on the shoulder*): Excellent, young man! Excellent! Some day I should like to have you on my platform.

VICKY (*To committee*): Well, gang, it looks as if our rehearsal has been a success. Now, remember, not a word to anyone about this. Keep your flashlights out of sight till the very last minute. One blink at the wrong time would spoil the whole thing.

ALL: O.K. We understand.

MR. DEANE: Perhaps Uncle Joe has something to say to your committee.

ALL (*Applauding*): Speech! Speech!

UNCLE JOE: Well, boys and girls, Election Day has always been a great day for Americans. In the past, it was a day of torchlight processions, fireworks and great celebrations. It's only natural that Americans should make Election Day one of their Red Letter Days because so many Americans fought and died to secure the right to vote in a free election. Right now, you young folks are experiencing the first thrill of an election in which you have the right to vote. Some day you will have the same right as American citizens. I hope all of you will learn to appreciate and preserve that right. Election Day is the one day of the year when we are truly equal, when we all have equal power. Rich man, poor man—every man's vote counts the same. That is why it is so important to cast it wisely. Our great American poet, John Greenleaf Whittier, expressed this same thought in the poem entitled: *The Poor Voter on Election Day.*

"The proudest now is but my peer,
 The highest not more high:
Today of all the weary year,
 A king of men am I.
Today alike are great and small,
 The nameless and the known,
My palace is the people's hall,
 The Ballot-Box my home."

(*All applaud.*)

BOB: That was a fine speech, Senator Ames. I'll always remember it.

UNCLE JOE: Thank you, Bob.

VICKY: Thanks, Uncle Joe. (*To committee*) And now, if there is no further business, I declare the committee meeting adjourned. (*Committee exits with "Good-bye," "See you tomorrow," "So long," etc.* BOB *and* JIM *remain.*)

BOB: Thanks, Vicky, for all your help.

JIM: I'm sure the stunt will go off without a hitch. If anything else turns up, I'll call you.

BOB: It was wonderful to meet you, Senator Ames. The best of luck in your campaign.

JIM: That goes for me too, sir.

UNCLE JOE: The same to you, boys. And remember this, Bob, win or lose—you're still going to serve that school with all that's in you.

BOB: Right, sir. Good-bye, Mr. Deane. Thanks, Mrs. Deane, for letting our committee meet here.

JIM: This house has really been our campaign headquarters.

MRS. DEANE: We're always glad to have Vicky's friends here, boys. You know that.

MR. DEANE: And we wish we were young enough to vote, Bob. Maybe when you grow up and run for some town or state office, we'll still have a chance to vote for you.

BOB: Thanks a lot. Good-bye, Vicky. See you tomorrow. (*Exit* BOB *and* JIM.)

UNCLE JOE: Well, Vicky, I hope your candidate wins. He's a fine boy.

VICKY: Oh, he's bound to win, Uncle Joe. He just can't lose.

UNCLE JOE: Don't say that, child. Anything can happen in an election.

VICKY: But he's the best candidate. He really is, Uncle Joe. He has all the qualifications.

UNCLE JOE: It's still up to the voters to elect him.

MRS. DEANE: I've never seen Vicky so enthused about anything as this election.

MR. DEANE: I think it's a good thing. These boys and girls need to know how elections are run, how campaigns are conducted, and what it means to be a voter.

UNCLE JOE (*Sitting down.* VICKY *perches on arm of chair*): Yes, Fred, no American is too young to learn that every voter has a public trust which is both a privilege and a responsibility.

MRS. DEANE (*Sitting down*): How is your campaign shaping up, Joe?

UNCLE JOE: Pretty well. It all depends now on how well we succeed in getting out the vote.

VICKY: What do you mean, Uncle Joe? "Getting out the vote?"

UNCLE JOE: Getting people to the polls to cast their votes on election day.

VICKY: But doesn't everybody vote? That is—everybody who is old enough?

UNCLE JOE (*With a laugh*): I only wish they did, Vicky. In the last Presidential election only sixty-two and seven-tenths percent of the voting population actually went to the polls.

MR. DEANE: And that was a *Presidential* election. Last year at our local primaries only thirty-five percent of the voters cared enough about our city government to turn out.

VICKY: But why not? Why doesn't everybody vote?

UNCLE JOE: Lots of reasons: sickness, lack of interest . . .

MRS. DEANE: Some people I know just can't be bothered. They forget, or have other things to do.

VICKY: But how *could* you forget about such a thing as voting?

MR. DEANE: You're all steamed up and excited, Vicky, because this is your first big election. It's the first time you've had the right to vote.

UNCLE JOE: As a matter of fact, I doubt if all the pupils in your school will vote in your election.

VICKY: But they must! They've got to!

MR. DEANE: Oh no, they don't have to vote. Nobody's going to make them vote. How they vote, or whether they vote at all is a matter of individual decision.

UNCLE JOE: Don't look so worried, Vicky—although it's really something for us grownups to worry about. The United States has the lowest percentage in the world of eligible voters who actually vote.

VICKY: But, Uncle Joe, that's terrible!

UNCLE JOE: It's not very good. But maybe when you grow up, you and your friends will take voting more seriously. At least, you're getting a good start in your school. (*Looking at watch*) Sakes alive! It's later than I thought. Here it is—time to leave, and I haven't told you why I came.

VICKY: You said it was to see me.

UNCLE JOE: That's exactly right. I came to ask to borrow Vicky for next Tuesday afternoon.

VICKY: Borrow me? What for?

UNCLE JOE: To sit on the platform with me at the big rally in Capital City.

VICKY: Oh, Uncle Joe! That would be wonderful! But what about school?

MR. DEANE: I think such a trip would come under the heading of an educational experience.

UNCLE JOE: Besides, they're going to open the new bridge at Capital City and I'm privileged to invite the lady of my choice to cut the official silver ribbon when I make the speech of dedication.

VICKY (*Hopping up and down with excitement*): Oh, Mother! May I go?

MRS. DEANE: I think it's wonderful that Uncle Joe asked you, dear. What do you think, Fred?

MR. DEANE: I think it's quite an honor.

UNCLE JOE: Then it's all settled. I'll pick you up next Tuesday morning.

MRS. DEANE: That will give me time to finish your new dress, Vicky.

UNCLE JOE: Now I must be on my way. Good luck with your campaign, Vicky, and I'll see you Tuesday.

VICKY: Oh, Uncle Joe, I can hardly wait! I'm ready to die of excitement! The election on Monday and this on Tuesday. (*Hugs herself with delight*) It's simply super!

MR. DEANE: I'll see you out to the car, Joe.

UNCLE JOE: If you want to get in touch with me in the meantime, I'll be at the Washington House in Capital City.

VICKY: Good-bye, Uncle Joe, and thanks a million.

MRS. DEANE: We'll try to make you proud of her, Uncle Joe. I'm sure she'll do her very best.

UNCLE JOE: I know she will. That's why I asked her. This young lady is beginning to have a sense of responsibility toward public affairs. Good-bye, Vicky. (*All exit but* VICKY. *Phone rings and she answers.*)

VICKY: Hello. Yes, this is Vicky. Oh, hello, Bob. No, I haven't seen the paper. Ours hasn't come yet. What? What furnace are you talking about? What? But they can't do that! They simply can't. (JIM *enters waving evening paper.*)

JIM: Vicky, have you seen the paper?

VICKY (*At phone*): Wait a minute, Bob, Jim just came in. O.K., I'll call you later. (*Hangs up*)

JIM: Boy oh boy! Here's some good news! Listen to this: "Pupils of Valley View to Have Extra-Long Weekend. School Closed Friday to Tuesday to Install New Furnace!" Now there's something that happens once in a lifetime.

VICKY: But they can't do that!

JIM: Why not? They've been waiting for the new parts for that furnace for weeks. Now we have a day off!

VICKY: But, Jim, that means the election will be postponed from Monday to Tuesday.

JIM: So what? It won't make any real difference.

VICKY: But it makes a difference to me. I won't be here Tuesday.

JIM: You won't be here? Why not? Where are you going?

VICKY: I'm going to Capital City with Uncle Joe.

JIM: Well, you'll just have to tell him you can't go. You'll have to be here to vote.

VICKY: But, Jim, I can't. I'm going to sit on the platform with Uncle Joe at the big rally. I'm going to cut the ribbon at the new bridge dedication. It's terribly important.

JIM: Well, it's not as important as this election. Your Uncle Joe himself said nothing was more important than voting.

VICKY: But, Jim, what's one vote more or less? Bob can win the election without my vote.

JIM: What kind of talk is that, Vicky Deane? You know this is going to be a close election. That Polly Douglas will pull a lot of votes, especially in the fourth and fifth grades. You don't want her to win, do you?

VICKY: Of course not, but . . .

JIM: Then stay home and vote. Good grief! You're the Campaign Chairman. You can't walk out now.

VICKY: But my work is finished. I've done everything I can do. The posters are out, the tags are ready to be distributed. I've written all the speeches, the stunt is ready for tomorrow. There's really nothing else for me to do.

JIM: Except vote! And that's the most important part of the whole election! (*Enter* MR. *and* MRS. DEANE)

VICKY: Well, I can't help it. I'm not going to let Uncle Joe down.

MRS. DEANE: What's this about letting Uncle Joe down?

VICKY: Oh, Mother, they're postponing our election all on account of an old furnace!

MR. DEANE: A furnace? What furnace?

JIM: It's all in the paper, Mr. Deane. The parts have come for the school furnace and they're closing down from Friday till Tuesday in order to install it.

MR. DEANE: Well, it's about time that furnace was repaired.

VICKY: But, Daddy! It means I won't be here to vote. I've got to go to Capital City with Uncle Joe.

MR. DEANE: You don't exactly *have* to go, Vicky. Nobody's making you.

VICKY: You mean you don't want me to go?

MR. DEANE: I mean you must decide for yourself. Uncle Joe gave you an invitation . . . not an order.

MRS. DEANE: Uncle Joe would understand, Vicky. He knows how much this election means to you.

VICKY: But, Mother, I can't give up that marvelous trip just to stay home and vote!

MR. DEANE: Plenty of men in our shop who live out of town give up a whole day's pay in order to go home and do their duty as American citizens.

VICKY: But that's different.

JIM: What's different about it? We're citizens of our school, aren't we? Is this a real election to you or are you just playing games?

VICKY: Of course, it's a real election. Haven't I worked as

hard as anybody to get Bob Lightner elected Junior Mayor?

JIM: Sure you worked hard as long as it was what you wanted to do and you were having fun. Now, when you have something better to do—you forget all about your wonderful right to vote in a school election.

MR. DEANE: Whether it's a school election or a community election, Vicky, voting is a serious business.

JIM: What will Bob think if you duck out on election day?

VICKY: Bob doesn't need my one poor little vote.

JIM: Suppose everybody felt that way about it? Besides, your Uncle Joe said an election's never won till the last vote is counted.

VICKY: It's Uncle Joe I'm thinking of.

JIM: Your Uncle Joe's a great guy. My Dad says he's the best senator this state ever had. He's really doing his best to serve his country. And somehow, I don't think your Uncle Joe would want anybody sitting beside him on that platform who would walk out on his job as a voter.

VICKY (*Thoughtfully*): Maybe you're right, Jim. Maybe you're right. (*Sitting down at table.*) I guess I just didn't think it through. (*Picks up paper and pen and begins to write. There is a short pause.*)

MRS. DEANE: What are you writing, Vicky?

VICKY: Is Capital City spelled with an *al* or *ol,* Daddy?

MR. DEANE: It's *al,* Vicky.

JIM (*Looking over her shoulder*): "Dear Uncle Joe: I'm sorry about the trip to Capital City, but our election has been postponed until Tuesday and you can understand that I MUST be here to cast my vote." (*Pounding her on the shoulder*) Good for you, Vicky. You're really the greatest!

MR. DEANE: Uncle Joe was right, Vicky, when he said you were really developing a sense of responsibility toward public affairs.

MRS. DEANE: I think this will make Uncle Joe prouder than if you cut all the ribbons on all the bridges between here and California.

VICKY: Someone else can cut the ribbon but no one else can cast my vote! (*Curtain*)

THE END

The Christmas Umbrella

Characters

TING, LING — *Santa's elves*
MRS. SANTA CLAUS
SANTA CLAUS
GRANDMAMMA
MAMMA UMBERTO
PAPA UMBERTO
THERESA, CARLOS, JOE, STEVE, BETTINA, ROSA, MARIA, JOHNNY, NICK — *the nine Umbertos*
EIGHT NEIGHBORS

SCENE 1

TIME: *Christmas Eve.*
SETTING: *Santa's Workshop. It is a deserted place. The*

shelves are empty except for one big box and a few scattered toys.

AT RISE: MRS. SANTA CLAUS *is sitting in a rocking chair. Her glasses have fallen down on her nose and she is taking a nap.* TING *and* LING, *Santa's elves, are seated at a table doing a crossword puzzle.*

TING: What is a four letter word beginning with Y that means *Christmas?*

LING: That's easy. *Yule.* Y-u-l-e.

TING: That's right. (*Prints slowly*) Y-u-l-e. Now let me see. Where am I? Oh yes! 23 down. "A spicy holiday drink." Now what in the world could that be? Seven letters. The third letter could be an S or maybe an X.

LING: S is right. The word is *wassail.*

TING: How do you spell it?

LING: W-a-s-s-a-i-l. Haven't you ever heard of a *wassail bowl?*

TING: No. What does a wassail bowl have to do with Christmas?

LING: For a Christmas Elf employed by Santa Claus you certainly don't know very much about Christmas customs. A wassail bowl holds the wassail that people drink on Christmas.

TING: I think I'd like lemonade better.

LING: Lemonade! That's not a Christmas drink, silly.

TING: I didn't say it was. I just said I think I'd like lemonade better than wassail. Now, tell me what is a French word meaning *crib?* I don't know any French words.

LING: Everybody knows *that* French word. It's *crèche.* C-r-è-c-h-e.

TING: That's exactly right. It fits perfectly.

LING: Of course, it fits.

TING: You're terribly smart, Ling. Maybe you'd better do this puzzle instead of me.

LING: I don't feel like doing puzzles. I'm worried about Santa.

TING: What are you worried about?

LING: He should be home by now. Maybe something happened to him.

TING: What could have happened to him?

LING: Maybe he got tangled up in one of those television aerials!

TING: Not a good driver like Santa.

LING: Well, anyhow, I'm worried. I'm going outside and look for him. (*Exit* LING. *As he goes out* MRS. SANTA *wakes with a start.*)

MRS. SANTA: Is that you, Santa?

TING: Not yet, Mrs. Santa. He's a little late.

MRS. SANTA: I thought I heard a door.

TING: It was just Ling going outside to look for the reindeer and the sleigh.

MRS. SANTA: It must be almost dawn. I'm glad the kettle's boiling so he'll have a good hot drink when he comes in. (*Sound of bells offstage and* SANTA *shouting "Whoa" to his reindeer.*)

TING: He's coming! He's coming! I'll go help Ling unharness the reindeer.

MRS. SANTA: And I'll pour his cup of tea. (*Busies herself at the fireplace, pouring the tea and setting a plate of cakes on the table. By the time she has finished,* SANTA *enters, pulling off his gloves and rubbing his hands.*)

SANTA: Merry Christmas, my dear! It's good to be home again.

MRS. SANTA: Now sit right down and have a good, hot cup of tea. You must be half frozen.

SANTA: Nonsense! You know I never get cold on Christmas Eve. I enjoy myself so much that I'm as warm as toast. Nevertheless, a cup of tea will taste good. (*Seeing plate of cakes*) And bless my whiskers, if you haven't baked a batch of snickerdoodles! Mrs. Santa, you're a real treasure!

MRS. SANTA: Now! Now! Now! None of your pretty speeches, Santa. You save them for the children.

SANTA (*Sits at table and drinks his tea*): The trip was more wonderful than ever this year, Mrs. Santa. So many good boys and girls in the world! It just amazes me!

MRS. SANTA: What about the bad ones?

SANTA (*Sternly*): There *are* no bad ones! Not on Christmas Eve, anyway. They're all as good as gold. (*Chuckling*) And they'll be rewarded on Christmas morning when they come downstairs and see what I've brought them. By the way, were there any calls?

MRS. SANTA: Nothing but some sort of message about a Christmas tree shortage some place or other. But the connection was so bad I couldn't make it out.

SANTA: Oh well! It will doubtless straighten itself out! Those things always do. (*Enter* TING *and* LING.)

SANTA: You finished in record time, my good elves. Did you take a look at Dasher's right front foot?

TING: Nothing serious, Santa. Just a little piece of slate roofing. We got it out and he's as fit as a fiddle.

LING: Did you have a good trip, Santa?

SANTA: Marvelous! In fact, I think it gets better every year. Won't you join me in a cup of tea? And do try some of these snickerdoodles. They're remarkable.

TING *and* LING (*Seating themselves at table and sampling the cakes, as* MRS. SANTA *brings more tea*): Thanks, Santa.

SANTA (*Looking around with satisfaction*): I don't believe I've ever seen the workshop so cleaned out. There's almost nothing left.

TING: I hope we don't get any last-minute requests.

SANTA: Don't worry, we won't. It's almost Christmas morning. By the way, Ting, what's in that big box? Looks as if we could fill plenty of orders with that.

TING: Oh, that's just an extra box of umbrellas. Hardly anyone wanted an umbrella this year, you know.

LING: Umbrellas! That's not a box of umbrellas. That's a box of toys!

TING: No, you're mistaken, Ling. Those are the umbrellas. I stacked them away for next year.

LING: But I tell you I looked inside that box right after Santa left. It's a box of toys. I can even tell you what they are—a pair of roller skates, a tricycle, three dolls, a toy train, a small radio, a painting set, and a chemistry set.

SANTA: Sounds mighty peculiar to me. All those toys left over!

MRS. SANTA (*Inspecting the box*): Here's a label. (*Adjusting her glasses and peering intently at the box*) It says . . . The Nine . . . The Nine Umbertos. Now what does that mean?

TING: Those are the nine Umberto children. They live at 217 LaPlata Street in Diaz City.

SANTA: 217 LaPlata Street, Diaz City. Why, that's where I took the box of nine umbrellas. Bless my soul! I must have read the label wrong, in my order book.

MRS. SANTA: I've told you, Santa, you should have your glasses changed.

SANTA: That's exactly what I did. The *Nine Umbertos* looked like *Nine Umbrellas* to me, so I delivered the umbrellas to that address.

TING: Oh Santa! How could you have made such a mistake!

SANTA (*In anger*): Mistake—you know Santa Claus never makes a mistake.

LING: But, Santa, you just said you read the label wrong.

SANTA: So I did.

LING: Then wasn't that a mistake?

SANTA: Of course not. I read the label wrong because I was supposed to read it wrong. Santa never makes a mistake. It's impossible.

TING: I don't see how you figure, Santa. Those children are going to be terribly disappointed when they go to look for their toys and find umbrellas instead.

SANTA: Disappointed! How can you say such a thing! You, my very own elves! You know perfectly well I've never disappointed a single child in my ancient and honorable career.

MRS. SANTA: Of course, you haven't, my dear! What a ridiculous thing to say!

TING: But it isn't a bit ridiculous! Imagine those poor little Umbertos trooping downstairs on Christmas morning, which is only a few hours away, and finding those hateful umbrellas instead of the toys they ordered.

LING: How could they help being disappointed?

SANTA: So! You've lost faith in your old Santa Claus. You think I disappointed the children! You think I make mistakes! Alas! I might just as well retire!

TING: Now, don't get so upset, Santa. It may not be too late to correct your error.

SANTA: Stop talking to me about correcting errors. There has been no error. I have not made a mistake.

LING: I give up!

SANTA: You forget, my friends, that I am Santa Claus. Santa Claus always knows what the children want.

TING: But the Umberto children told you what they wanted. And instead you brought them umbrellas.

LING: Then you say they won't be disappointed.

MRS. SANTA: I guess you little fellows are too young to understand.

TING: We're old enough to understand that if a boy wants a pair of roller skates for Christmas and gets an umbrella instead, he'll be disappointed.

SANTA: But you don't seem to understand that by the time this little boy gets the umbrella, he will no longer want the roller skates. He'll be tickled pink with the umbrella! (TING *and* LING *look at each other helplessly.*) You find that hard to believe, don't you?

TING *and* LING (*Nodding their heads*): Very, very hard.

SANTA: Listen to me closely, and I'll tell you a real Christmas secret. When you give a Christmas present with real love, there can be no mistake. Those umbrellas were packed in a box that was chock full of love. Therefore, the little Umbertos are bound to be happy with them. (TING *and* LING *still shake their heads.*)

MRS. SANTA: I guess you'll just have to prove it to them, Santa.

SANTA: You still don't believe me, do you?

TING *and* LING (*With embarrassment*): We don't see how it can be possible, Santa!

SANTA: Fudge and peanut brittle! Who cares about what

is possible and impossible at Christmas time? Most grown-ups think it's impossible for me to get down their chimneys, but they discover on Christmas morning that I've been there, so they have to admit the impossible is possible.

TING: Yes, but that's different.

SANTA: It's not different at all. It's the same thing. If I am an impossible character then I can do impossible things.

LING: Well, making the Umberto children happy over nine umbrellas on Christmas morning is the most impossible thing I've ever heard of.

SANTA: Very well. Ting, go harness up the reindeer. Ling, carry this box out into the sleigh.

TING: Hurray! Hurray! You're going to take the toys to the Umbertos after all.

SANTA: I'm going to do no such thing. *You* are going to take the toys to the Umbertos. When you arrive at the Umberto house, leave the toys in the sleigh until you see how the children receive the umbrellas. If they are unhappy or disappointed, you may deliver the toys. But if you find them happy and contented with the umbrellas, bring the toys back to me lickety-split.

LING: That's a bargain, Santa. I couldn't have enjoyed a bite of my Christmas dinner for worrying about those Umberto children.

TING: Bring the box, Ling. I'll have the reindeer ready in a jiffy. (*Exits*)

LING (*Picking up the box*): Thanks, Santa, for letting us take the toys.

MRS. SANTA (*Offering him two tinsel-printed signs saying,* "INVISIBLE"): Here, I'll stick these in the top of the box. Don't forget to wear them when you go inside the Umberto house. Goodbye, and good luck.

SANTA: Drive carefully and watch out for those consarned television aerials. (LING *exits with box.*)

CURTAIN

* * * *

SCENE 2

TIME: *Several hours later.*

SETTING: *The Umberto living room.*

AT RISE: GRANDMAMMA, MAMMA, THERESA, *and* CARLOS UMBERTO *are waiting for the return of* PAPA UMBERTO.

THERESA: Surely Papa will come home soon! It is almost daylight.

MAMMA: Your papa's one determined man when his mind is made up. And he has his mind made up to find Christmas trees this night.

CARLOS: But surely he knows by this time that no shipments will arrive in time.

MAMMA: Your papa does not give up. For years this neighborhood count on Papa Umberto for Christmas trees. Now they will be disappointed.

GRANDMAMMA (*Sniffing in disdain*): Christmas trees! Pah! In Old Country we have the *Ceppo*—the Christmas Log.

MAMMA: I know, Mamma, but even in Old Country now they have Christmas tree.

THERESA: Poor Papa! He is so disappointed.

MAMMA: He is disappointed for you too, my children. Without the Christmas tree business this year, your presents will not be like last year.

THERESA: Do not worry, Mamma Mia. This year the presents are taken care of.

MAMMA: How do you mean?

THERESA: Early in the month I have helped the little ones write to Santa Claus. Carlos helped too, with the spelling.

CARLOS: They asked for everything they wanted.

THERESA: And even I, the oldest, asked for something too! (TING *and* LING *enter quietly on apron of the stage. They listen closely to the conversation, look at each other doubtfully, and then sit down at the fold of the open curtain. They wear their signs saying* "INVISIBLE.")

MAMMA: You, Theresa, you believe in Santa Claus?

THERESA: When I was writing the letters, I believed. Now I am not so sure. (TING *and* LING *shake their heads.*)

GRANDMAMMA: Santa Claus! In Old Country it is the Befano who brings the little ones the gifts on Twelfth-night.

CARLOS: Who is this Befano she talks about?

THERESA: Befano—Carlos, you have heard it a thousand times.

MAMMA: Let her tell it again. Hear, Mamma, Carlos asks you about the good Befano. The old tale will help us pass the time. (*Children sit by* GRANDMAMMA.)

GRANDMAMMA: La Befano was an old woman like myself. But she was not lucky like me. She had no one at home, no grandchildren to live with. She lived by herself near the great highway where caravans of camels used to pass. One night, the 6th of January it was, three tall men stopped at her door. They wore rich velvet gowns and golden crowns.

THERESA: They were the Three Kings.

GRANDMAMMA: That is right, child. They asked Befano

the way to Bethlehem, but alas, the good woman did not know. They told her about the Blessed Babe and showed her the gifts they were taking to the Child.

CARLOS: Didn't they ask La Befano to join them?

GRANDMAMMA: Si, they did, but La Befano thought she must care for her own workaday affairs. She did not go. She watched the great travelers go their way, following a single star that shone in the sky. Soon a shepherd came to her door. He too told the wonderful story of the Babe in Bethlehem, but still La Befano could not make up her mind to go. But after the shepherd had gone, La Befano began to think what she could have taken to the Child.

CARLOS: Was she not a very poor woman?

GRANDMAMMA: Very poor, indeed, but she had treasures of her own. She went to her great chest and found the small toys her own baby used to play with. These she decided she would take to the Baby at Bethlehem.

CARLOS: And did she take her gifts?

GRANDMAMMA: Alas, she could not find the way. The star had disappeared while she hesitated. She wandered from place to place, from town to town, looking everywhere for the Holy Child. And she is wandering even now. Every Twelfth-night when the Wise Men journey to Bethlehem, La Befano goes from house to house peering in at windows and leaving gifts on the sill in hopes she will be presenting them to the right Child.

THERESA: It's a beautiful story, Grandmamma. But here it is Christmas Eve and Christmas Day that children get their presents.

CARLOS: And the little ones believe Santa Claus will bring them what they want. (*Sound of door opening and closing*)

MAMMA: Perhaps it is your father. (*Enter* TONY UMBERTO *carrying box of umbrellas.*) Tony, Tony, is that you?

PAPA: Yes, Mamma. I have come home! Theresa and Carlos, are you still up?

THERESA: We were waiting for you, Papa.

CARLOS: Did the trees come? Did you find any?

PAPA (*Putting box on floor and sitting down*): Not a one! Not a single one to be had. (*Buries his head in his hands*) Not only our own Christmas but so many others will be ruined. Papa Umberto has failed them.

MAMMA: Nonsense, Tony. Everyone knows you did your best to find trees.

CARLOS: What's in the box, Papa? (TING *and* LING *crouch closer to the curtains listening intently.*)

PAPA: I do not know. I found it by the chimney place in the kitchen.

THERESA: It's from Santa Claus! I know it! I know it! See, Carlos, it was by the chimney place. It must be from him.

PAPA: What is this foolishness?

THERESA: It is not foolish, Papa. Carlos and I helped the little ones write their letters. They asked Santa Claus for gifts and here they are . . . roller skates for Joe, a tricycle for Steve, dolls for Bettina, Rosa, and Maria, a chemistry set for Carlos, and a little radio for me. . . . The little radio I asked for so Mamma and Grandmamma can hear the music all day long.

CARLOS: Let's open the box, Papa. Hurry, hurry!

MAMMA: Yes, Papa, do hurry.

GRANDMAMMA: Perhaps La Befano comes early this year. (*As they open the box,* TING *and* LING *rise to their feet and stand poised for flight.*)

CARLOS: What is it?

THERESA: Careful, Papa, you might break one of the dolls!

MAMMA: Let me see.

GRANDMAMMA: Such a big box! (PAPA UMBERTO *holds up an umbrella.*)

ALL: An umbrella!

THERESA: Look again, Papa. The toys must be underneath. (PAPA *pulls out eight more umbrellas.*)

CARLOS: Nothing but umbrellas!

THERESA: But no one ordered an umbrella! Not a single one!

MAMMA: Such good quality, these umbrellas.

GRANDMAMMA: Umbrellas! Fah! The good Befano did not leave these! When it rains, I wear shawl over my head!

PAPA: They are very fine umbrellas, but so many of them! I wonder who could have sent them.

MAMMA: Maybe they go to wrong house.

THERESA: No . . . the label says . . . The Nine Umbrellas!

CARLOS: They're for us all right!

THERESA: I don't believe these umbrellas are from Santa Claus. He could never have made such a mistake.

CARLOS: He sure must be a dope to send nine children nine umbrellas. (TING *and* LING *shake their heads and pantomime their decision to go for toys*)

THERESA: I am so disappointed I could cry.

PAPA: Silly girl! Umbrellas are useful. They are good for something, and besides they are presents. You do not cry over presents.

THERESA: I could cry over these. They are not the presents the children ordered. And they have been so good, so patient, and they believed so firmly Santa would come.

GRANDMAMMA: In Old Country everything is better. La Befano is better, the Ceppo is better. You remember, my daughter, the handsome Christmas log your father used to make with tier after tier of decorations built on a frame above the log.

MAMMA: I remember. It looked like a great, golden triangle, with all the sparkling . . . Papa! Papa! I have been struck! I have been struck!

PAPA: Maria! Maria! What is the matter?

CHILDREN: Mamma! Mamma, what is it?

MAMMA: I have been struck by a great idea. I am inspired.

CHILDREN: What is it? What is it?

MAMMA: These umbrellas! They are a gift from the good St. Nicholas. They have come when we need them most. (TING *and* LING *turn back in astonishment and wait.*)

CARLOS: What do we need them for? It is not raining.

MAMMA: Hush! You have heard Grandmamma tell of the Ceppo. The Christmas log decorated and trimmed with Christmas pretties. In some countries I have heard they decorate a sheaf of wheat, in others they make paper Christmas lanterns.

THERESA: In Mexico they have a Piñata . . . a great paper mask filled with presents.

MAMMA: So why not the umbrella?

CARLOS: What about the umbrellas?

MAMMA: We decorate them. They become our Christmas trees.

ALL: What?

MAMMA: In magazine I read article. Quick. I show you! You come with me. (*Grabs up armful of umbrellas*) To the kitchen, march! (*All follow her to the kitchen except* CARLOS *who exits in the opposite direction as his mother calls*) Run, Carlos, run upstairs and bring the Christmas ornaments from the chest. (TING *and* LING *move center as others exit.*)

TING: Shall we get the toys?

LING: Not yet. We'll wait and see what happens.

TING: Do you think Santa may be right after all?

LING: It's possible. Maybe you and I have made the mistake in doubting him. Quick, here comes that boy again. (CARLOS *enters with trimmings and* TING *and* LING *return to positions at curtain's edge.*)

CARLOS (*Calling*): Here are the trimmings, Mamma. All the tinsel, and balls and strings of lights. (MAMMA *and her procession enter.* MAMMA *carries an umbrella stripped of the covering. The ribs are wound with tinsel. She puts the umbrella on the table in a little stand which has been previously made for it.*)

MAMMA (*Proudly*): Now for the trimmings. Papa, you arrange the lights. (*Quickly the* UMBERTOS *trim the umbrella with Christmas lights, balls and icicles.*)

THERESA: Another blue ball, Carlos. Now a red one! (CARLOS *hands the trimmings.*)

GRANDMAMMA: Let me put on the icicles. Always I put the icicles on the tree.

MAMMA: Oh, it is beautiful.

PAPA: It is not bad, Mamma. Not bad at all. In fact, it is pretty, very, very pretty. I think you have great idea.

THERESA: Oh, this is such fun. I never thought an umbrella could be so wonderful. Another red ball, Carlos.

MAMMA: And the star! Do not forget the star. (*Puts star on top as* PAPA *turns on the lights*)

ALL: Wonderful! Beautiful! Almost as good as a real tree.

THERESA: I can hardly wait for the little ones to see! (*Knock at door*)

PAPA: Visitors at this hour? (*At door*) Come in and a happy Christmas to you. (*Eight* NEIGHBORS *enter.*)

1ST NEIGHBOR: We saw you come home, Tony. Did you get the trees?

2ND NEIGHBOR: I told the children you would not fail us. They would have a tree on Christmas morning.

3RD NEIGHBOR: But what is this? (*Sighting the umbrella*)

PAPA: It is our Umbrella Tree. Mamma and the children, they made it up. You like?

ALL: It is beautiful!

4TH NEIGHBOR: But it is an umbrella!

5TH NEIGHBOR: Just an ordinary umbrella.

MAMMA: Not just an ordinary umbrella, friend. This is a Christmas Umbrella. In our house it becomes our Christmas tree.

6TH NEIGHBOR: But umbrellas are expensive. We have none to spare.

7TH NEIGHBOR: Good Umberto, do you have another one of these . . . another umbrella like this one?

8TH NEIGHBOR: My little ones would be delighted.

PAPA (*Proudly*): Yes, yes! Your good neighbor will not fail you. You shall have your Christmas umbrellas, if not your Christmas trees. Carlos, bring in the rest of the umbrellas. (CARLOS *exits to kitchen and returns with umbrellas.*)

1ST NEIGHBOR (*Reaching into pocket*): How much? How much money do we owe you, friend?

PAPA: Nothing! Not a cent. These umbrellas are gifts to us and gifts they shall be to our neighbors. (CARLOS *deals out umbrellas.*)

2ND NEIGHBOR: But surely we can pay you something. The winter has been a hard one, neighbor. Perhaps a toy for your little ones. My own children have grown too old for some of theirs. My Angela has a beautiful doll so big. She no longer plays with it.

THERESA: Oh, please! Please, Papa! A doll for Rosa, please.

3RD *and* 4TH NEIGHBORS: We also have dolls we can bring you, Papa Umberto. Little girls always love a dolly for Christmas.

1ST NEIGHBOR: And I have a painting set, just right for a little boy like Johnny.

5TH NEIGHBOR: My children no longer play with the little train. How about that for Nick?

6TH NEIGHBOR: Perhaps your Carlos would enjoy a chemistry set. My Albert has two of them.

7TH NEIGHBOR: Our tricycle would be just the right size for your Steve.

8TH NEIGHBOR: I've heard your little Joe asking for roller skates. Let me give you a pair in exchange for the umbrella.

PAPA: You are too kind, too kind.

NEIGHBORS: You have saved our Christmas with your umbrellas. Thank you. Thank you. (*Exit* NEIGHBORS *with umbrellas*)

THERESA: Oh, isn't it wonderful, Mamma? Just like a fairy story.

CARLOS: The children will have their tree.

THERESA: And their presents too. I can hardly believe it.

PAPA: But what about you, little daughter? Did you not order something from Santa Claus?

THERESA: I did, Papa, but I am perhaps too old. He brings presents only for little children.

PAPA: You may be right, child. Santa leaves some things for the Papas to bring. Go look on the kitchen table. (THERESA *runs out and runs in again clasping a small radio.*)

THERESA: Oh, Papa! Papa! A radio! See, Mamma. See, Grandmamma . . . . It will play all the beautiful music. Plug it in, Papa. Let's hear how it sounds. (PAPA *attaches radio and they tune in on "Deck the Halls with Boughs of Holly." As the music plays, the seven little Umbertos appear in the doorway.*)

BETTINA: Is it Christmas yet, Mamma?

ROSA: Has Santa Claus been here?

MARIA: Did he bring my dolly?

ALL: Look! Look! The tree! The tree! The beautiful tree! (*All join hands and dance around the table singing "Deck the Halls" as the curtains close leaving* TING *and* LING *outside.*)

TING: We two are still invisible,

LING: Except to *you* and *you*.

TING: And we have surely learned a lot,

LING: At least a thing or two.

TING: We know that Santa can't do wrong,

LING: To any girl or boy

TING: For every single gift he brings

LING: Is packed with Christmas joy.

TING: So if you get a curious gift

LING: Say . . . like an umbrella,

TING: Just count yourself a lucky girl

LING: Or lucky little fella.

TING: For every gift upon the earth

LING: Or from the sky above

TING: Is sure to brings its happiness

LING: If packed with Christmas love.

(*They exit.*)

THE END

Softy the Snow Man

Characters

SANTA CLAUS
SIX DEPARTMENT STORE SANTAS
SPUNKY, *head of Santa's workshop*
MRS. SANTA
MR. SNOW MAN
MARY, RUTH, BETSY — *a committee*

SETTING: *The display room of Santa's workshop.*

AT RISE: SANTA CLAUS *is demonstrating a mechanical toy to six young department store* SANTAS. *The store* SANTAS *are dressed just like the real* SANTA CLAUS *except that they are not padded and do not have beards. Each store* SANTA *wears a placard announcing the name of his store.*

SANTA (*From behind desk, as the mechanical toy runs down*): There! That's how it works, boys. Isn't it wonderful? Won't the children love it?

STACY'S SANTA: Well, sir, it's all right, but . . .

SANTA: All right? All right? Is that all you have to say about it? Why, it's wonderful. The child who finds this toy in his stocking on Christmas morning will be the happiest youngster in the block.

BON TON SANTA: That all depends.

SANTA: On what? I tell you this toy is a sure-fire hit.

GRIMBLE'S SANTA: I think it depends on the age of a child.

SANTA: Why, you young whippersnappers! What do you know about children? You're still new at the job. You don't even have a beard, and you're trying to tell me what children will and will not like.

BONAMAKER'S SANTA: You don't have to grow a beard to know what children like, Mr. Santa.

SANTA: Is that so? Then suppose you tell me what is wrong with this toy.

GRAY'S SANTA: That's what we're trying to tell you, Mr. Santa, but you won't listen.

SANTA: Well, I'm listening now. Go on and tell me. Don't you think this is an amazing toy?

BELL'S SANTA: Of course it is!

SANTA: Then what's the matter with it?

STACY'S SANTA: It's fine for older children, Mr. Santa, but little children won't like it.

SANTA: Nonsense! It will make them laugh.

BON TON SANTA: It might frighten them.

GRIMBLE'S SANTA: Besides, it isn't lovable.

BONAMAKER'S SANTA: No little boy or girl will want to take it along to bed.

BELL'S SANTA: It isn't cuddly.

GRAY'S SANTA: And it isn't washable.

SANTA: Cuddly! Washable! Phooey! We have hundreds of cuddly, washable toys for small children.

BONAMAKER'S SANTA: But the children are tired of stuffed dogs and cats and rabbits and pandas and teddy bears. They want something new.

SANTA: Of course they do, and this is the newest thing on the market.

DEPARTMENT STORE SANTAS (*Shaking their heads sadly*): It isn't cuddly.

SANTA (*Pounding his desk*): Will you please stop repeating that silly word—cuddly! I find it revolting.

DEPARTMENT STORE SANTAS (*Stiffly*): Very well. (*They start to exit.*)

SANTA: One moment. Where are you going?

STACY'S SANTA: If you do not value our opinion, we might as well leave.

GRIMBLE'S SANTA: After all, we department store Santas have direct contacts with the boys and girls.

BON TON SANTA: They climb up on our laps and tell us what they want.

BELL'S SANTA: We have inside information.

BONAMAKER'S SANTA: We study the toy market.

GRAY'S SANTA: We know what makes a toy popular or unpopular.

DEPARTMENT STORE SANTAS: And we know children like toys that are . . .

SANTA: Don't say it! Don't say it! There's that awful word again. Perhaps you had better go before I lose my temper.

DEPARTMENT STORE SANTAS: Very well. We bid you good day. (*Exit*)

SANTA: Good riddance! What do they know about children? Trying to tell old Santa how to run his workshop, are they? Well, I'll show them. (*Rings hand bell on desk*) Spunky will know all the answers. (*Rings bell louder and* SPUNKY, *who looks as if he might be first cousin to one of Snow White's Seven Dwarfs, enters.*)

SPUNKY: You sent for me, Santa?

SANTA: Yes, I did, Spunky. Have you tallied the Christmas letters for this year?

SPUNKY: Yes, sir. I have all the figures. Anything special you'd like to know?

SANTA: Among the children between the ages of one and six, how many requests did you find for mechanical toys?

SPUNKY: Well, I don't rightly know the exact figure, Santa, but I should say about three million.

SANTA: Good. And from children of the same age group, how many requests did you have for—(*Clears throat*) cuddly toys?

SPUNKY: Now that number I can remember, Santa, because it was the largest single item in the lot. Six million, sir.

SANTA: Six million!

SPUNKY: That's right, sir. The little children always ask for toys they can pet and hug and take to bed at night. And mothers always add a little note to make them washable.

SANTA: Bless my whiskers! Those smart alecks were right! This puts me in a pretty kettle of fish.

SPUNKY (*Misunderstanding*): No one asked for fish, sir. Not a single one.

SANTA: I didn't ask you that, Spunky. I said I am in a pretty kettle of fish. That means I'm in a stew, in other words, I'm on the spot.

SPUNKY: Is something troubling you?

SANTA: That's putting it mildly. Spunky, what kind of stuffed, cuddly toys do we have on hand?

SPUNKY: Oh, the usual, sir . . . dogs, rabbits, pandas, teddy bears. . . .

SANTA: Don't we have anything new?

SPUNKY: Not a thing, sir. In fact, I was going to bring it to your attention. Couldn't we have some new cuddly toys this year? The children love them so.

SANTA: Please, Spunky. I hate that word "cuddly."

SPUNKY: Then I won't use it, sir. I'll say—"squshy" instead.

SANTA: That's even worse. If you mean *cuddly,* I suppose you must say *cuddly*. But try not to use it unless you absolutely must. You see, those young sprouts from the department stores have been pestering me.

SPUNKY: The department store Santas?

SANTA: Yes, they agree with you that we must put out a brand new toy this year that is . . . er . . . well, you know what I mean.

SPUNKY: Yes, indeed, sir.

SANTA: And that's where I'm stuck. I don't have any new ideas in that field. We've been making dogs and cats and pandas and teddy bears for so long that I can't think of anything new. Do you have any ideas?

SPUNKY (*Shaking his head sadly*): None at all, sir. In fact, I am having so much trouble in the workshop now, that I don't see how we're going to get everything finished—to say nothing of developing a new product.

SANTA: Trouble in the workshop? What in the world is the matter?

SPUNKY: It's Mr. Snow Man! He slows up production at every turn.

SANTA: Oh, dear! What has he done now?

SPUNKY: Yesterday he told all the workers in the paint department to take the afternoon off.

SANTA: But why? Why? Why did he ever do such a thing right in the midst of our busiest season?

SPUNKY: He said the men needed time to do their Christmas shopping.

SANTA: He did, did he? And who is he to give orders around this shop? Spunky, send that man to me at once. At once, do you hear? This time, I'm really going to . . .

SPUNKY: Are you going to fire him? Mrs. Santa would never approve.

SANTA: Well, er. . . . I've had just about enough of his foolishness. This time, I'm really going to . . . Oh, well, send him in right away.

SPUNKY: Yes, sir. Right away. (*Exit* SPUNKY.)

SANTA (*Getting record book from his desk*): Mrs. Santa thinks Spunky is too hard on Mr. Snow Man, but his record is a poor one. In fact, there are so many black marks against him now, there's hardly room for another one. (*Opening book*) Late every morning last week! Fell asleep on the job twice on Tuesday afternoon. Absent entirely all day Wednesday! And now this! (MR. SNOW MAN *enters. He removes his battered hat politely and stands leaning on his broom.*) Oh, there you are, Snow Man.

SNOW MAN: Spunky told me you wanted to see me, sir. I hope it's not about my work. That is—I hope everything is satisfactory.

SANTA: Satisfactory? (*Waving record book under his nose*) You call this a satisfactory record? Late every morning last week. . . .

SNOW MAN: Oh, dear me! So I was. But I had such a good reason. You see, Mr. Santa, every morning on my way to work, I pass Billy Barclay's house. You know little Billy Barclay, don't you?

SANTA: Of course, I know him. Everybody knows Billy. But what does he have to do with your case?

SNOW MAN: Well, ever since Billy had polio, he has been wanting to get out in the yard during a snowstorm and build a snow man, but of course, he was never strong enough. Then last Sunday he had his chance. And he built quite a nice snow man—for such a little boy. Naturally by Monday morning, it was badly melted and out of shape . . . so I've just been helping his mother fool him a little bit.

SANTA: Fool him? How?

SNOW MAN: Well, you see, Billy loves his snow man so much that every morning as soon as he is awake, his mother carries him to the front window to see it.

SANTA: But I thought you said it was melted the very first day.

SNOW MAN: It was. But I've been taking its place. I stand in the front yard until Billy looks out the window and then I hurry to work. Since Billy doesn't wake up until almost nine o'clock, it does make me a little late. But, oh, Santa, it's such a small pleasure for such a good little boy.

SANTA (*Clearing his throat*): Ahem! Very thoughtful of you, Snow Man, and very kind. Under the circumstances, I guess we'll have to excuse you . . . but what about these other offenses? It seems you fell asleep on the job Tuesday afternoon.

SNOW MAN: Dear me! I'm sorry about that. But you see, I had had scarcely any sleep on Monday night.

SANTA: That's a poor excuse. What were you doing?

SNOW MAN: I was porch sitting.

SANTA: Porch sitting?

SNOW MAN: It sounds easy, doesn't it? But it's really very

tiring. You see, the Mulligan family, the Plum Street Mulligans, were giving a big party and they didn't want to spend any money for decorations. So they invited me to stand on the porch all evening.

SANTA: But you weren't very smart to tire yourself out like that.

SNOW MAN: Perhaps not. But the Mulligans are such nice people. I wanted to help them out.

SANTA: And what about Wednesday, the day you were absent?

SNOW MAN: I really couldn't afford that day off, Mr. Santa, but I just had to help little Piny.

SANTA: Who on earth is little Piny?

SNOW MAN: Little Piny is the small pine tree on the old Watson farm right near the highway. Piny is such a little tree his mother couldn't bear to see him cut down this year. The Christmas tree men were coming on Wednesday, and Piny and his mother were frantic. Christmas tree cutters choose little trees like Piny because they're so easy to chop down.

SANTA: How could you help?

SNOW MAN: The whole forest knew that the tree cutters would arrive on Wednesday so I just took the day off and went down.

SANTA: But what did you do?

SNOW MAN: I stood in front of little Piny and concealed him. The men never even saw him. His mother was so happy she almost cried and Piny fairly trembled with joy.

SANTA: Mr. Snow Man, you are the limit. You leave your job to protect a baby pine tree and then come back and give the painters a half-holiday.

SNOW MAN: But for good cause—their Christmas shopping.

SANTA: But you slowed up production. Mr. Snow Man, your trouble is that you are just too soft-hearted for your own good.

SNOW MAN: That's what my family tells me all the time. In fact, that is why they call me "Softy."

SANTA: Softy the Snow Man! That's a good name for you. Well, Softy, just because I'm soft-hearted too, I'll give you one more chance. But mind you, the very next time you get into trouble, out you go.

SNOW MAN: You mean I'll be fired? Oh, Santa, you couldn't do a thing like that. What would I do? Where would I go, if I couldn't work here with you? You and Mrs. Santa are the only ones who understand me.

SANTA: But can't you understand that our work must be done on time? December 25th is our deadline. Already we're behind schedule and my advisors tell me that six million children will be disappointed on Christmas morning because we haven't had time to design a new cuddle toy.

SNOW MAN: Oh, dear! That's too bad. Maybe I could think of something.

SANTA: You keep your mind on your own job. That's all I ask you. Now get back to your workbench before we waste any more time. (*Enter* MRS. SANTA *carrying a white teddy bear.*)

MRS. SANTA: Santa! Santa! Look! Look! Oh, this is terrible.

SANTA: What's the matter?

MRS. SANTA: I was just down in the workshop and what do you think I found? Three thousand teddy bears ruined, just ruined.

SANTA: Who did it? Who is responsible?

MRS. SANTA: Spunky says it was Mickey, Mickey Ryan.

SANTA: Impossible. Mickey is our most careful worker. He never makes mistakes.

MRS. SANTA: But he did this time. He forgot to refill the spray gun with brown paint instead of white and now we have three thousand teddy bears the wrong color.

SANTA: This is terrible. Send for Mickey at once.

MRS. SANTA: Spunky is looking for him now! I guess he was so terrified when he saw what he had done that he ran away.

SNOW MAN: Oh, no. He didn't run away. He went to the dentist.

BOTH: The dentist!

SNOW MAN: Yes. The poor boy had such a toothache it just melted my heart to see him suffer, so I told him to run along to the dentist and I would work the spray gun. I forgot all about changing the paint.

SANTA: Then it was your fault! I might have known! Well, this ends it. You're fired.

MRS. SANTA: But, Santa, you can't fire Softy. We couldn't get along without him.

SANTA: I could get along very well without him.

MRS. SANTA: And who would sweep the snow off our sidewalk every morning? Who would take extra blankets out to the reindeer in the middle of the night? Who would work after hours to do the packing and load the sleigh? Who would help you in and out of the chimneys when your rheumatism is bothering you? I'm glad somebody around this place has a soft heart.

SANTA: But he's *too* soft-hearted. That's the trouble.

SNOW MAN: I just can't seem to help it. Whenever I see someone in trouble or in need, my heart just seems to melt and go all squishy-squashy. (*Enter* SPUNKY *with three little girls.*)

SPUNKY: Sorry to interrupt at a time like this, sir, but here is the committee from the Children's Home to select this year's toys. I see you've found out about Mickey's terrible mistake. I hope you won't be too hard on him, sir.

SANTA: It wasn't Mickey's mistake at all, Spunky. It was Mr. Snow Man's fault, as we might have guessed in the first place. I'll talk to you about it later after our little guests have made their decision. Have you seen all the toys in the workshop, my little dears?

GIRLS: Yes, sir, all of them.

SANTA: And now you've come to tell old Santa what to take to the children in the home. Is your list ready?

MARY: We have the list for the older children, Santa. Here it is.

SANTA: Good for you, Mary. (*Glancing at list*) Very good indeed. I think we can fill your order down to the very last ball and bat.

RUTH: And here is the list for the in-betweeners, Mr. Santa. We found some lovely things.

SANTA: Thank you, Ruth. I'm glad you like this year's toys.

BETTY: But we don't know what to do about the little children, Santa. They always want cuddly toys.

SANTA (*Grabbing his head with both hands and moaning*): I knew it! I knew it!

SPUNKY: I showed them all we had, sir, but they weren't satisfied.

BETTY: Oh, they're very nice, Santa, but we had hoped for something new and different.

RUTH: And extra soft and squshy.

The Birds' Christmas Carol

Characters

THE CAROLERS
NARRATOR
GRANDMA BIRD
DONALD, HUGH, PAUL, CAROL — *the Bird children*
NURSE PARKER
UNCLE JACK
MRS. RUGGLES
NINE RUGGLES CHILDREN
MRS. BIRD

BEFORE RISE: CAROLERS *enter on apron of stage.*

1ST CAROLER: Is this our last stop? My feet are nearly frozen!
LEADER: Yes, this is the last one. Then home to my house for plenty of hot chocolate.
2ND CAROLER: Someone must be up late in that big house

Adapted from the original story by Kate Douglas Wiggin

across the street. All of the windows on the second floor are lighted.

3RD CAROLER: Maybe they'll invite us in to get warm.

LEADER: Think about the music instead of your feet, and you won't be so cold. Now, this is our last performance, so let's do our very best. (CAROLERS *sing several selections.*) That was truly beautiful. I'm sure anyone who was listening would feel the real spirit of Christmas in your music.

2ND CAROLER: I wonder if they were listening in that big house. The lights are still on, but no one is opening the door.

3RD CAROLER: I wonder how many people have heard our carols tonight, and what they thought of them.

LEADER: That's something we'll never know. But I have an idea that our Christmas caroling affects people more than we imagine. Who knows but what Christmas will take on a deeper meaning to some folks, just because of the carols we sang tonight. (CAROLERS *exit, all but one who serves as* NARRATOR.)

NARRATOR: And even our leader would have been surprised at the results of our carol-singing in the big, brownstone house. The family's name was Bird, and the reason why the Birds' Nest was all lighted up in the small hours of Christmas morning was that a new little fledgling, a very precious Baby Bird, had come into the world shortly after midnight. As the other children gather in the living room after breakfast, their Christmas gifts are almost forgotten in the excitement of hearing about their baby sister. (*Exits*)

* * *

SCENE 1

SETTING: *A living room decorated for Christmas.*

AT RISE: *Three small boys are gathered about their grandmother.*

HUGH: What's the baby's name, Grandma? What are they going to call her?

GRANDMA: I can't say for sure, dear, but I think your mother's going to call her *Lucy*. Would you like that?

HUGH: Oh, yes, well enough. It will do . . . for a *girl!* If it had been a boy, I think *Texas* would be a good name.

DONALD (*In disgust*): Aw, Texas isn't a real boy's name. It's the name of a state.

HUGH: It can also be a boy's name. Lots of boys are named *Texas!*

DONALD: Only in stories. Not for real! Anyhow, the baby's not a boy, it's a girl, so what are we arguing about?

PAUL: I think Luella's a pretty name.

HUGH: Yeah! Ever since you had that pretty nurse in the hospital named Luella, that's your favorite name. You even wanted to name our puppy Luella.

DONALD: Dorothy's a good name, too.

HUGH: Especially when it belongs to Dorothy Hagen, the girl who sits across the aisle from you.

DONALD: Now listen, you. . . .

GRANDMA: Children! Children! Not so loud! We don't want to disturb your mother or wake the baby! Anyhow, we can't be absolutely sure what the baby's name is until we hear from your mother.

PAUL: Maybe Dad will have a good idea for a name.

HUGH: Nope. Dad named all three of us boys. He says it's Mother's turn this time.

DONALD: Uncle Jack says a first girl baby should always be named for its mother.

GRANDMA: Well, one thing you can be sure of. Your mother will never allow her baby to go overnight without a name. In fact, I wouldn't be surprised if the matter has already been settled.

PAUL: When are we going to see the baby?

GRANDMA: As soon as the nurse says you may go up.

DONALD: Aw, I don't want to see it. I'd rather ride my new tricycle around the block.

GRANDMA: Donald Bird! What a dreadful thing to say! Of course, you want to see your little sister. (*Enter* NURSE)

NURSE (*To* GRANDMA): Excuse me, ma'am, but Mrs. Bird would like you to bring the boys upstairs now to see the baby.

GRANDMA: That's wonderful, Nurse. We'll be right up.

PAUL: What's the baby's name, Miss Parker? Has Mother decided yet?

NURSE: Indeed, she has, and I think she has selected the most perfect name in the world for a Christmas baby. *Carol.* Isn't that a sweet name?

ALL: Carol?

GRANDMA: Is it short for Caroline?

NURSE: No, indeed. It means just what it says. . . . *Carol* —a song of joy for Christmastide.

GRANDMA: Strange, she never even mentioned that name before.

NURSE: No, the idea came to her early this morning. Right after the baby was born, Mrs. Bird heard the carolers singing on the corner, and said the music was so sweet, it sounded as if the angels were bidding the baby welcome. "Carol" . . . she said . . . "She's Mother's little Christmas Carol," and that's how she decided on the name. A lovely thought if you ask me, ma'am.

PAUL: Gee Willikers! I guess if she had been born on the Fourth of July, they'd have named her *Independence!*

HUGH: If it had been February twenty-second, they might have called her *Georgiana* or maybe even *Cherry!*

DONALD: Carol! I think that's a pretty name. What are we waiting for? Let's go and see her. (*Starts for door*)

GRANDMA: Not so fast, young man! I thought you didn't want to see the new baby at all.

DONALD: Well, I've changed my mind since I know her name is *Carol.* I think it will be fun to have a little Christmas Carol around the house 365 days in the year.

CURTAIN

* * *

NARRATOR (*Entering*): And it *was* fun to have Carol around the house 365 days in the year. Perhaps because she was born at holiday time, Carol was a very happy baby, and also a very beautiful baby. Her cheeks and lips were red as holly berries; her hair was for all the world the color of a Christmas candle flame; her eyes were bright as stars; her laugh like a chime of Christmas bells, and her tiny hands were forever outstretched in giving.

But by the time ten Christmases had come and gone, a sad change had come over the Birds' Nest; for the little child who once brought such an added blessing to the day, lay month after month a patient, helpless invalid. A famous doctor had warned the family that someday soon Carol would slip quietly away from those who loved her so dearly. But in spite of their sorrow, the Birds determined to make Carol's tenth birthday the very best Christmas ever. Carol herself had planned the day down to the last detail, and she could hardly wait to describe her plans to her beloved Uncle Jack, just home from England in time for the holidays. (*Exits*)

* * *

Scene 2

SETTING: *A corner of* CAROL'S *bedroom.*

AT RISE: CAROL *is in bed, propped up on pillows.* UNCLE JACK *is seated near her.*

CAROL: I want to tell you about my plans for Christmas, Uncle Jack, because it will be the loveliest one I've ever had. You know, ever since I discovered how wonderful it is to be born on Christmas Day, I've tried to make someone extra happy on my birthday, and this year it's to be the Ruggleses.

UNCLE JACK: That large brood of children in the little house at the end of the back garden?

CAROL: Yes. Isn't it nice to see so many together? Uncle Jack, why do *big* families always live in small houses and the small families in big houses?

UNCLE JACK: That's pretty hard to explain, Carol.

CAROL: Well, don't bother. I'm sure the Ruggleses have a good time in their little house. Ever since they moved in, I've watched them play in their back yard. One day when they were extra noisy, and I had a headache, Donald asked them not to scream quite so loud, and what do you think they did?

UNCLE JACK: I hope they listened to Donald.

CAROL: Oh, they did. They played Deaf and Dumb Asylum all afternoon so they wouldn't disturb me.

UNCLE JACK (*Laughing*): Quite an obliging family, I must say.

CAROL: Now, Sarah Maud, she's the oldest, stops every day to see how I am before they start their games. Then she and Peter tell the others what to play.

UNCLE JACK: Which is the pretty, little red-haired girl?

CAROL: That's Kitty.

UNCLE JACK: And the fat one?

CAROL: Little Larry. He's the youngest.

UNCLE JACK: And the most freckled one?

CAROL: Now, don't laugh! That's Peoria.

UNCLE JACK: Carol, you're joking.

CAROL: No, really, Uncle Jack, she was born in Peoria, Illinois.

UNCLE JACK: And is there a Chicago and Cincinnati?

CAROL: No. The others are Susan and Clement and Eily and Cornelius and Peter.

UNCLE JACK: How did you ever learn their names?

CAROL: I have a window-school. When the weather is warm, I sit on the balcony, and the Ruggleses climb up and walk along our garden fence, and sit on the roof of our carriage house, and I tell them stories.

UNCLE JACK: And how do these children fit into your Christmas plans?

CAROL: I want to give the nine Ruggles children a grand Christmas dinner, and afterwards a tree, just blooming with presents. Here, I've written the invitation. Please read it and tell me if it's all right.

UNCLE JACK (*Reading*): "Birds' Nest, December 17th: Dear Mrs. Ruggles: I am going to have a dinner party on Christmas Day, and I would like to have all your children come. I want them every one, please, from Sarah Maud to little Larry. Mamma says dinner will be at half-past five, and the Christmas tree at seven; so you may expect them home at nine o'clock. Wishing you a Merry Christmas and a Happy New Year, I am

Yours truly,
Carol Bird."

CURTAIN

* * *

NARRATOR (*Entering*): That invitation caused a tumult of excitement in the Ruggles household. Poor Mrs. Ruggles was almost beside herself with preparations. Such a washing and scrubbing and mending of clothes you never saw. Larry had a new suit made out of his mother's old plaid shawl. Sarah Maud trimmed her skirt with a row of brass buttons off her uncle's policeman's uniform, and Peoria gave half her candy to the next-door neighbor in exchange for a pair of stockings that matched. Finally the great day came, and after an extra tubbing and scrubbing, Mrs. Ruggles lined them up on a row of chairs in the kitchen for final inspection and a lesson in manners. (*Exits*)

* * *

SCENE 3

SETTING: *The Ruggles home.*

AT RISE: *The nine Ruggles children are lined up on kitchen chairs, a wood box and a coal hod.* MRS. RUGGLES *inspects them.*

MRS. RUGGLES: Well, if I do say so, I've never seen a cleaner, more stylish mess of children in my life! I do wish your father could look at you for a minute. (*Crossly*) Larry Ruggles, how many times have I told you not to keep pulling at your sash! Haven't I told you if it comes untied, your waist and trousers'll part company in the middle . . . and then where'll you be? (*Severely*) Now look me in the eye, all of you! I've often told you what kind of family the McGrills was. I've reason to be proud, goodness knows! Your uncle is on the police force of New York City, and I can't have my children fetched up common, like some folks. When my children go out, they've got to have clothes and learn to act decent. Now, I want to see how you're going to behave when you get there tonight! Isn't as easy as you think. Let's start in at the beginning and act out the whole business. Pile into the bedroom there, every last one of you, and show me how you're going to go into the parlor. This'll be the parlor, and I'll be Mrs. Bird. (*Children go off stage and* MRS. RUGGLES *assumes exaggerated pose of a society woman. On signal from their mother, the children straggle in,* SARAH MAUD *in the lead.* LARRY *is at the tail end, but suddenly he makes a mad dash, slips and slides into home base.*)

MRS. RUGGLES (*In complete disgust*): There! I knew you'd do it some such fool way. Now, go in there and try it again, and if Larry can't come in on two legs, he can stay at home, do you hear? (*Children exit again and re-enter in lock step, single file*) No! No! No! That's worse yet! You look for all the world like a gang of prisoners! There isn't any style to that! Spread out more, can't you, and act kind of careless-like! Nobody's going to kill you! That isn't what a dinner party is.

(*Children try again, do better, and seat themselves once more on the chairs.*) Now you know there aren't enough decent hats to go around, and if there were, I don't know as I'd let you wear 'em, for the boys would never think to take them off when they got inside. Now, look me in the eye! You're only goin' just around the corner. You needn't wear hats, any of you! When you get into the parlor, and Mrs. Bird asks you to take off your hats, Sara Maud must speak up and say it was such a pleasant evening, and such a short walk, that you left your hats at home. Now can you remember?

ALL: Yes, ma'am.

MRS. RUGGLES: What have *you* got to do with it? Wasn't I talking to your sister, Sarah Maud?

ALL (*Meekly*): Yes, ma'am.

MRS. RUGGLES: Now we won't leave anything to chance. Get up, all of you, and try it. (*Children rise.*) Speak up, Sarah Maud. (SARAH MAUD *swallows again and again in stage fright.*) Quick! Speak up!

SARAH MAUD (*In desperation*): Ma thought that it was such a pleasant hat, that we'd better leave our short walk at home. (*Roars of laughter from the children*)

MRS. RUGGLES: Oh, whatever shall I do with you? I suppose I've got to teach it to you word by word. Now try it again. The rest of you, sit down!

SARAH MAUD: Ma thought it was such a pleasant evening and such a short walk that we left our hats at home.

MRS. RUGGLES: Again! (SARAH MAUD *repeats phrase.*) There! I guess you've got it! Now, Cornelius, what are *you* gonna say to make yourself good company?

CORNELIUS (*Startled*): Who? Me? I dunno!

MRS. RUGGLES: Well, you aren't going to sit there like a bump on a log, without saying a word to pay for your vittles, are you? Ask Mrs. Bird how she feels this evening or if Mr. Bird's having a busy season or how this weather agrees with him, or something like that. Now, we'll make believe we're having dinner. That won't be hard, cause you'll have something to do. If they have napkins, Sarah Maud down to Peory, may put 'em in their laps, and the rest of you, tuck 'em in your necks. Don't eat with your fingers! Don't grab anything off one another's plates! Don't reach out for anything! Wait till you're asked! And if you never get asked, don't get up and grab it! Don't spill anything on the tablecloth, or like as not, Mrs. Bird'll send you away from the table. Susan, keep your handkerchief in your lap where Peory can borrow it if she needs it! And I hope she knows when she does need it, though I don't expect it! Now, we'll try a few things to see how they go. (*Adopting society pose*) Mr. Clement, do you eat cranberry sauce?

CLEMENT: You bet your life!

MRS. RUGGLES: Clement McGrill Ruggles! Do you mean to tell me you'd say that at a dinner party? I'll give you one more chance. Mr. Clement, will you take some of the cranberry?

CLEMENT (*Meekly*): Yes, ma'am, thank you kindly, if you happen to have any handy.

MRS. RUGGLES: Very good indeed! But they won't give you two tries tonight. Miss Peory, do you speak for white or dark meat?

PEORIA: I'm not particular as to color. Anything nobody else wants will suit me!

MRS. RUGGLES: First-rate! Nobody could speak more genteel than that! Miss Kitty, will you have hard or soft sauce on your pudding?

KITTY: Hard or soft? Oh, a little of both, please, and I'm much obliged.

PETER: What a pig!

ALL: Piggy! Piggy! (*They make grunting noises.*)

MRS. RUGGLES: None of that, and stop your grunting, Peter Ruggles. That wasn't greedy. That was all right! It's not so much *what* you say, as the way you say it. And don't keep staring cross-eyed at your necktie pin, or I'll take it off and sew it on Clem or Cornelius. Sarah Maud'll keep her eye on it, and if it turns broken side out, she'll tell you. Gracious! You'd think you'd never worn jewelry in your whole life!

Eily and Larry are too little to train, so you two just look at the rest and do as they do! Lord have mercy on you and help you to act decent! Now, is there anything more you'd like to practice?

PETER: If you tell me one thing more, I can't sit up and eat! I'm so cram full of manners now, I'm ready to bust without any dinner at all!

CORNELIUS: Me, too!

MRS. RUGGLES (*With sarcasm*): Well, I'm sorry for you both! Now, Sarah Maud, after dinner, every once in a while, you must get up and say: "I guess we'd better be going." Then, if they say: "Oh, no, stay a while longer," you can sit down. But if they don't say anything, you've got to get up and go! Now, have you got that into your head?

SARAH MAUD (*Mournfully*) It seems as if this whole dinner party sets right square on top of me! Maybe I could manage my own manners, but to manage nine manners is worse than staying at home.

MRS. RUGGLES (*Cheerfully*): Oh, don't fret! I guess you'll get along. Well, it's a quarter past five, and you can go now. (*Children line up to depart.* MRS. RUGGLES *follows them off stage, giving directions till the last child is out of sight and the curtains close.*) Remember about the hats! Don't all talk at once! Susan, lend your handkerchief to Peory! Cornelius, hold your head up! Sarah Maud, don't take your eyes off Larry! Larry, you keep tight hold of Sarah Maud and do just as she says! And whatever you do, all of you . . . never forget for one second. . . . (*Shouting*) THAT YOUR MOTHER WAS A McGRILL!

CURTAIN

* * *

NARRATOR (*Entering*): There never was such a party! There were turkey and chicken, with delicious gravy and stuffing, and there were half a dozen vegetables, with cranberry jelly, and celery and pickles; and after these delicacies were served, there were plum pudding, mince pie and ice cream; and there were more nuts and raisins and oranges than anyone could possibly eat. Then there was the tree with the presents! By nine o'clock the Ruggleses could hardly stagger home with their boxes, bags, bundles and packages. All in all, it was a Christmas the children would never, never forget. (*Ruggles children come across the stage, each one laden with gifts.*)

SARAH MAUD (*Carries a large paper bag in one hand, and holds onto* LARRY *with the other*): This is a bag of oranges Mrs. Bird sent along home to Ma. It's so heavy I can hardly carry it!

LARRY: I have a Noah's Ark with all the animals!

CORNELIUS: Would you believe it . . . every fellow had his own particular butter and there were pictures stuck right fast on to the dishes!

PETER: Wait a minute, everybody! I have to see what time it is on my new watch!

CLEMENT: You'll wear that watch out taking it in and out of your pocket. Be careful you don't break it before Ma sees it!

CORNELIUS: If he does break it, I can fix it with my new set of tools.

PEORIA: I can hardly wait to wear my beautiful new dress!

SUSAN: Me, too! And I bet my new coat is warm as toast!

KITTY: I love my doll baby! She has the most beautiful clothes in the world!

EILY: No, no! Mine are the prettiest! Aren't mine the prettiest, Sarah Maud?

SARAH MAUD: Everything's just lovely, Eily. Now come along while we can still walk! Ma'll be worried about us. And remember, not any of you is to tell her that Larry got stuck in the hall rack behind all those canes and umbrellas.

ALL: We won't! We won't!

KITTY: I wish Ma could have had some of that wonderful dinner and tasted that plum pudding!

PETER: Don't worry. She did! Mr. Bird told me they sent a whole dinner over to our house with ice cream and everything.

PEORIA: I'm glad! I hope she got a drumstick like mine.

LARRY: And I got the wishbone! (*Making a chant of it as the children exit*) I got the wishbone! I got the wishbone!

NARRATOR (*As children exit*): And if the Ruggleses had a wonderful time, Carol Bird, their little hostess, enjoyed it even more. She and her mother talked it all over when Mrs. Bird came in to say goodnight. (*Exits*)

* * *

SCENE 4

SETTING: *A corner of Carol's bedroom.*

AT RISE: CAROL *is propped up on pillows, ready for the night. Her* MOTHER *sits on the edge of the bed.*

CAROL: Oh, wasn't it a lovely, lovely time, Mother?

MOTHER: It certainly was, darling, but I'm afraid you've had enough excitement for one day.

CAROL: From first to last, everything was just exactly right! I'll never forget little Larry's face when he saw the turkey, nor Peter's when he looked at his watch! And, Mother, did you see Kitty's smile when she kissed her dolly, and Sarah Maud's eyes when she saw her new books!

MOTHER: We mustn't talk any longer about it tonight, dear. You're far too tired.

CAROL: I'm not so tired. In fact, I've felt fine all day, not a pain anywhere. Perhaps this has done me good.

MOTHER: I hope so. There was no noise or confusion, just a happy, happy time. Now, I'm going to close the door for a little while so you can get some rest. There's a little surprise for you later on.

CAROL: Surprise?

MOTHER: Yes, dear. The Carolers did not come this way last night, and so they're paying us a special visit this evening just so you may hear your favorite carol. Isn't that nice of them?

CAROL: Wonderful, Mother, wonderful! I will stay awake to hear them.

MOTHER: Oh, they'll be here early. We asked them to come before ten o'clock because after that, you might be asleep.

CAROL: I'll listen to every word. And please, will you raise the shades. This morning, I woke ever so early, and one bright, beautiful star shone in the eastern window. I never noticed it before, and I thought of the Star in the East that guided the Wise Men to Bethlehem. Good night, Mother. Such a happy, happy day!

MOTHER: Good night, my precious Christmas Carol. Goodnight.

CAROL (*Calling her mother back*): And, Mother dear, I do think we have kept Christmas this time just as *He* would like it. Don't you?

MRS. BIRD: I'm sure of it, my darling. I'm sure of it. (*Curtains close as* MOTHER *leans over to kiss* CAROL *good night. On apron of the stage, the* CAROLERS *quietly assemble.*)

LEADER: We are here, as you know, by special invitation to sing for little Carol Bird. Eleven Christmases ago, the music of one of our caroling groups inspired Mrs. Bird to name her baby daughter *Carol.* So tonight, we'll sing the same carols that were sung on the little girl's birth day. (*Announces same carols used in prologue and* CAROLERS *sing them*)

1ST CAROLER: It's after ten o'clock. I do hope she heard us.

2ND CAROLER: Oh, dear! I hope she wasn't asleep! (*To* LEADER) Do you think Carol heard the music? Do you think she is still awake?

LEADER *(Looking up in the direction of* CAROL'S *window)*: I can't be sure, child. Perhaps she *has* fallen asleep! But somehow, even if she did, I feel quite sure she heard the music, after all! (CAROLERS *leave stage softly humming the last carol as stage lights darken and house lights come on.*)

THE END

The Santa Claus Twins

Characters

MISS JINGLE
CHRISTMAS FAIRY
JACK-IN-THE-BOX
TOY SOLDIER
NED
FRED
RAG DOLL
FRENCH DOLL
CLOWN
COWBOY
WEIGHER
MEASURER
TEDDY BEAR
MESSENGER
SOLDIERS
CHILDREN

SETTING: *Classroom stage with no decoration except a Christmas tree.*

AT RISE: MISS JINGLE, *the teacher, is ready to rehearse her Christmas play.*

MISS JINGLE:
I'm putting on a Christmas play!
And it's a lot of trouble!
Sometimes I get so tired that
I think I'm seeing double!
The children are as good as gold.
They learned their parts with ease.
And now, the cast! I'll call your names.

Assemble, if you please. (*Enter* CHRISTMAS FAIRY, JACK-IN-THE-BOX *and* TOY SOLDIER)
Now, little Christmas Fairy,
Why do you wear a frown?
I see you have your silver wand,
And lovely, sparkly crown.

FAIRY: I'm just as nervous as can be!
Suppose I should forget!

MISS JINGLE:
Oh, nonsense! You know every word!
On that it's safe to bet. (CHRISTMAS FAIRY *moves to one side of stage.*)

MISS JINGLE:
Now, let me see! Oh yes, it's Jack!
But where on earth's your box?

JACK: Too heavy, Teacher! And it feels
As if it's filled with rocks!
But Dad will make another
Especially for the play.

MISS JINGLE:
All right! I guess we'll do without,
And make believe today!
Toy Soldier next! Come let me see
Your shiny sword and gun.

TOY SOLDIER:
My mother's finished with the suit,
But gee! . . . the hat's not done!

MISS JINGLE:
Oh, never mind. You look first-rate,
So stand up straight and tall.
Remember, you're the captain bold,
Commander of them all!

TOY SOLDIER (*Saluting*): 'Ten shun! Forward march! (*Other toy soldiers enter and drill.*)

MISS JINGLE:

Bravo! Bravo! (*Applauds the drill*)
I'm proud of you. You marched without a pause.
And now it's time we take a look
At Mr. Santa Claus! (*Two boys enter, one from each side of the stage, dressed exactly alike in Santa Claus suits.*)

ALL: Two Santa Clauses!

MISS JINGLE: What's this? What's this? I told you yesterday
That only *one* could take the part
Of Santa in our play.

NED:

I got here first! I know my lines!
And I can say them too!

FRED: But I have talent! I can act!
I'm better far than you!

NED: You're not!

FRED: I am! My mother says so!

MISS JINGLE:

Boys! Boys! Behave yourselves!
Now listen, both, to me.
We need *one* Santa Claus . . . no more
Beside our Christmas tree!
It may be Ned; it may be Fred.
We'll put you to the test,
And let the children help decide
Which one of you is best. (*Clapping hands as a summons*)
Come, children! Quickly gather round. (*Children enter*)

Now you must cast your vote
For Fred or Ned, and which should wear
The Santa pants and coat. (*Children assemble in groups on the stage.*)

RAG DOLL: Oh, please, Miss Jingle, please explain
How we can pick and choose.
I do not know how we can tell
Which is the best to use.

MISS JINGLE: Well, well! I guess we'll have to think
Of what he needs to do,
And choose the one who is the best
At picking up his cue.

RAG DOLL: A Santa must be merry,
And speak up loud and strong,
And shout a "Merry Christmas"
Or even sing a song!

FRED: Anything you can shout, I can shout louder! I can shout anything louder than you!

NED: No, you can't!

FRED: Yes, I can!

NED: No, you can't!

FRED: Yes, I can!

BOTH (*At the top of their lungs*): MERRY CHRISTMAS!

FRENCH DOLL (*Hands over ears*): We have to cover up our ears!

TOY SOLDIER: That must have been a tie!

RAG DOLL: But what about a Christmas song?

MISS JINGLE: We'll give each one a try. (*Each contestant sings one verse of a Christmas song.*)

COWBOY:
You boys know how to rope a song!

You really know your staff!
But Santa must be jolly—
I'd like to hear you laugh. (*There is a loud chorus of Ho-Ho-Ho's and Ha-Ha-Ha's, each Santa trying to out-laugh the other. All children begin to laugh.*)

MISS JINGLE:
Enough! Enough! Now call a halt!
We're getting indigestion!
Attention, children. Quiet, please!
We must decide this question. (*Children quiet down.*)

FRED:
My mother's coming to the play
And all my aunts and cousins.

NED: My relatives are coming, too,
And I have simply dozens!

FRED:
They want to see me on the stage
With Santa's bulging pack.

NED: And if *I* don't play Santa Claus,
They'll want their money back!

MISS JINGLE:
Well, children, it is up to you,
And I would know your pleasure.

CLOWN: I guess we'll have to take their weight
And also take their measure.

MISS JINGLE: Go get the tape, go get the scales. (*Children bring in tape measure and scales.*)
We'll judge on pounds and inches.

FRED (*Stepping on scales*): You'll find I am a heavyweight!

NED (*As child pulls tape around his chest*): Ouch! Ouch!
That tape line pinches. (NED *and* FRED *are weighed and measured.*)

THE WEIGHER:
Alack! Alas! They weigh the same!
No difference by the pound!
THE MEASURER:
They're just as tall, and just as broad,
And just as big around!
TEDDY BEAR:
Oh dear, oh dear! It's getting worse.
I can't make up my mind.
But one big thing we 'most forgot,
A Santa's always kind.
MISS JINGLE:
Then who can speak for Ned or Fred
And name a kindly deed?
Step forward quickly, if you will,
And testify with speed.
CLOWN:
Fred helps his mother every day,
Runs errands to the store.
COWBOY: Ned mows the lawn and rakes the leaves
And scrubs the cellar floor.
RAG DOLL:
Fred never never picks a fight
Or teases little girls!
FRENCH DOLL:
Ned helps his little sister out
And never pulls her curls.
TOY SOLDIER:
Fred always feeds a dog or cat
That has a hungry look.
JACK-IN-THE-BOX:
Ned shares with others all the time—

A game, or toy or book.

MISS JINGLE:

We'll have to put it to a vote,
Raise hands, if you're for Fred.
(*Half the group votes for* FRED)
And you who do not raise your hands
Are casting votes for Ned. (*Naturally the vote is a tie*)

MISS JINGLE:

Oh, goodness gracious, it's a tie!
Whatever shall we do? (*Enter* MESSENGER BOY *with telegram*)

MESSENGER BOY: Telegram for Miss Jingle! Telegram for Miss Jingle!

MISS JINGLE: I'm Miss Jingle, boy.

MESSENGER BOY: Then here's a wire for you!

ALL: A telegram! A telegram!

MISS JINGLE: Dear me! It's from the North Pole!

ALL: From the North Pole!

MISS JINGLE: Why, it's from Santa Claus. The *real* Santa Claus.

ALL: What does it say?

MISS JINGLE: Oh, dear, I'm so excited. It says: Dear Miss Jingle:

ALL: Dear Miss Jingle!

MISS JINGLE (*Reading*):

The Christmas Fairy in your play
Has told me you're in trouble.
Instead of *one* boy Santa Claus,
You're really seeing double.
I understand that both these boys
Are fully qualified,
And when you put it to a vote,
You found the vote was tied.

I hear you're in a dither now
Deciding what to do.
The answer's very simple for
You'd better use the *two*.

ALL: Two Santa Clauses! Who ever heard of such a thing?

MISS JINGLE (*Continuing reading*):
Experience has taught me that
Two hands are not enough.
You need at least an extra pair
To handle Christmas stuff.
For every year at Christmas when
The holiday begins . . .
I have a very solemn wish:
I wish that I were twins!

ALL (*Laughing*): The Santa Claus Twins! Hurrah for the Santa Claus Twins.

MISS JINGLE (*Continuing reading*):
I hope this solves your problem
Of putting on your play.
And now, to all your players . . .
A merry Christmas Day!

Signed
Santa Claus
St. Nicholas
Kris Kringle Incorporated

FRED: Now tell me, Christmas Fairy,
How did you do this trick?

NED: Did you write to Mr. Santa,
Or telephone St. Nick?

CHRISTMAS FAIRY:
Oh, no. I used my magic wand
And wished with all my heart
That Santa Claus himself would choose

The best boy for the part.

TOY SOLDIER:

And now the matter's settled—
The best man always wins,
And here you see the only pair
Of Father Christmas twins.

ALL (*Singing the following song to the tune of "Up on the Housetop"*):

Up on the housetop the job begins
Out jump both our Santa Twins;
Down through the chimney with
lots of toys,
Doubling all your Christmas joys!
(*Chorus*) Ho, ho, ho! Who wouldn't go!
Ho, ho, ho! Who wouldn't go!
Up on the roof with merry grins,
Down through the chimney with Santa Twins!

First comes the stocking of little Nell,
Oh, dear Santas, fill it well.
She wants a dolly that laughs and cries,
Let it be twins as a big surprise!
(*Chorus*)
Next is the stocking of little Bill.
Both of you must work to fill.
He wants a train and a mile of track,
Lucky for him there's an extra pack!

(*Chorus*)

THE END

The Christmas Runaways

Characters

JOEY, *a runaway boy*
DOODLES, *his little sister*
BRAD, *a schoolboy*
SKIPPER, *his pal*
POKEY, *a friend*
THE LADY

SETTING: *A stable.*

AT RISE: *The stage is empty. Then two children enter. They wear heavy coats and each carries a bundle. The little girl holds a doll.*

DOODLES: Can't we stay here, Joey? I'm so tired and Betsy is hungry.

JOEY: Stop whining, Doodles. I told you this would be rough, and it is. You said you would be game.

DOODLES: I *am* game, but it's Betsy. She hasn't eaten anything for hours and if she isn't fed soon she'll begin to cry.

JOEY (*Laughing*): You and that doll! Every time you want something, you pretend it's for Betsy.

DOODLES: Boys just don't understand about dolls. Anyhow,

she's not cold. I have her wrapped in a good warm blanket.

JOEY: Well, put her down somewhere and take off your coat. It doesn't seem very cold in here.

DOODLES (*Taking off coat and unwrapping the doll which she lays on a pile of hay*): What are we going to have for supper, Joey?

JOEY: Same thing we had for lunch . . . sandwiches.

DOODLES (*With a sigh*): They were such dry sandwiches. Don't we have any milk or a little hot soup?

JOEY: Hot soup! What do you think this is . . . a hotel?

DOODLES: Silly! It's a barn. Even I know that much.

JOEY: Well, then, stop talking about hot soup. Next thing you'll be mentioning roast turkey and mashed potatoes and gravy and cranberry sauce . . .

DOODLES: No, I won't, Joey. That's for tomorrow. That's what we'll have for Christmas dinner when we get to Cousin Ellen's house in the city.

JOEY: You mean *if* we get to Cousin Ellen's house in the city.

DOODLES: How much further is it, Joey? We've come an awful long way.

JOEY: We've come exactly five miles, if you want to know. And the city is at least thirty miles from here.

DOODLES: I told you we had come a long way. Five miles is as far as . . . well I guess it's almost as far as the moon.

JOEY: Doodles, you're a character.

DOODLES: What's a character, Joey? Is it something nice?

JOEY: Oh, it's nice enough, I guess. Come on now, (*Opening his bundle*) eat your sandwich. As soon as we've rested a bit we can start out again.

DOODLES: Aren't we going to sleep here?

JOEY: How do you expect we'll ever get to the city if we sleep here? We've got to travel all night if we want to get there in time for Christmas.

DOODLES: I don't think Betsy will like this sandwich one bit, but I'll offer her a bite. (*Goes to doll and pretends to feed her a bite of sandwich*)

JOEY: If she's smart, she'll eat it whether she likes it or not; it's all we've got.

DOODLES: I'll tell her about the turkey dinner we're having tomorrow at Cousin Ellen's. That should encourage her.

JOEY: Talk won't fill her stomach or yours either. Now eat your sandwich and stop jabbering. If you eat every crumb of it, I'll give you a bite of chocolate bar.

DOODLES (*With delight*): A chocolate bar? Joey, you're almost as good as Santa Claus for surprises. Where did you get a chocolate bar?

JOEY: I've been saving it for an emergency and I guess this is it.

DOODLES (*Stuffing sandwich into her mouth*): I'll eat every bit, Joey. There! It's all gone.

JOEY (*Taking candy bar from pocket and breaking off a piece*): Here's a piece for now. (*Putting the rest back in pocket*) The rest is for later.

DOODLES (*Munching candy bar*): I'll eat it very, very slowly. Maybe I can make it last till we light the light.

JOEY: Light what light?

DOODLES: That lantern. It's beginning to get dark in here.

JOEY: We're not going to light any lantern, you little goose. Do you want to set fire to the barn or something? Besides, we don't want anyone to know we're here.

DOODLES: That's right. I keep forgetting we're running away.

JOEY: How could you forget such a thing for a single minute?

DOODLES: I don't know. It's easy. I guess I just have a good forgetter.

JOEY: Well, remember this much. If anyone should happen to come in here, we hide and keep perfectly quiet. Understand?

DOODLES: I understand and it makes me feel all shivery inside when I think about it. Do you think Aunt Sarah and Uncle William have missed us yet?

JOEY: Not yet. They'll think we're at the entertainment, and when they discover that we're not there, they'll have our note about going to Cousin Ellen's. (*Voices are heard offstage*) Sh! What's that?

DOODLES: Somebody's coming.

JOEY: Quick, let's hide. Now remember, you must be absolutely quiet. (*Children hide behind some equipment, right stage. The beam of a flashlight plays over the barn and three boys enter. They are older than* JOEY *and* DOODLES *and wear good hiking clothes. They carry camping equipment.*)

BRAD (*Shining flashlight all around*): The coast's clear. Come on, fellows.

SKIPPER: Say! This looks like a good place. It's dry and snug, and not very cold.

POKEY: And best of all, it's deserted. Not a soul around.

BRAD: It's too far from the house for anybody to come nosing about here tonight. Let's make ourselves at home. (*Boys pile in and begin to unpack their gear.*)

SKIPPER: Rustle up that grub, Pokey. I'm starved.

BRAD: A cup of hot cocoa will taste good to me.

POKEY: We have cocoa every night for supper at school and you never drink yours.

BRAD: Oh, this is different. Even those baked beans will taste good right out of the can. (*Boys unpack picnic goods, pour cocoa from thermos and begin to eat. They sit on the floor leaning against the bale of hay.*)

SKIPPER (*Stretching in sheer comfort*): Boy oh boy! This is the life. No books, no lessons, no professors . . .

POKEY: And no Christmas carols!

BRAD: Yeah . . . it's not school we're running away from, it's Christmas.

POKEY: Another Christmas shut up in that school would have driven me crazy. Three years I've been there now. Same old Christmas Eve party, same old Christmas tree, same old entertainment and tomorrow the same old Christmas dinner.

SKIPPER: With just about a dozen of us in a dining room built for three hundred!

BRAD: Your idea of this camping trip just about saved my life, Skipper.

POKEY: Mine, too. Boy, oh boy! Was I glad to get away some place where we wouldn't hear or see anything connected with Christmas! More beans, fellas?

SKIPPER *and* BRAD: Sure thing. Pile 'em up. Where are the rest of the buns? How about some of those pickles? What happened to the potato chips?

POKEY: Don't eat everything the first meal. We've got to have something for tomorrow.

BRAD: We've got the corned beef hash and by that time we should be up in the mountains where we can build a fire and roast some potatoes.

SKIPPER: Sounds good to me. I'll eat anything at all, just so it isn't turkey and mashed potatoes and filling and gravy and cranberry . . . (*Suddenly sees doll on bale of hay*) Well, bless my great Aunt Susie! What's this? (*Holds up doll.* DOODLES *makes a frantic effort to crawl out of hiding but* JOEY *pulls her back.*)

BRAD: Looks like a doll to me.

POKEY: I wonder how such a thing ever got into a barn.

SKIPPER: That's not such a tough mystery. Some little kid must have left it here. Look . . . here's a blanket, too.

SKIPPER (*Suddenly ties doll up in blanket*): Here! Want to play beanbag? Catch! (*He tosses doll to* BRAD, *who quickly throws it to* POKEY, *etc. This is too much for* DOODLES. *She tears away from* JOEY, *runs across the stage and hurls herself on the boy who happens to have the doll at that moment.*)

DOODLES: Stop! Stop! Stop it, I say! You're hurting her! You're hurting my darling Betsy. (*Succeeds in snatching doll from boy. Struggles to unfasten blanket*) Oh, dear! She's probably smothered by now! You mean, cruel, wicked boys! How could you ever do such a thing! (*Boys stand still in amazement.*) There! There, darling! Don't cry. You're safe now.

SKIPPER: Where in the world did you come from?

BRAD: How did you get here?

POKEY: Who are you?

DOODLES: I wouldn't even speak to such awful . . . such awful . . . characters! (*Boys laugh.*)

SKIPPER: Say, you're a spunky little trick. What's your name?

DOODLES: I won't tell you. (JOEY *emerges from hiding place.*)

JOEY: Her name is Drusilla but everybody calls her Doodles.

SKIPPER: Jehosophat! This empty barn is crawling with people.

POKEY: Are your mother and father and the rest of the children here too?

JOEY: We don't have a mother or father and this is all the children we are. We're running away.

BRAD: Well, that makes us buddies. So are we.

JOEY: Yes, I . . . we . . . heard you talking.

DOODLES: I don't like these boys, Joey. They're running away from Christmas.

SKIPPER: Is that so terrible, sister?

JOEY: It's terrible to Doodles because we're running away to find Christmas.

POKEY: This is too deep for me. Let's have some light on the conversation. There's a lantern that looks as if it has some oil in it.

DOODLES: Now you'll burn down the barn!

POKEY: Not your Uncle Pokey, little girl. I've had Boy Scout training and I know how to be careful with lanterns. We'll set it up here on top of this barrel so no one will knock it over. (*Pretends to light lantern. Stage lights come up.*) There! Isn't that more cozy?

JOEY: Suppose someone sees the light?

BRAD: Not much danger. It's pretty deserted around here. Besides, everybody sticks close to home on Christmas Eve.

DOODLES (*Going up to* JOEY): Oh, Joey, I wish we were home. I don't like it here with these horrid boys. And Betsy doesn't like it, either. Let's go back to Aunt Sarah and Uncle William.

JOEY: Come now, Doodles. That's no way to act. Remember what a dreary Christmas we had last year with no tree, and hardly any presents and no regular Christmas dinner? Remember how we planned for a real Christmas this year with Cousin Ellen?

DOODLES: Does Cousin Ellen believe in Santa Claus for sure?

JOEY: Of course, she does. Didn't she send us a card with his picture?

DOODLES: That's right, she did. And will she let us hang up our stockings?

JOEY: Well, we'll be getting there too late to hang up our stockings, but it will be a million times better than Christmas with Aunt Sarah and Uncle William. They don't even approve of Santa Claus and Christmas trees and big dinners.

SKIPPER: Golly! That's just the kind of Christmas we're running away from, isn't it, fellas?

BRAD: Yeah. But I guess it's all right for little kids.

POKEY: I guess it would be all right for big kids too, if they were home with their families instead of away at boarding school.

BRAD: Look, Doodles, wouldn't you like a nice hot cup of cocoa?

SKIPPER: And some beans? How about some good, fresh beans, right out of the can?

POKEY (*With sudden inspiration*): I bet that poor doll is plenty hungry. How about it, Doodles? Shall we give Betsy some cocoa?

DOODLES: I guess you're not such bad boys after all. Yes, thank you, Betsy and I would like some cocoa and some beans. And I bet Joey would like some too.

POKEY: Sure, Joey, there's plenty for all of us.

JOEY: Thanks. It looks good, just like a picnic.

BRAD: It's a picnic all right; and we're going to have a picnic camping way up in the woods where there are no colored lights and no decorations and nothing to remind us of Christmas. (*Sound of automobile horn. Everyone is startled.*) Golly! I hope no one is stopping here.

JOEY: Maybe we should put out the lantern.

SKIPPER: The light doesn't show from the road.

DOODLES: I'm scared, Joey.

JOEY: Nobody's going to hurt you.

POKEY: How about some more food?

JOEY: No, thanks. Doodles and I must be on our way. Come on, Doodles. Here's your coat.

DOODLES: I have to wrap Betsy in her blanket first.

BRAD: You two are pretty small fry to be out alone on Christmas Eve.

JOEY: You're not so much older yourself.

BRAD: You'll have to admit that little sister of yours should be home in bed, waiting for Santa Claus.

JOEY: I know. But this year we aren't waiting for Santa Claus. We're going to meet him at my Cousin Ellen's house in the city.

SKIPPER: Is she expecting you, your Cousin Ellen?

JOEY: Well . . . er . . . not exactly. It's to be sort of a surprise.

POKEY: How do you know she'll be home?

JOEY: Oh, she'll be home all right. I'm sure of that. Hurry up, Doodles, here's your coat. (*He helps her with her coat and they each pick up a bundle.*)

SKIPPER (*Doubtfully*): I hope you know what you're doing.

JOEY: Of course, we know what we're doing. Come along, Doodles. Thanks, fellas, for all the food and everything. And good luck on your camping trip.

POKEY: And good luck to you.

BRAD: Hope you get to your cousin's house O.K.

SKIPPER: No hard feelings, Doodles, about using Betsy as a beanbag?

DOODLES: No. Betsy wasn't hurt and she understands you didn't mean to be rough.

SKIPPER: Well, that's good! So long, you two.

ALL: Merry Christmas! (*Just as they say "Merry Christmas," the* LADY *enters. She is wearing a blue raincoat and hood.*)

LADY: Well, a Merry Christmas to you, too, whoever you are.

POKEY: Jiminy Crickets! Where did you come from?

LADY: From the highway. My car bogged down. Didn't you hear me blowing?

SKIPPER: Yeah, we heard.

LADY: Then I saw the light and thought I could get some help. Do any of you know how to change a tire?

BRAD: I guess I'm the mechanic of the crew, ma'am. I'll be glad to help.

LADY (*To* DOODLES *and* JOEY): My goodness! Where are you two going? What a beautiful doll you have there, little girl.

DOODLES: Her name is Betsy. She's a little sleepy right now, or I'd let you hold her. I think she's upset with all these strange people and running away and everything.

LADY: Running away? Are you really running away?

DOODLES (*Clapping her hand over her mouth*): Oh dear, Joey! I didn't mean to tell. Honest, I didn't. Don't be mad at me!

LADY: Of course, he won't be mad at you. Are you the little girl's brother?

JOEY: Yes, ma'am. But don't pay any attention to her, ma'am. She's always had a terrific imagination.

LADY: But I don't think that was her imagination. I think you really *are* running away. Well, don't let that worry you. The fact is, I'm running away too.

ALL: What?

LADY: Yes, I really am.

JOEY: What are you running away from?

LADY: I'm running away from the city.

DOODLES: Oh, I'm so glad you're not running away from Christmas.

LADY: Running away from Christmas? Why, whoever heard of such a thing!

DOODLES (*Pointing to boys*): They told me. I heard them say they're running away from Christmas.

BRAD: That sister of yours is sure no good at keeping secrets, Joey.

SKIPPER: Doodles is right, Miss. We *are* running away from Christmas.

POKEY: But it isn't like running away from home, Miss, or anything like that. It's only running away from school.

LADY: Running away from school?

BRAD: You make it sound terrible, Pokey. You see, we all go to Hilltop, the big boarding school about ten miles from here. All three of us live too far away to go home for the holidays and anyhow our parents are all abroad. So we just decided to go on a camping trip over the holidays.

SKIPPER: And forget all about Christmas.

LADY: Forget all about Christmas? But that's impossible.

POKEY: We've done all right so far, Miss. We've gotten away from holly and mistletoe and Christmas carols and Christmas trees and presents, and turkey dinners, and . . .

LADY: But just as I came in you were all shouting "Merry Christmas."

POKEY: Oh, yes, I know. But that was just for Doodles. She's still such a little girl. We wouldn't want her to forget about Christmas.

BRAD: And anyhow, they're running away to *find* Christmas.

LADY (*Laughing*): This is the funniest thing I ever heard of. Here *you* are, running away from Christmas; and here *they* are running to look for Christmas, and look where you've all wound up.

ALL (*Puzzled*): Where?

LADY: Why, right here. Right in a stable. Had you forgotten that Christmas really began in a stable? (*All look at each other in astonishment.*)

SKIPPER: She's right.

POKEY: We never thought of that. (LADY *seats herself on the bale of hay. The manger is beside her.*)

LADY (*Softly*): It might have looked very much like this, you know, that first Christmas. The stable, so small and dim, the hay, so clean and fresh.

DOODLES (*Laying the doll in the manger*): And the little Baby in the manger.

LADY: And the shepherd boys, and maybe some children from the inn gathered round, in wonder. (*The grouping of children around the* LADY *resembles the Manger scene.*)

DOODLES: It's just like the song. (*Sings softly*)

"Away in a Manger, no crib for His bed.
The little Lord Jesus lay down His sweet head.
The stars in the heavens looked down where He lay,
The little Lord Jesus asleep in the hay." (*There is a pause after the song.*)

BRAD: I guess you can't ever run away from Christmas, ma'am.

POKEY: Maybe our camping trip wasn't such a good idea.

SKIPPER: I don't believe any of us ever really wanted to forget Christmas. Thanks, lady, for helping us find it again.

LADY: You're not the first to find Christmas in a stable, you know. And what about *you?* (*To* JOEY *and* DOODLES) Where did you expect to find Christmas?

JOEY: In the city.

DOODLES: At our Cousin Ellen's house.

LADY (*Startled*): Your Cousin Ellen?

JOEY: Yes, she's a lovely lady who really understands what children like for Christmas. We were going to visit her.

DOODLES: It was to be a surprise.

LADY: And it *is* a surprise . . . a big surprise. Tell me . . . are you Joey and Doodles who live with their Aunt Sarah and Uncle William?

BOTH: Yes! How did you know?

LADY: Because I am your Cousin Ellen.

BOTH: You are? But how did you get here?

LADY: I was on my way to visit you with a carload of Christmas gifts. Oh, it's wonderful to find you here. (*Hugs the children*)

JOEY: What about Aunt Sarah and Uncle William? Do they know you are coming?

LADY: Of course, they know. In fact, they know a great many things that may surprise you.

JOEY: Do you mean they know we ran away?

LADY: No, they don't know that. But they know you were unhappy about last Christmas. (*Sits down again and takes letter from her bag*) This is the letter they wrote me. (*Reads*)

Dear Ellen:

Please try to spend Christmas with us this year. The children need you. William and I seem to have forgotten what Christmas means to little folks. We know they were terribly disappointed by our rather sensible celebration last year. So pack up your car with all the trimmings, and we'll see if we can make it up to them with plenty of extra surprises. William and I have a few of our own tucked up our sleeves. We're going to try to fill the old house with Christmas from attic to cellar and we want you to be with us.

Fondly,

Sarah.

JOEY: I guess we didn't understand Aunt Sarah and Uncle William very well.

DOODLES: Maybe we didn't understand Christmas very well.

BRAD: I think I'll go take a look at your car, ma'am. I can change that tire in a jiffy.

LADY: I hope so because it's time we got started. And . . . wait a minute, now. How would you and your friends like to join us for a real old-fashioned, homey Christmas with Aunt Sarah and Uncle William?

BRAD: Gosh, we'd love it . . . but . . .

SKIPPER: That would be swell.

POKEY: But nobody wants three extra boys with extra appetites for Christmas dinner.

JOEY: They said they wanted to fill the house from attic to cellar.

LADY: And three boys would help to fill in the extra places at the big dining room table. How about it? (*Boys look at each other and nod their heads.*)

SKIPPER: We accept.

POKEY: Let's remember to call the school when we can get to a phone. We'd better tell them where we're going to spend Christmas.

BRAD (*Putting on his coat*): I'll blow the horn when I get the tire changed.

SKIPPER: Need any help, Brad?

BRAD: No, you two would just be in the way. I can work faster alone. (*At door*) This is a real Christmas Eve. The stars are crystal clear, and there's one big one that seems to hang right over this stable door. (*He exits.* ELLEN *seats herself on the hay,* DOODLES *nestles close to her and the others group themselves around her. Softly they sing the first verse of "Silent Night" as the curtains close.*)

THE END

Santa Claus for President

Characters

PROLOGUE	PERUVIAN CHILD
SANTA CLAUS	DUTCH CHILD
MRS. SANTA	MEXICAN CHILD
JINGLE } *elves*	FRENCH CHILD
JANGLE } *elves*	DANISH CHILD
THREE REPORTERS	ITALIAN CHILD
ENGLISH CHILD	THREE AMERICAN CHILDREN

PROLOGUE (*Before the curtain*):

My Daddy says that politics
Present a serious question.
And that is why at Christmas time,
We have a good suggestion.

If you would have a President
Who's great in every way
Just leave it to the boys and girls
Throughout the U.S.A.

We now present our candidate,
A gentleman of note:

We know that Mr. Santa Claus
Is sure to get your vote.

* * *

SETTING: *Santa's workshop.*

AT RISE: MRS. SANTA *is listing telegrams as the two elves,* JINGLE *and* JANGLE, *call them off to her.* SANTA CLAUS, *his hands behind his back, is pacing up and down.*

JINGLE: Pottstown, Pennsylvania.
JANGLE: Albany, New York.
JINGLE: Kansas City, Kansas.
JANGLE: Portland, Maine.
JINGLE: Hollywood, California.
JANGLE: Dallas, Texas.
JINGLE: And here's the last one—Richmond, Virginia.
MRS. SANTA: The last one! Good! That makes five million telegrams asking Santa Claus to be President of the United States. (*Shakes head and makes disapproving sounds*) And I don't approve of it one bit! Not a single bit!
JINGLE: But, Mrs. Santa, the children want him.
JANGLE: Five million of them. We counted them.
MRS. SANTA: But do children always know what's best?
SANTA: Of course they do. We wouldn't have toy trains, or dolls, or lollypops, or ice cream, if it weren't for the children. The little dears always know what's best.
MRS. SANTA: That's where you're wrong. If children always knew what's best, we wouldn't have stomach-aches from eating too much candy and green apples.
SANTA: Nevertheless, if the children want me to be President, I think it is my duty to please them.

MRS. SANTA: Fiddlededee! It's your duty to stay right here and make hobby horses and candy canes and doll babies and sleds and roller skates.

JINGLE *and* JANGLE: Besides, Santa, it wouldn't be any fun.

SANTA: FUN? Who's talking about fun?

JINGLE *and* JANGLE: We are. We think fun is important.

SANTA: Don't you think the President has any fun? (JINGLE *and* JANGLE *shake their heads "No."*)

JINGLE: If you were President, you couldn't live at the North Pole.

JANGLE: You'd have to live in Washington.

JINGLE: And you couldn't keep your reindeer in the White House.

JANGLE: And you couldn't ride in your sleigh.

JINGLE: And you couldn't come down chimneys.

BOTH: It wouldn't be proper.

SANTA: I never thought of that.

MRS. SANTA: There's plenty you never thought about.

SANTA: Still, if the children want me . . . (*Sound of sleighbells*)

MRS. SANTA: There's someone at the door. Jingle and Jangle, you may answer it. (*Exit* JINGLE *and* JANGLE) Please, Santa, take my advice. Don't run for President. You won't be happy.

SANTA: But if I could make *the children* happy. . . . (JINGLE *and* JANGLE *enter with three* REPORTERS. *Each wears a "Press" sign in his hat and carries a big red notebook, oversized green pencil.*)

JINGLE *and* JANGLE (*Announcing*): The Gentlemen of the Press!

REPORTERS (*Bowing*): Good evening, Santa. Good evening, Mrs. Santa.

SANTA *and* MRS. SANTA: Good evening, gentlemen.

FIRST REPORTER: Is it true that you are going to run for President, sir?

SECOND REPORTER: We'd like to get the whole story.

THIRD REPORTER: And we'd also like a few pictures.

SANTA: I'm afraid you are too early, gentlemen. I have not yet decided.

FIRST REPORTER: But, sir, the whole world is waiting for your answer.

SANTA: If I were only sure that all the children want me.

SECOND REPORTER: Oh, but they do, sir.

THIRD REPORTER: Think what it would mean to them.

FIRST REPORTER: Free toys for all.

SECOND REPORTER: Christmas every day.

THIRD REPORTER: The children of the United States would be the happiest, luckiest boys and girls in the world.

SANTA: In that case, my answer must be *yes.*

REPORTERS: May we print that, Santa?

MRS. SANTA: Oh dear, oh dear, oh dear! (*Goes over to* JINGLE *and* JANGLE *who try to comfort her.*)

FIRST REPORTER: This is the best news of the year.

SECOND REPORTER: The biggest Big Story in the world!

THIRD REPORTER: Santa Claus for President! What a headline!

FIRST REPORTER: Please, Sir, may we have some pictures?

SECOND REPORTER: You and Mrs. Santa and perhaps a few of your elves?

SANTA: Of course. (*To* MRS. SANTA) Come, my dear. They want to take your picture as the future Madame President. (*Sleighbells jingle violently.*)

FIRST REPORTER: May we keep your company waiting until after the pictures? (JINGLE *and* JANGLE *run to the door.*)

JINGLE *and* JANGLE: There are children to see Mr. Santa.

SANTA: In that case, we cannot keep them waiting. Santa Claus is never too busy to see children. Tell them to come in. (*Exit* JINGLE *and* JANGLE)

SECOND REPORTER: I suppose these are more children who want you to run for President.

THIRD REPORTER: They'll be glad to know it's all settled. (JINGLE *and* JANGLE *enter, heading a parade of children from foreign countries. Each child bears a banner with the name of his country. They march in and salute* SANTA CLAUS.)

SANTA: Welcome! Welcome, boys and girls! I am always glad to see my little friends, and I can guess why you have come to see me. You want me to be President. Am I right?

ALL: NO!

SANTA: What? You don't want me to be President of the United States?

ALL: No, indeed!

SANTA: But why? Tell me why.

ENGLAND: We represent the boys and girls,
From far across the sea.
If you become a President,
Where will *our* children be?

PERU: If you are strictly U.S.A.
Then what about Peru?
How will we spend our Christmas
If we do not have you?

HOLLAND: And who will fill our wooden shoes
With candy and with toys?
If you stay here in U.S.A.
We'll have no Christmas joys.

MEXICO: You'll be so tired with taxes

And all affairs of state,
That Christmas treats in other lands,
Will simply have to wait.

FRANCE: Dear Santa, you're a friend of all,
The whole wide world around.
You make all children happy
Wherever you are found.

DENMARK: No single country has the right
To claim you for its own,
To shed your blessings on one land
And leave the rest alone!

ITALY: So please, dear Santa, don't you see
You *can't* accept this post,
For in one land you'd have to stay
And serve that country most.

ALL (*Kneeling*):
We beg you, Santa, on our knees
Before we have to go,
Oh, Santa, Santa, won't you please
Tell them your answer's *no!*

SANTA: Why bless my soul! I had no idea the rest of the children in the world would feel like this.

ALL: We won't give you up. You belong to us. You belong to every child in every land!

MRS. SANTA: The children are right. You yourself said that children know best.

SANTA: But what about the children of the United States? I belong to them too, you know. How will they feel if I refuse to be their President?

MRS. SANTA: Let's ask them and find out. (*To audience*) Dear children of America, you've heard the voices of your little friends across the sea. They too love our Santa Claus. They depend on him to fill their stockings and put up their Christmas trees and bring them toys. Do you still want him to be your President and leave the rest of the world without a Santa?

CHILDREN IN AUDIENCE: No! Christmas is for everybody. (*Three children come to the stage with American flags.*)

FIRST AMERICAN: The children of the U.S.A.
Can understand your plight.
If we kept Santa for ourselves
We'd not be doing right.

SECOND AMERICAN: And Christmas is the time of year
To love and help each other,
For everyone throughout the world
To be a friend and brother.

THIRD AMERICAN: It's better to be right, they say,
Than to be President.
And Santa's international—
A world-wide resident.

SANTA: Gentlemen of the Press, you've heard the children. I've changed my mind. My answer is *no*.

ALL: Hurrah! Hurrah! Hurrah! (*Cast and audience join in closing song, to the tune of "Up on the House Top."*)

Santa belongs to the whole wide world,
Matters not what flag's unfurled.
Over the ocean with lots of toys
All for the good little girls and boys.

Chorus:

Ho, ho, ho, there he will go,
Ho, ho, ho, there he will go.
All 'round the world he'll click, click, click
Down ev'ry chimney comes good Saint Nick!

THE END

Mystery at Knob Creek Farm

Characters

AL, *from Alabama*
CANDY, *from Kansas*
CAL, *from California*
TEX, *from Texas*
FLORENCE, *from Florida*
MINNIE, *from Minnesota*
MITCH, *from Michigan*
PENNY, *from Pennsylvania*
MARY, *from Maryland*
VERNON, *from Vermont*
A BOY FROM KENTUCKY

SETTING: *A picnic grove on Knob Creek Farm, Kentucky.*

AT RISE: *The boys and girls from the Travelvue Sightseeing Bus are seated around a picnic table, holding cameras, maps, Lincoln souvenirs, sandwiches, etc.*

AL: Boy, oh boy! I never saw so many different license plates in my life! All those cars in the Knob Creek Farm parking lot! People are here from every state in the Union.

CANDY: There were even more parked at Hodgenville.

FLORENCE: I was lucky enough to go down to Rock Spring when there wasn't another soul there. It was so quiet and peaceful. I could just imagine how Nancy Hanks Lincoln took her baby down there on a hot summer afternoon to sit by that lovely, cool spring.

MINNIE: I'll bet she didn't have much time for resting. Pioneer women had too much work to do.

CAL: How could there have been so much housework with just that tiny one-room cabin?

PENNY: That shows how much you know about it. There was all the cooking and washing to do and they weren't able to buy a single thing at a store.

FLORENCE: And then, there was the sewing, to say nothing of the spinning, and weaving, and looking after the children.

MITCH: I liked the birthplace the best. It was wonderful to see that little log cabin enclosed in a marble temple.

MARY: I felt almost as if I were in church.

VERNON: That's the way you're supposed to feel when you visit a real historic shrine.

TEX: I don't feel that way here at Knob Creek Farm.

AL: Neither do I. But somehow, I feel more Lincolnish here than I did at Hodgenville.

MARY: That's a funny thing to say. What do you mean by feeling *Lincolnish?*

AL: Oh, I don't know exactly. Lincoln seems more real here. After all, he was only three years old when his parents left Rock Creek. He was little more than a baby. He lived here until he was seven, and I can just imagine him roaming through these woods and doing the chores on this farm.

CAL: What did you buy at the souvenir shop? I got some colored slides to show on our projector.

FLORENCE: I got some more postcards. It seems the more I send, the more names I remember.

CANDY: I didn't buy anything. I'm tired of souvenir shops. They're all the same.

PENNY: It was a wonderful idea for the tour director to arrange this picnic for us. The grownups will be down in that shop for ages.

MITCH: If it's a picnic, when do we eat? I'm starved.

FLORENCE: You boys are always starved. All you do is eat.

TEX: Just the same, I bet you'll put away your share of sandwiches when you get started.

AL: Yes, there's no such thing as a girl with a delicate appetite these days. (*Children busy themselves arranging picnic plates, etc. While this is going on,* MARY *rises from the table and goes through a mysterious performance at one side of stage. She presses one hand against her forehead, and, with eyes closed, walks eight or ten steps around in a circle, then turns and reverses her course.*)

PENNY: Don't pour the lemonade now! It will get too warm.

VERNON: Where are the cheese sandwiches?

MINNIE (*As* CAL *reaches for the potato chips*): Keep out of those potato chips till we have the lunch unpacked.

CANDY: Tex, see if you can open these pickles, please. The lid's too tight.

TEX: I never saw a girl yet who could open a pickle jar.

AL (*Noticing* MARY'S *ritual*): Hey, Mary, what in the world are you doing? You'll get dizzy!

MARY (*Continuing*): Don't bother me. I'm concentrating. (*All stop their work and watch* MARY.)

TEX: What is this? Some sort of hocus-pocus?

MITCH: What are you trying to do, anyhow?

MARY (*Stopping in disgust*): Oh, dear! Now you've spoiled it! I wasn't supposed to talk till I had been around seven times!

FLORENCE: Are you trying to work some sort of magic?

MARY (*Joining the others*): I know you'll laugh. But it's something I bought at the souvenir shop.

ALL: What? What is it?

MARY (*Opening her hand and showing the others a small stone*): It's a wishing stone.

TEX: A what?

MARY: A wishing stone.

CANDY: I didn't see anything like this at the shop.

MARY: I didn't exactly get it at the shop. I bought it from an old woman outside.

AL (*Examining it*): Looks like an ordinary piece of rock to me.

PENNY: It's an odd color—sort of greenish.

VERNON: What's it supposed to do?

MARY: It's supposed to make your wish come true. (*All laugh.*)

CAL: Don't tell me you paid real money for that thing!

MARY: I paid a quarter for it!

MINNIE: Oh, Mary! You didn't! Why, that's just throwing your money away.

MARY: I don't care. I wanted to see if it would work.

MITCH: Well, now you know! It's a fake. You've been had. Now, what do you say we eat?

PENNY: What did you wish, Mary?

MARY: I'm not going to tell. Wishes never come true unless you keep them a secret. (*As the children talk, a boy enters from the woods. He wears a coonskin cap and a long hunting shirt. His feet are bare. He carries a wooden pail.*)

CANDY: Come on, forget about wishing stones and have a sandwich. We're all hungry.

MITCH (*Spotting boy*): Hello, stranger. Where did you come from?

BOY: From back yonder in the woods, back of Muldraugh's Hill.

AL: Won't you have some lunch?

BOY: No, thank you kindly. I'm not hungry. I've been eatin' blueberries all mornin'.

PENNY: Blueberries? Do they grow around here?

BOY: Sure. The woods are full of blueberries and wild currants. Lots of wild grapes too and crab apples.

FLORENCE: You must live around here to know so much about the woods. Do you go to school?

BOY: Sometimes.

PENNY: Sometimes! You don't sound like a very regular pupil. Where is your school?

BOY: 'Bout two miles from here. It's not much of a school but Mr. Caleb Hazel is a mighty fine teacher. Never saw you folks hereabouts. Did you come from far?

AL: We sure did, boy. I came all the way from Alabama. Cal here is from California, Minnie's from Minnesota, Mitch is from Michigan. Fact is—we're all from different states.

BOY (*Puzzled*): Different states? Aren't you from the United States?

FLORENCE: Of course, we're from the United States. I'm from Florida.

BOY: But those names. I never heard of such names.

PENNY: Surely you've heard of Pennsylvania.

MARY: And Maryland?

BOY: Yes. I recollect those names, but folks round Knob Crick never talk of those other places.

TEX: Well, here. Take a look at this map. You can see Texas right away. (*Children group around map.*)

CANDY: Here's Kansas. That's my state.

VERNON: Up here's mine—The Green Mountain State, we call it, but Vermont is what it says on the map.

BOY: Where's Kaintuck?

AL (*Pointing*): Right here—south of Indiana.

BOY: Indiany? My folks are moving to Indiany right soon. Pappy says he can get a lot of rich land for two dollars an acre.

CANDY: It's exciting to move. When we moved from Nebraska to Kansas, we packed most of our things in the station wagon. It was like going on a big vacation.

BOY: Station wagon?

CANDY: Yes. What kind of car do you have?

BOY: I don't rightly understand you. Pappy aims to take all our household goods by flatboat down the Ohio River.

CANDY: That should be fun. I've never been on a river boat.

PENNY (*Brushing at mosquitoes*): I don't believe this was a very good place for our picnic—too many bugs.

BOY: Skeeters are bad this time o' year for sure. Going to rain tomorrow, that's one reason they're so pesky.

AL: The radio says it's going to be clear tomorrow.

BOY: Radio? What's that?

MINNIE: Dear me! You really must live in the backwoods if you don't know what a radio is. We always get our weather reports on the radio.

BOY: Last night our roosters were crowin' like all possessed when they went to roost. That's always a sure sign of rain.

AL: That's a new one. I never heard that before.

BOY: Folks set great store by weather signs in these parts.

Farmers have to know about the rain so they can drop their seeds at the right time and gather their crops.

CAL: That's one thing we don't have to worry about in California. The weather takes care of itself.

BOY: California—that's a right smart word. I like the feel of it when I say it.

CAL: California's a right smart state too, if anybody should ask you, my friend.

MITCH: Aw, you and Tex are always bragging about California and Texas. You should really come to Michigan if you want to see something.

BOY: Michigan. That's another word it pleasures me to say. I like words—big words that sort of fill up your mouth and roll off your tongue smooth and easy-like. *Independent*—now there's a word I like to say.

PENNY: Now where did a little boy like you hear a big word like that?

BOY: Fourth o' July I heard it for the first time. Pappy came out the cabin door in the morning and shot off his long rifle right up in the sky. Like to scared the daylights out o' Mammy and Sairy.

VERNON: What was he trying to do? Make his own fireworks?

BOY: He said that's what everybody does on Fourth o' July, because that's the day the United States first called itself a free and independent nation. "Free and independent nation." I like the sound o' those words, too. Sound mighty important-like.

FLORENCE: What in the world do you find to do around here? There aren't any movies or anything, and I don't see any television aerials.

BOY: Movies? Television aerials? My! My! What a lot o'

words there are. I have an idea not even Doc Graham or Zachariah Riney ever heard words the likes of those.

AL: Do you read a lot?

BOY: I read all I can, but books are scarce here in the wilderness. We are mostly poor folks without much learnin'. Mammy's got a big Bible she reads to Sairy and me. It's got pages and pages with more words than you ever heard of. Sometime I aim to read 'em all.

MINNIE: Well, what *do* you do when you're not working or going to school?

MARY: She means what do you do to have fun?

BOY: Fun? (*Laughing*) I'm always havin' fun, at least it seems that way. Over the top of Muldraugh's Hill there's a pretty good swimmin' hole, and there are all sorts of things to do in the woods—trees to climb, cricks to wade, places to look for nuts and wild honey. Yes, I reckon I have a good bit of fun.

MITCH: What about fellows to play with? Do any other boys live near you?

BOY: Austin Gollaher. He's always ready to go swimmin', or fishin', or huntin'. Yesterday he played a trick on me, he did!

VERNON: What did he do?

BOY (*Taking off cap*): See this cap? Well, I shinnied up a pawpaw tree, and dropped a big, ripe pawpaw into his cap. Trouble was, Austin outsmarted me. He switched caps, so I had to clean the mess out of my own cap. That Austin! He's a foxy one, he is!

VERNON (*Examining cap*): Well, it doesn't look any the worse for wear. This is a neat cap. Did you buy it at the souvenir shop?

BOY: Buy it? Nope. Mammy made it last time Pappy shot a coon. My old one was plumb wore out.

FLORENCE: You really lead an exciting life. It makes ours seem dull—just going to school and coming home and going to school again, except, of course, during vacation.

PENNY: What are you going to do when you grow up? Stay here and be a farmer?

BOY: I don't rightly know, for certain. Sometimes I get a funny feelin'. Sometimes at night I get a-wonderin' and a-dreamin', and then I get lonesome-like and scared. 'Pears to me as if growin' up isn't so easy. I think I'd rather just stay here and do the farm chores, but Mammy says when my feet get further away from my head, I'll feel different. I hope she's right. (*A loud blast of an automobile horn is heard offstage.*)

CANDY: That's the bus driver blowing for us. We'll have to fly.

MITCH: Give me another sandwich before you shut the picnic basket. (*Grabs sandwich as others pile things in the basket*)

AL: Be sure you get everything. Don't leave anything behind or the bus driver will be mad. (*Another blast from the bus. There is a scramble as children run offstage yelling, "We're coming! We're coming!" In the rush,* MARY *picks up a camera.* PENNY *gets out her autograph book.*)

PENNY: Wait a minute. (*To* BOY) Would you sign my autograph book?

BOY: Your what?

PENNY: Just put your name right here. (*Handing* BOY *a pen and book.*)

BOY: I don't aim to spoil your book. I can't write so good, you understand, but I can spell out my name for you if you like. (*Signs name in book*)

PENNY: Thank you. (*She turns to put book in her handbag.*)

MARY (*Aiming camera*): Now let me take your picture. (*As* MARY *sights through camera,* BOY *moves out of her range and offstage.*) Stand still. I can't get you in focus. Hey, where are you? (*Looking up from camera*) Why, that's funny!

PENNY (*Turning around*): What's funny?

MARY: The boy! He's gone! I couldn't focus him in my range-finder at all. Nothing but a shadow.

PENNY: Maybe you scared him off with that camera. He certainly was the shy type. Maybe he's never seen a camera.

MARY: Penny! Do you suppose?

PENNY: Do I suppose what?

MARY: Penny! It's true! It's true! Oh dear! Now I've lost it! (*Drops to her knees and begins to search on the ground*)

PENNY: What's come over you, Mary? What have you lost?

MARY: My stone! My precious wishing stone! I must have dropped it.

PENNY: Well, don't waste time hunting for that old thing! It was no good, anyway.

MARY: But it was, Penny. It was a real wishing stone.

PENNY: It was no such thing! And we'll be late for the bus, hunting for it. It was just a stone like any other stone.

MARY: It wasn't just like any other stone. It really made my wish come true.

PENNY: What?

MARY: It really did, Penny, honestly and truly. You see—I wished that I could really see Abe Lincoln as he actually was, when he was a little boy and lived here on Knob Creek Farm.

PENNY: And how did your wish come true?

MARY: That boy, Penny. He was no ordinary boy. Think how he was dressed and how he talked.

PENNY: He talked just like any other backwoods country boy who had never been out of these hills.

MARY: But he had never heard of Michigan or California or Texas. Don't you understand why?

PENNY: Because he hadn't been to school long enough.

MARY: No, because those places weren't even states when Lincoln was a boy.

PENNY: You don't mean to stand there and tell me you honestly think that boy we were talking to was Abe Lincoln?

MARY: That's what I think, Penny. That's what I honestly think.

PENNY: Then you're crazy. You're absolutely crazy.

MARY: No, I'm not. Didn't you notice something strange about him? Something—well, sort of different?

PENNY: Of course, he was different. He would naturally be different from the boys we know.

MARY: But this was a *different* difference, Penny. I—I just can't explain it, but somehow I know. Let me see that book. Your autograph book. What did he write?

PENNY (*Opening book*): There! There's the page.

MARY: And look! Look what he wrote! A. L-I-N-K-H-O-R-N.

PENNY: That goes to show you he's some sort of joker. Anybody knows that's not the way to spell *Lincoln*.

MARY: But I read somewhere that lots of people spelled it that way years ago.

TEX (*Running onstage*): Come on, you two! You're holding us up.

PENNY: Oh, Mary's poking around looking for that stone of hers. She insists it's magic. She actually believes that boy from the backwoods was young Abe Lincoln! Did you ever hear anything so crazy in your life?

TEX: Well, it could be! After all, these trips are supposed to make history come alive!

PENNY: Now don't tell me you agree with her! You don't really think he was Abe Lincoln, do you?

TEX: It doesn't matter what I think. Get a move on! It will be something to argue about on the bus. (TEX *seizes* PENNY'S *arm and propels her across the stage.* MARY *follows. When she reaches center stage, she turns, and speaks her last line to the audience.*)

MARY: And it will be something for *you* to argue about, too! Do you think we saw the real Abe Lincoln, or just a little shirt-tail boy from the hills? (*Curtain*)

THE END

Melody for Lincoln

Characters

THERESA ALVAREZ
MRS. ALVAREZ, *her mother*
RAMÓN ALVAREZ, *her brother*
MISS LUCINDA, *Theresa's music teacher*
NAOMI
SARAH JANE
CLARISSA
MR. EHRHART, *the director*

TIME: *The present.*
SETTING: *The Alvarez living room.*
AT RISE: MISS LUCINDA *is seated at the piano. Beside the piano is a small dressing case.* MRS. ALVAREZ *is speaking to* RAMÓN.

MRS. ALVAREZ: Please, Ramón. Run down to the school and look for your sister. It is not like her to be so late, especially when she knows Miss Lucinda is here for her lesson.
RAMÓN: But, Mother, the school is long since closed. Everyone is gone.
MRS. ALVAREZ: Then perhaps she is with her friends—

Naomi, Sarah Jane, maybe the new little girl, Clarissa.

RAMÓN: I'll go look for her, Mother, and don't worry. I'm sure nothing has happened to her. She's just gone off somewhere and forgotten all about time, the way she always does.

MRS. ALVAREZ: Ramón! Please! Theresa would not be so impolite as to keep Miss Lucinda waiting.

RAMÓN: You know Theresa, Mother, when she starts daydreaming.

MRS. ALVAREZ: Yes, yes, I know. Such a one for pretending and making up stories, that little one!

MISS LUCINDA: You can be glad she has such a fine imagination, Mrs. Alvarez. That is one reason she is making such progress at the piano. I'm really glad she is a bit late this afternoon. It gives me a chance to talk with you.

RAMÓN: I'll send her home a-flying, if I find her, Mother. (*Exit* RAMÓN.)

MRS. ALVAREZ: I, too, am happy to speak with you, Miss Lucinda. I am not good with the words to tell you how grateful we are for your time and interest in our Teresita. We are not long in this country, and it is good to have a stranger be so kind.

MISS LUCINDA: I am not exactly a stranger, Mrs. Alvarez. I am a teacher. We both have the interest of your little girl at heart. That makes us friends, doesn't it?

MRS. ALVAREZ: That is such a good word—*friends*. You think Theresa has the talent for music, Miss Lucinda?

MISS LUCINDA: I am sure of it. She is one of the most unusual children I have ever taught. Her response is amazing. Mrs. Alvarez, I would like Theresa to go to the city this winter to study with a better teacher.

There is a very fine musician I know who would take her as his pupil if he heard her play.

MRS. ALVAREZ: So good you are, Miss Lucinda. But the city—no. We do not have money for city lessons.

MISS LUCINDA: Let's not talk about money, Mrs. Alvarez. I am sure we can work something out if you will let Theresa go.

MRS. ALVAREZ: When we left our home in Venezuela, I never dreamed to find such good friend so soon in strange country. But, yes, she may go, if you say it is a wise thing for her.

MISS LUCINDA: Of course, Theresa will have to work, and work hard. But I think we can depend on her to do that, Mrs. Alvarez.

MRS. ALVAREZ: Since she was very small, my Teresita loved the music. When she was tiny baby, I would sit at the piano and hold her on my lap. Before she could talk, she would try to sing with the piano.

MISS LUCINDA: I'm so glad we had this chance to talk, Mrs. Alvarez, because the gentleman I was telling you about will be here for the Lincoln Festival. Then it will be possible for him to meet Theresa.

MRS. ALVAREZ (*In excitement*): The Lincoln Festival! I had forgotten! That is where Theresa is, Miss Lucinda. All week she has talked of nothing else.

MISS LUCINDA: I'm glad to hear she is so interested.

MRS. ALVAREZ: It is the play! Tonight they are holding the—the what you call it—the try-outs for the children. She and her little friends were going to read for the Señor Director this afternoon after school. How could I have forgotten!

MISS LUCINDA: I didn't know she wanted a part in the play!

MRS. ALVAREZ: Oh, yes! Yes! For days she has been talking and play-acting! (*Doorbell*)

MISS LUCINDA: There is someone at your door. Perhaps I should be leaving.

MRS. ALVAREZ: No, no! Please stay. I will see who it is. (*Runs to door and re-enters with* NAOMI, SARAH JANE *and* CLARISSA)

NAOMI: We just stopped by to see if Theresa is here so we can tell her the good news.

SARAH JANE: Hello, Miss Lucinda. We're so excited. We all got parts in the play for the Lincoln Festival. I am to be Sarah Lincoln and Naomi is to be Sarah Johnston, my half-sister.

CLARISSA: Even I got a part! I never expected it since I just moved here. But I'm going to be Grace Bedelle.

MISS LUCINDA: Grace Bedelle?

CLARISSA: Yes, she was the little girl from New York State who wrote Mr. Lincoln a letter suggesting that he wear whiskers like the other stylish gentlemen of his time.

MRS. ALVAREZ: But Theresa? What about her? Where is she?

NAOMI: That's why we stopped, Mrs. Alvarez. We wondered if she got a part too.

CLARISSA: She went flying out of the auditorium right after she read her lines, and we haven't seen her since.

MRS. ALVAREZ: Aiee! So worried I am. It is not like her to be late. Already she has kept Miss Lucinda waiting for her lesson. Perhaps an accident!

NAOMI: Don't worry, Mrs. Alvarez. I'm sure she'll be here soon.

SARAH JANE: Tell her we all got parts in the play, won't you, Mrs. Alvarez?

CLARISSA: I'm sure she got one too. Theresa is very good at reading.

MRS. ALVAREZ: Always play-acting she is!

SARAH JANE: Goodbye, Mrs. Alvarez. And don't worry about Theresa.

NAOMI, SARAH JANE *and* CLARISSA: Goodbye, Miss Lucinda. (*Exit*)

MRS. ALVAREZ: Miss Lucinda, I am frightened. Something bad has happened to my Teresita.

MISS LUCINDA: Now now, Mrs. Alvarez, don't get excited. Listen! I think she's here now.

THERESA (*Offstage*): I won't go in! I won't! I won't!

RAMÓN (*Offstage*): You must. Mother is worried and Miss Lucinda is waiting for you. (RAMÓN *enters, half dragging* THERESA *who is in a storm of tears.*)

THERESA: I don't want to see anyone. I want to be by myself.

RAMÓN: Here she is, Mother. I found her in the park.

MRS. ALVAREZ: Teresita! What is the matter? Are you hurt?

MISS LUCINDA: What in the world is the matter?

THERESA (*Throwing herself in her mother's arms*): Oh Mamacita! Mamacita! My heart is broken!

MRS. ALVAREZ (*Stroking her hair*): There! There! Teresita. Nothing can be so bad. Tell me. What is it?

THERESA: It is the play! The beautiful play!

RAMÓN: Is that all?

THERESA: "Is that all"? You are a boy, Ramón! You do not understand. To me it is everything!

RAMÓN: I can't see why you'd be crying your eyes out over a silly old play!

THERESA (*Fiercely*): It is because I did not get a part—

that is why. Everyone else—Naomi, Sarah Jane, Clarissa, all my friends, got parts! Speaking parts to say on the stage! They will wear costumes! They will go to all the rehearsals! Even the boys—that Billy Scott in our room will be Mr. Lincoln's son, Tad; Joe Bowman will play the little Willie who died in the White House. Only I—Theresa Alvarez—have no part at all! (*Burst of tears*) It is not fair! It is not fair! I read my lines as well as the others. I know I did.

MRS. ALVAREZ: Hush, Teresita. Do not cry any more. See, here is Miss Lucinda for your music lesson. You have not even spoken to her a greeting.

THERESA: Miss Lucinda! I am sorry, but I do not wish the piano lesson.

MISS LUCINDA: I know, dear. You are too upset right now. But next time we will have a long lesson. There is so much I want to tell you. When you calm down a bit, we'll have a nice talk.

THERESA: You do not understand. I do not wish any more piano lessons ever!

MRS. ALVAREZ (*Shocked*): Theresa! What are you saying?

MISS LUCINDA: Theresa! I don't understand.

THERESA: It is the piano that has done this to me.

RAMÓN: What's got into you? There's something wrong with your head.

THERESA: No! It is the truth. It is because of this piano, because of my music I did not get the part in the play. (*Pounding top of piano with fist*) I hate it! I hate it!

MISS LUCINDA: You don't mean that, my dear.

THERESA: Yes, I do, Miss Lucinda. Ever since they find out at school I play piano, I do nothing else. Always—"Theresa will play for us." The others dance—I play piano. The others sing—I play piano! Now when all the rest of my friends get parts in the play—I must play piano!

MRS. ALVAREZ: Theresa, you did not tell us that. Then you will be in the Lincoln Festival after all?

RAMÓN: Then what are you squawking about?

THERESA: Sure, I will be in it. But for what? As usual—a piano solo. I play for the intermission. I play while the rest change their costumes or they move the scenery. It is not like being in the play. It is not like having a real part. They don't even need me. I just—how you say—I just fill in the gaps!

MISS LUCINDA (*Rising and putting an arm around* THERESA): You are all wrong about this, Theresa. You don't understand.

THERESA: Yes, I do, Miss Lucinda. Too often this has happened to me before. This time I tell them I will not do it.

MISS LUCINDA *and* MRS. ALVAREZ: You what?

THERESA: I tell them I will not play! I refuse. I walk out!

RAMÓN: That was a silly thing to do!

MRS. ALVAREZ: It was worse than silly, Ramón. It was impolite—rude! Theresa, I am ashamed.

THERESA: Mamacita, you do not understand!

MISS LUCINDA: No, Theresa, it is you who does not understand. You are quite wrong about not getting a part in the play.

THERESA: Why? Why did I not get a part like my friends?

MISS LUCINDA: Because you were not suited for those parts. Because they were not suited to you.

THERESA: I could read all the lines without a mistake.

MISS LUCINDA: Look at yourself, Theresa. You are a little Spanish girl from Venezuela. Do you think you look or speak like a pioneer child from Kentucky?

THERESA: I could act the part. I am good at pretending.

MISS LUCINDA: Not good enough, Theresa. Besides, with the part you are to play you don't need to pretend. You can be yourself.

THERESA: But, Miss Lucinda, it will be just another piano solo. It has nothing to do with the Lincoln story.

MISS LUCINDA: This is your day for being wrong, Theresa, and you are wrong again. (*Picking up small dressing case.*) What do you think I have in this case?

THERESA: More music? Another piece I am to learn?

MISS LUCINDA (*Laughing and opening case.*): Wrong again, my dear! (*Pulls out a lovely, full ruffled skirt*) It is your costume for the Lincoln Festival!

THERESA: My costume!

MRS. ALVAREZ: How beautiful.

RAMÓN: That's pretty!

MISS LUCINDA (*Slipping skirt over* THERESA'S *head and draping a lace scarf over her shoulders*): You see, my dear, you are not going to play just another piano solo at the Lincoln Festival. You are to play the part of a real character.

THERESA: You mean it will be like being in a play?

MISS LUCINDA: It *is* being in the play, Theresa. You see, you did not wait for the Director to explain who it is you are to be.

THERESA: Am I not to be myself—Theresa Alvarez playing the piano?

MISS LUCINDA: No, indeed. You are to be Theresa all right—but another Theresa—a Theresa you never heard of.

MRS. ALVAREZ: I believe I understand.

MISS LUCINDA: I'm sure you understand, Mrs. Alvarez. Because the Theresa this child is to play was a very famous pianist from your own Venezuela. Her name was Theresa Carreño!

MRS. ALVAREZ: The great Madame Carreño!

THERESA: Theresa Carreño! You say she too played the piano?

MISS LUCINDA: Like no one else, Theresa. When she was a little girl, just eight years old, her parents brought her to New York for a public concert. She was a sensation! The critics loved her. Then she went to Boston for more concerts. She became more and more famous. Then, one day, she received a wonderful invitation—a request to play at the White House for President Lincoln.

THERESA: She played for President Lincoln?

MISS LUCINDA: She did, indeed, my dear, when she was just ten years old.

THERESA: That is my age, Miss Lucinda. I am ten years old too.

MISS LUCINDA: And your name is Theresa, you play the piano, you are from Venezuela. Do you understand now why you and you alone could have been chosen for this important scene?

THERESA: It is wonderful! I can scarcely believe it. I really have a part, a real part—not just a solo between the acts!

MISS LUCINDA: If you had been a bit more patient, the Director would have explained everything.

THERESA (*Whirling around*): A part! A part! I too have a part in the Lincoln play!

RAMÓN: Not any more you don't. You turned it down—walked out! Now they'll get someone else.

THERESA (*Wildly*): They can't! They won't! They mustn't! Miss Lucinda, don't let them get someone else.

I will practice night and day. I will play as I never played before. Please, Miss Lucinda.

MRS. ALVAREZ: I am afraid your haste has cost you a real sorrow, Teresita.

RAMÓN: Mother is always telling you not to fly off the handle. Now you've really done it!

MRS. ALVAREZ: Hush, Ramón. You are only making your sister feel worse. (*Doorbell.*) Go answer the door. I will talk to Teresita. (RAMÓN *goes to door.*)

MRS. ALVAREZ: Theresa Carreño was a great artist. She delighted kings and queens with her skill. But always she thought of her music. She was not ready to give it up for the least disappointment.

THERESA: I know, Mamacita, I know. I did not really mean all I said. I—I guess I was just jealous of the others. But now, tell me, what can I do?

RAMÓN (*Returning with* MR. EHRHART.) A gentleman to see you, Mother.

MR. EHRHART: Ah, Mrs. Alvarez. Good afternoon. I am Franz Ehrhart, director of the Lincoln Festival. I have come to see you about your little girl. She ran away so fast this afternoon I did not have a chance to talk to her. (*Seeing* THERESA) Why, there you are, child! And in costume!

MISS LUCINDA: Good afternoon, Professor Ehrhart.

MR. EHRHART: Miss Lucinda! This is indeed a pleasure.

MRS. ALVAREZ: My daughter has done us much shame in her rudeness, Señor. There is much she would say to you.

THERESA: Sir, if you will just give me another chance! Miss Lucinda has told me about that other little girl, the one who played for Mr. Lincoln. I know I do not play as well as she did, but I will do my best.

MR. EHRHART: I am sure of that, Theresa. That is why I have come to see you. I thought we should discuss what you are to play on this great occasion.

THERESA: Then I am to have my part in the play in spite of all the stupid things I said?

MR. EHRHART: We all do and say stupid things from time to time, Theresa. Even the great artist whose name you bear sometimes acted like a very naughty child.

THERESA: She did?

MR. EHRHART: Yes, she did. And history tells us that she was not too well behaved the day she went to play at the White House.

RAMÓN: What did she do?

MR. EHRHART: It wasn't so much what she did as what she didn't do. The young lady refused to practice for the occasion. Indeed no one could get her to make up her mind ahead of time what she was to play. But you and I are going to decide that right now, aren't we?

THERESA: I will play my most difficult numbers, and I'll practice and practice until Miss Lucinda says they are just right.

MR. EHRHART: That will not be necessary, Theresa. We do not want a difficult, showy composition.

THERESA: For the President, sir, surely you would want the best.

MR. EHRHART: The best is not always the most brilliant. This is what you are to play, my child. (*Hands* THERESA *sheet of music*)

THERESA: *Listen to the Mocking Bird!* But, this is so simple. We sing it at school, Anyone who could read music could play this.

MRS. ALVAREZ: Your opinion has not been asked, Theresa.

MISS LUCINDA: Sit down at the piano, Theresa. It is a

familiar song. If you will play it for us, we will all help to sing. Mrs. Alvarez, Ramón, even Professor Ehrhart will join in the chorus. (*As* THERESA *plays,* MISS LUCINDA *sings the verse of the song; the others, grouped about the piano, sing the chorus.*)

I'm dreaming now of Hally, sweet Hally, sweet Hally,
I'm dreaming now of Hally, for the thought of her is one that never dies.
She's sleeping in the valley, the valley, the valley,
She's sleeping in the valley, and the mocking bird is singing where she lies.

Chorus:

Listen to the mocking bird, listen to the mocking bird,
The mocking bird still singing o'er her grave.
Listen to the mocking bird, listen to the mocking bird,
Still singing where the weeping willows wave.

THERESA: It is such a sad song to play for a festival.

MR. EHRHART: You forget. You are not playing for a festival. You are Theresa Carreño playing for Mr. Lincoln. That was the President's favorite song. He asked Theresa to play it for him.

THERESA: I wonder why he liked it so much. I still think it is a sad song.

MR. EHRHART: Mr. Lincoln was a sad man in the fall of 1863. Only a few short months before, his little son, Willie, had died of a fever. Not only was he grief-stricken over his own loss, but he also sorrowed for the mothers and fathers who were losing their sons on the battlefields of the Civil War. And yet, with all his griefs and burdens, he still had time to hear this famous child pianist, the little girl from South America. In her music he found a few minutes of peace and relaxation. After she had played one or two numbers of her own choosing, he asked her to play this—his favorite song.

THERESA: And did she play it well?

MR. EHRHART: The story goes that she played it as it had never been played before, with a multitude of changes and variations. She played it with such feeling that when she finished, the President's eyes were filled with tears. Her playing had touched his heart. Do you understand now, Theresa, how it is to be played?

THERESA: I think I understand, sir. I may not get it right the first time, but perhaps if I think of Mr. Lincoln as I play, the right feeling will come to me. (*She begins to play softly.** MR. EHRHART, MISS LUCINDA, MRS. ALVAREZ *and* RAMÓN *seat themselves at one side as the audience.*)

THERESA (*Playing*): The song is not all sad. The melody must remind Mr. Lincoln of his dear ones as they were in life—happy and smiling. (*Pause during which she plays through the song*) It must bring comfort to his heart, a smile to his lips. (*As she finishes*) If there are tears in his eyes, they must be tears of love and remembering—not tears of sorrow.

MR. EHRHART (*After a pause during which he wipes his eyes*): There *were* tears in Mr. Lincoln's eyes after that song, little friend. But I think, like mine, they were not the tears of sorrow.

THERESA: Then you think I played the melody as Mr. Lincoln would have liked it?

MR. EHRHART: I am sure of it, Theresa. So sure that I would like to have you as my pupil.

THERESA: I do not understand.

* *Music can be faked if necessary, or recording may be used.*

MISS LUCINDA: Professor Ehrhart is a great teacher, Theresa, a real musician. You are, indeed, a fortunate little girl. Mrs. Alvarez, this is the gentleman I was telling you about.

MRS. ALVAREZ: Gracias, Señor.

MR. EHRHART: Someday, Theresa, you may become a great pianist, like the lady whose name you bear.

MISS LUCINDA: Like the little girl who played for Lincoln.

RAMÓN: You might even give concerts, Theresa.

THERESA (*Still at piano, playing softly*): If I do, I will play this melody on every program—at every performance—just as if I were playing it for Mr. Lincoln himself.

MRS. ALVAREZ: Why will you do that, my child?

THERESA: So that others will know and love the song he loved, so that everyone may share the song that was in Mr. Lincoln's heart. (*Music up full as curtains close.*)

THE END

The Tree of Hearts

Characters

KING VALENTINO, *of Valentia*
PRINCE VALENTINO, *his son*
LORD CHANCELLOR
DALE DAWSON, *American tourist*
GAIL DAWSON, *his sister*
MR. GOOSEBERRY, *Head Gardener*
MRS. GOOSEBERRY, *his wife*
GOLDIE GOOSEBERRY, *their daughter*
CHILDREN OF VALENTIA

SCENE 1

SETTING: *Near the Head Gardener's hut, in the Palace Garden of Valentia.*

AT RISE: KING VALENTINO *is talking to* MR. GOOSEBERRY. *The* LORD CHANCELLOR *is taking notes on the conversation.*

KING: Those are my orders, Mr. Gooseberry. Are there any questions?

MR. GOOSEBERRY: If Your Majesty could just give me some clue as to the type of tree His Highness, the Prince, would prefer?

KING: That is *your* problem, Mr. Gooseberry. My Lord Chancellor has set forth the specifications. Repeat the order, Lord Chancellor.

LORD CHANCELLOR (*Reading from official scroll*): As King of Valentia, I hereby decree that our Royal Head Gardener develop a special tree for His Highness, the Prince of Valentia, for the occasion of the Prince's tenth birthday to be celebrated on February 14th. Said tree must possess such charm and power as will attract the Prince to the Palace Garden and revive his pleasure therein. Failure to produce such a tree by the date specified will result in the banishment of the Gardener and the Gardener's family from this realm forever. Signed . . . His Mighty Majesty, King Valentino of Valentia.

MR. GOOSEBERRY: But, Your Majesty, the development of a tree requires months—even years. It is impossible to create a new tree by February 14th. That is the day after tomorrow.

KING: You have heard the royal command. The rest is up to you. I need hardly explain how important it is to draw the Prince back into the garden. This place was once his favorite spot. Now he spends all of his time indoors, shut up in his room. He is growing thin and pale. If he does not soon find pleasure in the out-of-doors, he will sicken, and perhaps die. You are the Head Gardener. You must make the garden such a beautiful and fascinating place that he will want to spend hours out here in the sunshine. You have developed many wonderful trees in the past which have delighted the Prince. Surely your skill has not failed you. Come, Lord Chancellor, we have other business to transact within the hour. Mr. Gooseberry, we will await a report of your experiments.

LORD CHANCELLOR (*Stepping in front of the* KING *and leading the way offstage*): Make way! Make way for His Most Gracious Majesty, King Valentino of Valentia. (*Exit* KING *and* LORD CHANCELLOR.)

MR. GOOSEBERRY (*Sitting down on bench in an attitude of despair*): Alas! Alas! What is to become of us? Where will we go? What will we do? I have lived all my life in Valentia. I cannot bear to live anywhere else. (*Enter* MRS. GOOSEBERRY *with a small market basket. With her is* GOLDIE, *carrying a large straw hat.*)

GOLDIE (*Running to her father*): Look, look, Father. See what I've brought you from the market place. (*Perching the bright-colored hat on her father's head*) There's a brim large enough to keep the sun off your head even on the hottest days.

MRS. GOOSEBERRY: We don't want you having a sunstroke working on your flower beds, in this hot February sun. (*With a sigh*) I wonder how it must be living in a country where the summer lasts only a few months of the year.

MR. GOOSEBERRY: You may soon discover what it is like to live in a different country, good wife.

MRS. GOOSEBERRY: What do you mean?

GOLDIE: Why, Father, your eyes are full of tears. What is the matter?

MR. GOOSEBERRY: A terrible trouble has befallen us, my dear ones. The King was just here.

MRS. GOOSEBERRY: The King?

GOLDIE: The King? That old monster! He always brings trouble.

MR. GOOSEBERRY: Hush, Goldie! Do you want us hanged as well as banished?

MRS. GOOSEBERRY: Banished? Who's been talking to you about banishment? Surely not the King. Why, you're the best gardener he's ever had.

MR. GOOSEBERRY: But this time he demands the impossible.

GOLDIE: Nothing is impossible for you, Father.

MR. GOOSEBERRY: His Majesty has commanded that I create a special tree in time for the Prince's birthday.

MRS. GOOSEBERRY: But that's the day after tomorrow.

MR. GOOSEBERRY: And as if that's not bad enough, he has further decreed that the tree must be so beautiful and possess such charm that the Prince will want to spend all his waking hours in the garden.

MRS. GOOSEBERRY: But did you explain to the King how impossible that is?

MR. GOOSEBERRY: The King would hear no explanations. Either I produce such a tree or we are banished forever from Valentia.

MRS. GOOSEBERRY: Oh, my poor husband! How can he treat you so after a lifetime of faithful service?

GOLDIE: No kingdom in the world has such wonderful trees! And you have developed them all to please the Prince.

MRS. GOOSEBERRY: Remember the time you created the Lollipop Tree for the Prince?

GOLDIE: He spent days out here in the garden, stuffing himself with lollipops till he got a stomach-ache.

MRS. GOOSEBERRY: The same way with the Sugar Plum Tree and the Choc-a-Nut Tree.

GOLDIE: Then there was the Fig-a-Jig Tree and the Dreamland Tree, the Orange-Pineapple Tree and the wonderful Gumdrop Bush.

MRS. GOOSEBERRY: To say nothing of the Laughing Willow, the Golden Leaf Maple and the Penny-Bearing Pine.

MR. GOOSEBERRY: But none of those will help me now. Besides, the Prince lost interest in all of them, in a few days.

MRS. GOOSEBERRY: Well, don't worry about it, husband. What must be, must be. You can only do your best. Now, come into the house for awhile and rest. Maybe you'll think of something.

MR. GOOSEBERRY: I must think of something. We can't leave our home and everything we have worked for all these years.

MRS. GOOSEBERRY (*Patting his shoulder*): There! There! Don't fret yourself so.

GOLDIE: I'll stay outside and do a bit of weeding, Father. At least, I can try out your new garden hat. (*Takes hat from her father and puts it on.* MR. *and* MRS. GOOSEBERRY *exit.*)

GOLDIE (*Pretending to look for weeds*): Father is such a wonderful gardener, there are scarcely any weeds to be found. Oh, here are a few. (*Kneels and pretends to weed. As she is weeding,* DALE *and* GAIL *enter.* DALE *carries a guide book.*)

DALE: Excuse me. Is this the Royal Palace of Valentia?

GOLDIE (*Rising in surprise*): Yes, it is. But who are you? No one is admitted here except on official business to the Palace.

DALE: I am Dale Dawson and this is my sister, Gail.

GAIL: We are American tourists. My brother and I are

doing some sight-seeing of our own. Are you a member of the royal family?

GOLDIE: Goodness, no. I am Goldie Gooseberry. My father is the Royal Gardener.

GAIL: How exciting! You must see the King often.

GOLDIE: Yes, indeed. Sometimes too often. (*Claps her hand over her mouth*) Oh, dear! I shouldn't have said that.

DALE: Why not? Isn't Valentia a free country?

GAIL: What's the matter? Isn't the King a kind man?

GOLDIE: Oh, yes. The King is very kind . . . only . . . that is . . . well, *most* of the time he's very kind. He's been very good to Father and to us, too, until today.

DALE: I'm afraid we're asking too many questions. But, you see, we don't know very much about Kings. We've never seen any.

GAIL: That's why we're so curious to see a real palace and maybe get a glimpse of the King and Queen.

GOLDIE: Well, there isn't any Queen, you know. She died several years ago. There's just His Highness, the Prince.

DALE: How old is the Prince?

GOLDIE: His Highness will be ten years old day after tomorrow.

GAIL: Why that's Valentine's Day!

GOLDIE: Valentine's Day?

GAIL: Of course. Certainly the people of Valentia celebrate the fourteenth of February.

GOLDIE: Oh, we celebrate all right, but only because it's the birthday of His Royal Highness.

DALE: How strange! I thought every country in the world observed Valentine's Day.

GOLDIE: I've never even heard of it. What is it?

GAIL: Why, it's the day we send valentines to people we like.

GOLDIE: Valentines? What are they?

DALE: They're little greeting cards, usually in the shape of hearts. Sometimes they're decorated with roses and cupids and they always contain verses.

GOLDIE: What sort of verses?

GAIL: Verses that tell how much we love our friends, like —"Roses are red, violets are blue, sugar is sweet and so are you!"

GOLDIE (*Laughing*): I like that one.

GAIL: That's a very old one. We usually write our own.

DALE: Maybe you should send your prince a valentine especially since it's his birthday.

GOLDIE: We wouldn't dare. And anyhow, we're not likely to be here on the Prince's birthday.

GAIL: But don't you live here? Isn't this your home?

GOLDIE: Yes, but my father is in terrible trouble. You see, His Highness, the Prince, is a very sickly boy. He stays shut up in his room most of the time. His father, the King, wants him to spend more time in the garden, but the Prince hardly ever ventures out-of-doors.

DALE: That sounds more like a case for a doctor than a gardener. What does your father have to do with it?

GOLDIE: My father is almost a magician when it comes to trees. He has created all sorts of rare and wonderful specimens for the Prince's pleasure. But in a few days, he tires of them. Now the King has issued an order that my father must prepare a new tree, so marvelous that the Prince will spend hours and hours in the palace garden. Unless he can produce such a tree by February 14th, our whole family will be banished from Valentia forever.

DALE: Why, that's terrible. Your king must be a most unreasonable man.

GAIL: Didn't your father tell him it takes a long time to develop a new tree?

GOLDIE: Of course. But the King has made up his mind! (*Begins to cry*)

GAIL: Oh, dear! I wish we could help you. Surely there must be some way to make the King listen to reason.

DALE: What's the matter with the Prince? Why doesn't he want to stay in the garden? What does he do when he does come outside?

GOLDIE: Walks up and down the garden paths, or picks the flowers or looks at the trees. Mostly he looks at the trees, especially the ones Father has developed.

DALE: That doesn't sound like much fun to me. Doesn't he play any games or invite any of his friends in to play with him?

GOLDIE: Friends? He doesn't have any.

DALE: What makes him so unpopular?

GOLDIE: Oh, he isn't unpopular. Everybody loves him, especially the children. But, you see, he is the Prince. The King would never let him play with ordinary children.

DALE: I think your prince is lonely instead of sickly. No wonder he won't stay in the garden. There's nothing to do.

GAIL: Maybe he thinks no one likes him. How does he know the children love him if they never get a chance to tell him so?

DALE: What your prince seems to need is a Valentine party instead of a birthday party.

GAIL: Dale! Dale! I have a terrific idea.

DALE: Not another one! This sister of mine is always

having terrific ideas and usually they get *me* into trouble. What is it this time?

GAIL: Listen. (*Whispers in his ear*)

DALE: They'd never go for it, not in a million years.

GAIL: But they have nothing to lose! If they're to be banished anyhow, what difference would it make? Besides, don't you remember the Coleridge verse we had to learn in school last year on Valentine's Day?

> Flowers are lovely; love is flower-like;
> Friendship is a sheltering tree;
> Oh the joys that came down shower-like
> Of friendship, joy and liberty.

GOLDIE: Tree? Did I hear you say the word tree?

GAIL: Yes, you did, Goldie. We have an idea that might help you. Please let us talk to your father.

DALE: Remember, if we both land in the palace dungeon, it was *your* idea, not ours. But I'm willing to take a chance. Go ahead, Goldie, take us to your father. As I said before, you have nothing to lose.

GOLDIE: I know Father will be willing to try anything, if there's the slightest chance. This way, please. It's only a few steps. (*Calling*) Father! Father! I'm bringing someone to see you. Hurry, Mother! Open the door. We have company. (*The children exit as curtains close and reopen almost immediately on Scene 2.*)

CURTAIN

* * *

Scene 2

SETTING: *Same as Scene 1, except for a folding screen center stage on which is hung a sign:* HAPPY BIRTHDAY, YOUR HIGHNESS!

AT RISE: MR. *and* MRS. GOOSEBERRY *and* GOLDIE *are onstage.*

MRS. GOOSEBERRY (*Wringing her hands*): This is the craziest thing I have ever heard of. I think you are mad! Stark raving mad! We shall all lose our heads, before this day is done!

MR. GOOSEBERRY: Now, now, Mother! Calm yourself. As the children say, we have nothing to lose.

MRS. GOOSEBERRY: Only our heads!

MR. GOOSEBERRY: Nonsense, my dear! No one has been beheaded in Valentia for a hundred years. Beheading has gone out of fashion.

GOLDIE: Is everything ready, Father?

MR. GOOSEBERRY: Everything in *my* department is ready, child. If only your friends from the strange land of America do their part.

GOLDIE: Oh, I know they will. I know they will. When will the Prince and the King arrive?

MR. GOOSEBERRY: They should be here any minute now.

MRS. GOOSEBERRY: I know I'm going to faint! I'm sure of it.

MR. GOOSEBERRY: Then go in and lie down, my dear.

MRS. GOOSEBERRY: And miss all the excitement! I should say not! (*An offstage blast of trumpets is heard.*)

GOLDIE (*Jumping up and down*): They're coming! They're coming!

MRS. GOOSEBERRY: My smelling salts! Where are my smelling salts?

GOLDIE: In your apron pocket, Mother. Take a good sniff and keep your fingers crossed for luck.

LORD CHANCELLOR (*From offstage*): Make way! Make way for His Supreme Majesty, King Valentino, and His Royal Highness, the Prince of Valentia. (*Enter* KING, PRINCE *and* LORD CHANCELLOR.)

KING (*To* PRINCE): In just a few seconds now you will see your birthday surprise, my son.

PRINCE: Oh, dear! I'll bet it will be another tree!

KING: Of course, it will be another tree, my son. And what a tree! This time, Mr. Gooseberry assures me, he has outdone himself. Although I have not seen it, I can safely say there is no other like it in the whole wide world. (*To* MR. GOOSEBERRY) Ah, Mr. Gooseberry, I see everything is ready. At the sound of the trumpets, let the ceremony begin! (*As trumpets sound offstage,* MR. *and* MRS. GOOSEBERRY *take their places on either side of the folding screen.* GOLDIE *curtsies to the* PRINCE *as she recites.*)

GOLDIE: A happy birthday to our Prince,
So noble, brave, and true!
And now behold the Birthday Tree,
Especially for you!
(MR. *and* MRS. GOOSEBERRY *remove screen, revealing a bare tree planted in a green tub.*)

PRINCE: What is it? There's not a leaf or flower on it!

LORD CHANCELLOR: Is this some sort of joke?

KING: What is the meaning of this? Gooseberry, what do you have to say for yourself?

MRS. GOOSEBERRY: I begged him not to do such a thing, Your Majesty.

KING: This is an outrage. Surely, you cannot mean that this is the Prince's Birthday Tree.

MR. GOOSEBERRY: If Your Majesty will grant me a few minutes, everything will be explained.

GOLDIE (*Calling to* GAIL *and* DALE *offstage*): Gail! Dale! Let the March of the Children begin! (GAIL *and* DALE *enter, followed by a long procession of children, each carrying a red heart to which a wire hanger is attached. They march onstage and around the tree singing to the tune of "Oats, Peas, Beans and Barley Grow."*)

Oh happy birthday, Prince of mine,
We want you for our Valentine.
And now we offer you our hearts
With all the love this day imparts.

All happiness and joy be thine,
If you will be our Valentine! (*Repeat*)

KING: What's this? What's this? A new national anthem?

MR. GOOSEBERRY (*Holding up his hand for quiet*): Your Mighty Majesty, and Your Royal Highness, I beg to present two visitors from a strange land who have a message of the most vital importance—Dale Dawson and his sister, Gail, from the United States of America.

DALE: Your Majesty, Your Royal Highness! Gail and I just happened to be touring through your wonderful country when we heard of the Royal Palace and the beautiful gardens so we came to see them. When we arrived Mr. Gooseberry and his daughter, Goldie, told us about the Prince's birthday falling on the fourteenth of February. In America and in many countries of the world that day is celebrated as St. Valentine's Day.

PRINCE: You mean my birthday is celebrated in other lands and other countries?

DALE: Yes, Your Highness, and you are extremely fortunate to have been born on a day that is set aside for love and friendship, the two greatest gifts in the world.

PRINCE: But who was this St. Valentine you speak of, whose name day falls on my birthday?

GAIL: St. Valentine was a good and great man who was killed by his enemies on February 14th. It is said that a beautiful pink almond tree grew and blossomed over his grave. Ever since his death people have sent messages of love and friendship to their dear ones on the day which has become known as St. Valentine's Day.

PRINCE: Which is also my birthday?

DALE: Right! So when we heard that Mr. Gooseberry had been commanded to create a special tree in honor of your birthday, Sire, Gail suggested that he make you a Tree of Hearts and here it is. (*During speeches by* GAIL *and* DALE, *the children have clustered around the tree and hung their hearts on its branches so that it is literally a Tree of Hearts.*)

GOLDIE (*With a curtsy to the* PRINCE): Dear Prince, the children of Valentia love you with all their hearts. They welcome this opportunity to show you their love and loyalty. (*Children sing to the tune of "The King of France with Forty Thousand Men."*)

The tree of hearts
Is planted here to show
Our noble Prince
The children love you so!

PRINCE: I am deeply touched and honored. This tree is the most beautiful tree I have ever seen. I thank you with all my heart! (*Applause*) Look, Father, see how each heart on the tree is decorated. (*Peering more closely*) And bless my soul, there are verses on some of them. (*Reading*) "If you love me as I love you, no knife could cut our love in two!" How remarkable! Who is the author of this masterpiece? (*The children look shy and embarrassed.*)

GAIL: You must not ask questions, Your Highness. You don't have to sign your name to a valentine, you know. It's sort of a secret.

KING (*Reading*): And listen to this one, son. "I love you little, I love you big! With you I'd like to dance a jig!"

PRINCE (*Laughing*): That's a good idea. I think I'd like to dance a jig with any of these young ladies.

LORD CHANCELLOR (*Reading verses on hearts*): Here's a noble sentiment. "When you are sad and feeling blue, remember, Prince, we all love you."

PRINCE: That's the best of all. It makes me feel happy all over. I never knew I had so many friends before.

DALE: That's the whole idea of Valentine's Day, Sire. When you love somebody, that's the day you can tell him so without feeling shy or silly.

PRINCE: It will take me days to read all these verses.

GAIL: And days more to answer them. You see, Sire, Valentine's Day is a two-way proposition. The joy is not only in receiving them, the best part is in sending them.

PRINCE: A capital idea! Chancellor, get me paper and pencil at once. I must compose some verses.

MR. GOOSEBERRY: Excuse me, Sire, but I have a further suggestion.

KING: Whatever it is, Gooseberry, feel free to make it. Your Tree of Hearts is the most magnificent thing you have ever done! Chancellor, make a note to build the Gooseberrys the finest cottage in the land.

MRS. GOOSEBERRY: Then you are not sending us away?

KING: Sending you away, indeed! The Prince will want a Tree of Hearts every year after this, and perhaps the Chancellor and I would each like one of our own.

MR. GOOSEBERRY: As our little friends from America have pointed out, Sire, friendship is, indeed, a sheltering tree. And now for my suggestion.

KING: Chancellor, take pen in hand.

MR. GOOSEBERRY: I suggest first of all, that we turn the rest of the day over to Dale and Gail to be celebrated in the fashion of a true Valentine party. (*Applause*) Mrs. Gooseberry has baked some cakes for the occasion and Goldie is ready to serve ice cream in heart-shaped molds. (*Applause*)

KING: Very good! Excellent!

MR. GOOSEBERRY: And one further suggestion, Sire, about the care of the tree. A Tree of Hearts is not like other trees. It needs more than water and sunshine. It must have plenty of love and attention. It must always be within range of the sound of laughter and what it needs most is children playing underneath its branches. Without this kind of care, it will wither and die.

KING: Chancellor, prepare an edict. The Palace Garden henceforth is open every day to all children who wish to come inside and play with the Prince. (*Applause*)

PRINCE: Thank you, Father, thank you. This is the happiest birthday I have ever had. In fact, thanks to Gail and Dale, and the Gooseberrys and the Tree of Hearts, this is the happiest day of my life. Nevertheless, I have one more request.

KING: Whatever it is, it shall be granted, my son.

PRINCE: It is very simple. I merely wish to change my name from Prince Valentino to Prince Valentine in memory of the good saint we honor on my birthday.

KING: It shall be done. Chancellor, make official pronouncement.

LORD CHANCELLOR: Hear ye! Hear ye! From this day forth, the Crown Prince and Heir Apparent to the crown of Valentia shall be known as Prince Valentine.

DALE: Three cheers for Prince Valentine! (*Curtains close on cheering as children dance around the Tree of Hearts.*)

THE END

Crosspatch and Cupid

Characters

CROSSPATCH
CUPID
TEACHER
LAZY LUCY—LOVELY LUCY
HATEFUL HANNAH—HELPFUL HANNAH
CARELESS CARRIE—CAREFUL CARRIE
JEALOUS JUDY—JOLLY JUDY
SULKY SUE—SUNNY SUE
SCOWLING SAM—SMILING SAM
FIGHTING FREDDIE—FRIENDLY FREDDIE
ROWDY RUDOLF—RESPECTFUL RUDOLPH
PICKY PETER—POLITE PETER
CLUMSY CALVIN—CLEVER CALVIN

SETTING: *A classroom.*

AT RISE: *The five boys, five girls, and their* TEACHER *are at work. Seated on stools at either side of the stage are* CROSSPATCH *and* CUPID. *Each has a scoreboard mounted on an easel beside him, and a crayon to keep score.*

CROSSPATCH: Ho ho! Ha ha! Tee-hee! Tee-hee!
I can see *them* (*Points to children*), but they cannot see me!

My name is Crosspatch, and sternly I rule
The youthful scholars in this school.
This patch I wear upon my eye (*Points to eye patch*)
Conceals all good. Just *bad* I spy.
Here on this board I tally the score (*Points to board*)
Of *hate* words spoken on the floor.
Each time a child *hates* this or that
Is like a feather in my hat. (*Looks at* CUPID *scornfully*)
My neighbor, Cupid, on his stool,
Thinks *he's* the master of this school.
But during this, our little play,
You'll find that Crosspatch wins the day! (*He nods his head in confidence and folds his arms across his chest, as* CUPID *speaks.*)

CUPID: My name is Cupid. My law is love.
I'm gentle as the gentlest dove.
I keep my two eyes open wide
To see the *good* that's deep inside
Of every child who goes to school.
That's why I'm perched here on this stool. (*Indicates board and crayon*)
I draw a line, all bright and clear
For every *love* word that I hear.
Each time a child *loves* that or this
To me is like a hug and kiss. (*Grins at* CROSSPATCH)
Now Crosspatch thinks *he's* master here,
But love will make him disappear.
If you will watch our little play,
You'll soon find out who wins the day!

BOTH: Now school begins, as you can tell
The minute Teacher rings the bell. (TEACHER *taps bell for attention.*)

TEACHER: Good morning, girls and boys.
CHILDREN (*Gloomily*): Good morning, Teacher.
TEACHER (*With a sigh*): I know we all *hate* days like this
When rain sets all our plans amiss, (CROSSPATCH *scores.*)
But even though the sun won't shine,
We *must* begin this valentine. (*Moves a large heart-shaped wire frame center stage.*)
So bring your scissors, papers, paste,
That we may all proceed with haste.
LAZY LUCY: Oh dear! I *hate* to cut and trim! (CROSSPATCH *scores.*)
Let Sammy do it! Call on him!
TEACHER: That's *Lazy Lucy,* through and through!
She weakens when there's work to do!
SCOWLING SAM (*With a heavy frown*): I also *hate* to make this heart (CROSSPATCH *scores*)
But I will try to do my part. (*As children speak, they group themselves around the wire frame and gradually fashion a red paper heart. It can be prefabricated, ready to assemble. It should be a sorry-looking affair, crooked, streaked, and very carelessly made.*)
TEACHER: "Scowling Sam" and "Sulky Sue!"
I never saw a crosser crew!
SULKY SUE (*With a toss of her head as she goes to work*):
I know I'm sulky! I don't care!
I *hate* the way these papers tear! (CROSSPATCH *strokes again.*)
ROWDY RUDOLPH (*Charging at the heart as if ready to ruin it*): I'll go to work with might and main!
I *hate* the way these girls complain! (CROSSPATCH *scores with glee.*)
TEACHER: Rowdy Rudolph! Have a care!

That heart won't stand such wear and tear!

FIGHTING FREDDIE (*To* ROWDY RUDOLPH): You break that heart, and that's no joke,
You'll be surprised to get a poke! (CROSSPATCH *claps his hands silently in delight.*)

TEACHER: Now, Fighting Freddie, simmer down!
You're quite the crossest boy in town!

CARELESS CARRIE (*With a wail*): Oh, dear, oh, dear! Oh, what a waste!
Just look at me! I've spilled the paste!

TEACHER: Careless Carrie! What a mess!
Try not to get it on your dress!

CARELESS CARRIE (*Half in tears*): I always *hate* this stuff that spills!
And Mother *hates* the cleaning bills! (*Double score for* CROSSPATCH.)

TEACHER: Let Hannah help you with the paste.
Slow up a bit—not so much haste!

HATEFUL HANNAH: I'm cross at Carrie all this week!
We had a fight and we don't speak! (CROSSPATCH *is delighted as he makes a big black stroke.*)

TEACHER: I *hate* to hear you talking so. (*Another stroke*)
But, never mind! Just let it go!

JEALOUS JUDY: I've done more work than all the rest,
And I am sure it's done the best!

PICKY PETER (*Looking at the heart with a critical eye*):
I *hate* to say it, but it's true (CROSSPATCH *scores*)
This heart is very much askew.
It's crooked, and the paper's torn.
I think it looks a bit forlorn.
I'm surely glad it isn't mine!
I'd *hate* to get *this* valentine. (*Another score for* CROSSPATCH)

TEACHER: I think we all should have a rest
To give us back our pep and zest!
Here, Calvin, set the heart aside.
The rain has stopped. Go play outside. (*As* CLUMSY CALVIN *moves the easel, he knocks it over and steps on the heart.*)

CLUMSY CALVIN: Oh dear! How clumsy! What a shame!
I know it's my fault! I'm to blame!

FREDDIE (*In anger*): You Clumsy Calvin! What a sight!
Now you and I will have a fight!

TEACHER: No fighting, Freddie! (*With a sigh*) What a day!
Please, children, go outside and play. (*As children exit*)
This day is more than I can bear!
I think I need a breath of air! (*Exit* TEACHER)

CROSSPATCH: Ho ho! Ha ha! Tee-hee! Tee-hee!
The victory belongs to me!
Just look at this! Add up the score
Of all these *hate* words! More and more!
I know I owe a thing or two
To Lazy Lucy, Sulky Sue,
And all the rest like Fred and Sam
Who helped to put me where I am!
Alas for Cupid and his rule!
I guess he knows who runs this school!

CUPID: One minute, Crosspatch, not so fast!
You know the day is not yet past. (*Reaches into quiver for handful of paper darts*)
With these, my magic Cupid darts,
I know I'll reach the children's hearts.
Of play the pupils quickly tire.
When they return, I'll aim and fire!
Then, mark you, Crosspatch, count the score!

Those angry words you'll hear no more!

CROSSPATCH: Ho ho! Ha ha! Tee-hee! Tee-hee!
Go try your luck! We'll see! We'll see!

BOTH: Recess is over. Now for the fun!
Watch the children. Here they come! (*As children and* TEACHER *enter,* CUPID *hurls paper darts. As each child is struck, he examines the dart carefully.*)

TEACHER: Look, children, look! And read your name.
No two of these are quite the same.

LOVELY LUCY: This one cannot be for me, (*Looks at it carefully*)
Though Lucy's spelled as plain can be.
Lazy Lucy must disappear,
For *Lovely* Lucy's written here. (CUPID *scores.*)

HELPFUL HANNAH: *Hateful* Hannah was my name,
But *Helpful* Hannah's written plain. (CUPID *scores.*)

SUNNY SUE: I'm always *Sulky* Sue to you,
But now I feel like *Sunny* Sue. (*Score for* CUPID.)

SMILING SAM: *Scowling* Sam is straightway dead.
Henceforth, I'm *Smiling* Sam instead. (CUPID *scores.*)

ROWDY RUDOLPH: *Rowdy* Rudolph is no more.
(*With a bow*) *Respectful* Rudolph takes the floor. (CUPID *scores.*)

CAREFUL CARRIE: *Careless* Carrie took the blame.
Now *Careful* Carrie is my name. (CUPID *scores.*)

FRIENDLY FREDDIE: From now my fighting spirit ends.
What I want most of all is friends. (CUPID *scores.*)

POLITE PETER: *Polite* Peter will make folks smile.
Picky Peter's out of style. (CUPID *scores.*)

JOLLY JUDY: *Jealous* Judy is not for me.
It's *Jolly* Judy here you see. (CUPID *scores.*)

CLEVER CALVIN: Always clumsy! But today
Clever Calvin's here to stay. (CUPID *scores.*)

TEACHER: I think we've had a change of heart.
Let's try to make a brand-new start.

LOVELY LUCY: I love it when we work together! (CUPID *scores again.*)
Let's make this heart the best one ever! (*This time, as children work on the heart, they replace the old covering with beautiful paper arrangement.*)

SMILING SAM: I'd love to work a little while.
I feel much better with a smile. (CUPID *scores.*)

SUNNY SUE: I know, Sam, just the way you feel.
A smiling face has eye-appeal.
I'd love to help and do my share. (*Score for* CUPID)
And see . . . the paper doesn't tear!

RESPECTFUL RUDOLPH: I wonder why I felt so rough,
And tried so hard to be so tough. (CUPID *scores.*)

FRIENDLY FREDDIE: Somehow that little paper dart
Took all the fight out of my heart. (CUPID *scores.*)

CAREFUL CARRIE: And I've not spilled a single thing.
I feel so good, I want to sing. (CUPID *scores.*)
With *Helpful* Hannah by my side,
I'm really working in my stride.

HELPFUL HANNAH: I love to help! I never knew (CUPID *scores.*)
How helping hands bring friends to you.

JOLLY JUDY: My part is really very small,
But I am glad to work at all. (CUPID *scores.*)
I'm proud that I can have a part
In making this big, lovely heart.

POLITE PETER: It looks just great! It's really fine!
I'd *love* to get *this* valentine. (*Score for* CUPID)

CLEVER CALVIN: There's one thing missing. Oh, how stupid!
It needs a picture of a Cupid.

TEACHER: Well, Calvin, that's a clever plan.
Let's try to draw one, if we can. (*Children go to tables to draw.*)
To show you how he ought to look,
I have his picture in a book. (TEACHER *walks from child to child showing book. As children draw,* CUPID *speaks.*)

CUPID: Well, Crosspatch, what have you to say?
You must admit, I've won the day.

CROSSPATCH: Some trick you've used!
It isn't fair!
But look out, Cupid, have a care!
I'll soon undo this work you've done.
You cannot say the fight is won! (*As* CROSSPATCH *climbs down from stool,* CUPID *showers him with darts.*)

CUPID: Take that! And that! A lucky shot!
I've aimed and hit you on the spot!
We'll see if Crosspatch has a heart
That can be pierced by Cupid's dart.

CROSSPATCH (*Reeling under shower of darts*): Help! Help!
Before it's too late!
I feel I'm losing all my hate.

CUPID: I know you are. Now you'll behave,
And evermore must be my slave.

CROSSPATCH (*Kneeling before* CUPID): Just tell me what I am to do,
And faithfully I'll follow you.

CUPID: First take that black patch off your eye,
So all the good things you can spy.
So you can see these children here,
Just as they really do appear.
You'll learn to love them right away,
And you'll be glad you lost the fray!

CROSSPATCH: Dear me! Dear me! I think you're right.
These children are a real delight!
CUPID: Of course they are! Now we proceed
To other schools where children need
A goodly dose of Cupid's darts
To open up their little hearts.
Come on, Crosspatch, here we go.
And you may bear my pouch and bow. (*Hands* CROSSPATCH *his bow and pouch of arrows*)
But first I'll leave my photograph
Inscribed with my true autograph,
So when I really disappear,
They'll know that Cupid has been here. (CUPID *places a picture on the cardboard heart, and pretends to sign his name. Exit* CROSSPATCH *and* CUPID.)
TEACHER: Let's pause and put our work aside.
I know how very hard you've tried
To draw a Cupid. None the less,
I fear we've met with no success.
LOVELY LUCY: Look, Teacher, look!
A big surprise!
I scarcely can believe my eyes! (CHILDREN *and* TEACHER *crowd around heart with picture.*)
CLEVER CALVIN: It's really Cupid, just the same,
For, look, you see, he's signed his name.
ALL: Yours sincerely, Dan Cupid!
BOYS: How did it get here?
GIRLS: Where did it come from?
TEACHER: I do not know, but one thing's true,
He left his picture just for you.
We'll keep it to remind us of
The little winged god of love
Who taught these little folks of mine

To make a living valentine. (*Curtains close as* TEACHER *and children dance around the heart singing the following verses to the tune of "Reuben and Rachel":*)

ALL: Cupid, Cupid, I've been thinking
What a good world this would be
If we'd say to one another,
"I love you as you love me."

Cupid, Cupid, I've been thinking
How to build a world so fine
If we'd send our friends and neighbors
Every day a valentine!

THE END

The Washington Shilling

Characters

TOBY FREMONT, *a present-day boy*
TABBY FREMONT, *his sister*
MR. FREMONT } *their parents*
MRS. FREMONT }
JUDY } *Tabby's friends*
MAGGIE }
SANDRA }
MAC, *Toby's friend*
TOBIAS FREMONT, *a colonial boy*
TABITHA FREMONT, *his sister*
GEORGE WASHINGTON
OTHER COLONIAL CHILDREN
CLOWNS
A JUGGLER
TWO ACTORS
FOUR STREET CRIERS

SCENE 1

SETTING: *The Fremont living room.*

AT RISE: TABBY FREMONT, JUDY, MAGGIE, *and* SANDRA *are gathered around a small table on which there is a blue velvet jewel case.*

JUDY: I can hardly wait to see it, Tabby.

MAGGIE: Neither can I. Did the shilling really and truly belong to George Washington, Tabby?

TABBY: Yes, it really did. He gave it to one of my ancestors—the first Toby Fremont. Both my father and my brother are named for him.

SANDRA: Isn't it worth a lot of money?

MAGGIE: Oh, a shilling isn't worth very much, is it? Only about nineteen or twenty cents.

JUDY: But a shilling that belonged to George Washington would be worth ever so much more, wouldn't it, Tabby?

TABBY: I guess so. But Mother and Daddy wouldn't take anything for it.

SANDRA: Well, hurry up and open the case. I want to see it.

MAGGIE: I don't believe half of the boys and girls in our class really believed you when you said you had a shilling that belonged to George Washington.

TABBY: Well, we do! And right here it is! (*Opens box and displays it to girls*)

MAGGIE: Why, it's empty!

SANDRA: There's not a thing in it!

TABBY: What?

JUDY: See for yourself! What were you trying to do? Fool us with an empty box?

TABBY (*Stares at the box in disbelief*): Why, I can't believe it! It *must* be here! No one ever touches it!

MAGGIE: Then where is it?

SANDRA: It couldn't get out of the box by itself!

JUDY: Maybe we should call the police! You've been robbed!

TABBY: But it's impossible! Daddy always keeps it in his desk except on special occasions. He took it out last night because this is George Washington's birthday and he's invited some of the men from the office to come in this evening. One has a famous coin collection. He wanted to see our shilling.

SANDRA: Maybe your mother put it someplace.

TABBY: But where? Besides, Mother isn't home this afternoon. She went to a luncheon.

JUDY: Well, my goodness! Aren't you going to do something about it? Are we all going to stand around and do nothing when something valuable has been stolen?

TABBY: But how do we know it's been stolen?

MAGGIE: Well, it's disappeared, hasn't it? Unless there never was such a shilling in the first place.

TABBY: Maggie Russell! What a terrible thing to say! Of course, there was a shilling. Do you think I'd make the whole thing up?

MAGGIE: Oh, I didn't mean that exactly.

TABBY: Well, what did you mean?

SANDRA: There's no use quarreling about it, Tabby. I agree with Judy. You should do something about it.

TABBY: But what can I do? Maybe if we wait till Toby comes home, he'd know what to do.

JUDY: That would just be wasting more time. You know Toby always practices basketball after school.

MAGGIE: Why don't you phone your mother? Maybe she knows something about it.

TABBY: Yes, I could do that. Only it might upset her.

MAGGIE: Not if she knows where the coin is. She might have taken it with her to show her friends.

TABBY: I never thought of that, Maggie. But, then, why wouldn't she have taken the case?

MAGGIE: Why not call her and find out? That's one way of settling it.

TABBY: All right, I will. (*Goes to phone, tries it, then replaces receiver*) Oh, dear! I forgot! The phone is out of order. Mother said at noon she had reported it.

JUDY: You can come over to our house and phone from there.

TABBY: Thanks. Oh, I do hope she has it with her, or knows where it is! Come on, let's hurry. (*A moment after the girls leave,* TOBY *and* MAC *enter.*)

MAC: I hope you know what you're doing, Toby, but the way I look at it, you're just piling up more trouble for yourself.

TOBY: You don't know my Dad, Mac! He prizes that Washington shilling more than anything we own. Mom always says if the house should catch on fire, the first thing Dad would save would be that precious shilling.

MAC: If you knew he felt that way about it, why did you take it without asking him?

TOBY: That's the sixty-four-thousand-dollar question! I could kick myself around the block now that I did it. But well, at the time, I didn't see any special risk. And you know how the kids at school are! They wouldn't believe I had such a shilling. I don't think even Miss Parsons believed me.

MAC: So you had to show 'em! And now look where you are!

TOBY: Listen, Mac! It must be somewhere. It couldn't have disappeared into thin air. I figure if you let me stay all night at your house, maybe the janitor will find it when he sweeps the room. Then tomorrow I can bring it home and explain to Dad.

MAC: But you can't explain that you took it without asking him.

TOBY: Yeah, I know! That part will be rough! But it will

be a whole lot rougher if I have to tell him the shilling is lost. Thank goodness we have the house to ourselves. Mom's at a luncheon and Sis isn't home yet. If I hurry, I can make it. You wait here while I go stick some clothes in a bag. I'll leave a note for Mom that I'm spending the night with you. (*Exit*)

MAC: O.K., pal! But I still think you're making a mistake. (*With a low whistle*) I wouldn't be in his shoes for a million dollars! (TABBY *enters with a rush, stops short when she sees* MAC.)

TABBY: Hello, Mac! Is Toby home?

MAC (*With a gulp*): Yeah, he's home.

TABBY: Oh, thank goodness! Mac, the most terrible thing has happened. (*Seizing empty jewel box*) Look! Our Washington shilling is gone! I've just been over to Judy Lawson's trying to phone Mother, but she had already left! I can hardly wait to tell Toby. Maybe he can think of something to do.

TOBY (*Entering with small overnight case in one hand and a note in the other*): I'll prop up this note on the phone table so Mom will see it first thing. Oh, for Pete's sake! (*Seeing* TABBY) Are *you* home!

TABBY: Oh, Toby! (*Showing him the box she still has in her hand*) What will Dad say? The Washington shilling is gone.

TOBY (*Blankly*): Gone?

TABBY: Judy wanted me to call the police.

TOBY (*Horrified*): The police! Don't tell me you called the police!

TABBY: Of course not! Not without asking Mother. That's one reason I tried to reach her on the phone. She should be here any minute.

TOBY: Come on, Mac. Let's get going.

TABBY (*Noticing overnight case*): Toby, what's the matter? Where are you going?

TOBY: I'm going to spend the night with Mac. (*Thrusting note in her hand*) Here! Give this to Mom.

TABBY: But she'll be here any minute. She left the Watsons' about fifteen minutes ago. You can tell her yourself. Anyhow, Dad wanted us all home for dinner tonight. Those men are coming from the office. You'd better not go out to spend the night without asking Mother or Dad.

TOBY: Tabby, you don't understand. I've got to get out of this house without seeing either Mother or Dad . . . least of all Dad!

TABBY: Toby Fremont! What have you been up to?

TOBY (*With a hollow laugh*): What makes you think I've been up to anything?

TABBY: You're in some sort of trouble. It's written all over your face!

TOBY: Don't be silly. (*Pushing past her*) Come on, Mac.

TABBY: Toby, come back here! (*Runs after him*) Toby, you don't mean . . . you can't mean you know something about the Washington shilling!

TOBY: Oh, for goodness' sake! Let me alone, can't you?

MAC: You might as well tell her, chum. She's catching on!

TOBY: O.K. So I took the old Washington shilling to school to show the class and I lost it!

TABBY: Oh, Toby! You didn't! Not without asking Dad!

TOBY: What would have been the use of asking! You know how he is about that shilling.

TABBY: Yes, I know . . . But what possessed you to take such an awful risk?

TOBY: It was the kids at school mostly. They wouldn't believe me. Said I was making the whole thing up!

TABBY: Yes, I know. Judy and Maggie and Sandra didn't believe me, either. That's why I brought them in after school to show them.

TOBY: Ever since we moved to this town, I've never had anything important to take to school and this time I thought I'd really make 'em sit up and take notice! Now look what happened.

TABBY: What *did* happen? How did you lose it?

TOBY: I don't know. We were just passing it around the room and one of the fellows dropped it. We searched high and low, but it was gone.

MAC: Toby thought if he stayed at my house overnight, maybe your Dad would cool down and the janitor might find the coin when he sweeps.

TABBY: But, Toby, you can't do that!

TOBY: Why not? I've written a note to Mom. She often lets me stay all night at Mac's.

TABBY: But this is different.

TOBY: How?

TABBY: This is running away!

TOBY: It is not!

TABBY: It is so! You're afraid to face Dad, so you're running away!

TOBY: Of course, I'm afraid to face Dad. Who wouldn't be? But I'm not running away. I'm just going over to Mac's house overnight.

TABBY: Because you're afraid to tell Dad what you did.

TOBY: But I *will* tell him, Tabby. You know I will. And by morning, maybe I'll have the shilling back again. That's not running away.

TABBY: I'd call it running away, but maybe a better word is "hiding out." Either way you look at it, you're just making matters worse.

TOBY: Who asked you for any advice, anyhow?

TABBY: Nobody. But, Toby, don't you see? It really *is* running away. Listen to me. Have you forgotten the story of how we got the Washington shilling in the first place? Don't you remember the story of that other Toby Fremont—the one you were named for?

TOBY: *Yeah* . . . he had a sister, too.

TABBY: Surely you haven't forgotten, Toby. Dad has told it to us a hundred times. If anything could possibly mean more to Dad than the shilling itself, it's the story of how it came into our possession. I guess that other Toby and Tabby were just about our age, the day they decided to go to the street fair on High Street. (*Curtain.*)

* * * *

SCENE 2

BEFORE CURTAIN: *Child places large placard which reads,* STREET FAIR—COME ONE, COME ALL!, *on the apron of the stage. Another child places a bench to one side. To off-stage carnival music,* CLOWNS *tumble across stage, and a* JUGGLER *tosses balls into the air. The entertainers are followed by an admiring group of children, among them,* TOBIAS *and* TABITHA FREMONT. *Young* GEORGE WASHINGTON *is also in the group.*

TABITHA (*As children applaud the clowns and juggler*): What a merry sight, Tobias! I never thought to see such a clever juggler!

TOBIAS: Fie, Tabitha! I could do the same tricks myself, had I more time to practice. (TWO ACTORS *enter, each carrying a hand puppet.*)

1st Actor: Right this way, ladies and gentlemen! See the funniest show on earth!

2nd Actor: See the battle of the century between the masterful Punch and his daring wife, Judy!

1st Actor: Hear ye! Hear ye!
Have you a penny? Well, then, stay!
Haven't you any? Don't go away!
Punch holds receptions all through the day,
Squeaking aloud to gather a crowd,
Scolding at Toby, beating his wife,
Frightening the constable out of his life!

Tabitha: Let's go, Tobias! Did you hear? There's a *Toby* in the play— Let's go! Let's go!

Tobias: Be quiet, lass. Toby is the dog!

2nd Actor: Hear ye! Hear ye! It's really your duty
To come to the show and see Punch and Judy!
Now away we must jog, with Punch and his dog!
Our friends we will meet on the very next street!

Both: This way! This way! For the Punch and Judy show! Only a penny for a thousand laughs!

Tabitha (*As* Actors *exit, followed by several children*): Do let's go, Tobias! I want to see it!

Tobias: Did ye not hear what the fellow said? We must have a penny to see the show!

Tabitha: Oh, dear! I forgot!

Tobias: And even if we *did* have a penny, I would be loath to spend it on such a trifle. Now here is something more to my liking. (Four Street Criers *enter with large trays suspended around their necks. Each one is crying his wares.*)

1st Crier: All hot! All hot! Come buy! Come buy!
Three a penny is the price,
And if you my meat pies try,

You will find them very nice. (*Repeat at intervals*)

2ND CRIER: A penny for a sweetmeat! A penny for a sweetmeat! A penny for a sweetmeat! (*In a sing-song voice, over and over*)

3RD CRIER: Toys! Toys! Penny toys!
Toys for girls and toys for boys!
Toys for tots who scarce can crawl,
Toys for youngsters stout and tall,
Toys for prince and peasant, too,
Toys, my dears, for all of you!
Toys for girls and toys for boys!
Toys! Toys! Penny toys!

4TH CRIER: A penny, a penny, a penny a bun!
Buy a full dozen or buy only one!
Eat it with sugar, oh, what a treat!
A penny, a penny, a big bun to eat!

TABITHA (*Holding her ears*): I never knew a penny could buy so much!

TOBIAS: My mouth is fair watering for one of those buns!

TABITHA: If only we had a penny, we might buy some sweetmeats! (*The crowd swarms around the vendors.* GEORGE WASHINGTON *buys three buns, one of which he munches as he strolls about.*)

TOBIAS: Let's find a place to sit down, out of the crowd.

TABITHA (*Pointing to bench*): Here is a bench, but must we have a penny to sit on it? (GEORGE WASHINGTON *strolls up to the children in time to hear* TOBIAS *speak.*)

TOBIAS (*As they sit down*): Right now I am so hungry I could eat one of these pebbles on the ground.

GEORGE WASHINGTON: 'Twould be mighty hard eating, lad! And I venture to say you would have more of a toothache than a stomach-ache. Best try one of these buns instead. (*Offers the children each a bun.*)

TOBIAS: No thank you, sir. We have no money.

WASHINGTON: Who said aught of money, lad? Here, take the bun. And this one shall be for your sister.

TABITHA: My mother says we should take naught from strangers, sir.

WASHINGTON: Your mother speaks wisely, lass. But I am just a lad, not much older than your brother, I vow.

TOBIAS: The buns look very good, sir.

WASHINGTON (*Putting bun in his hand and giving one to* TABITHA): They're better than that. You'll be doing me a favor by keeping me company while I eat. I dislike eating alone.

TABITHA: Have you no friends at the fair?

WASHINGTON: Nay, child. I come from Virginia.

TOBIAS: But that is far away!

WASHINGTON: Aye! And this is one of the fairest towns I've seen. A fine change from the wilderness!

TOBIAS: The wilderness?

WASHINGTON: Aye. I am on a surveying mission for Lord Fairfax.

TOBIAS: You must have had great adventures.

WASHINGTON: More hardship than adventure, lad. Twice in the last week, the wind and rain swept away our tent and put out our campfire.

TABITHA: Are there Indians in the wilderness, sir?

WASHINGTON: Aye, we met a party of braves only a fortnight ago. They did a war dance for our special entertainment.

TOBIAS: Is it hard work being a surveyor? I think I should like to go into the wilderness.

WASHINGTON: Then stick to your books for a while, lad. A surveyor must have a head full of figures and an eye for a drawing board.

TOBIAS: Does the work pay well?

WASHINGTON: Lord Fairfax is a generous employer. He grants me a doubloon every day the weather permits my going out.

TOBIAS: A doubloon? Tabitha and I have a doubloon, sir.

WASHINGTON: A whole doubloon? But I thought you lacked even a penny for a sweetmeat or a bun.

TABITHA: The doubloon is not ours. Father gave it to us to take to Captain Oster on Canal Street. It is for a debt Father owes. 'Twas my brother's notion we should come by way of High Street and see the fair.

WASHINGTON: A doubloon is a large piece of money to be carrying at the fair, lad. You'd best be careful. In such crowds there are likely to be thieves and knaves.

TOBIAS: Oh, I have it quite safe in my jacket. (*Reaches in jacket and pulls out drawstring purse*) See! (*Opens purse. It is empty.*) It's gone!

TABITHA: No! No! It must be there!

TOBIAS: It isn't. It's lost! Stolen! What shall we do?

TABITHA: We must look for it at once.

TOBIAS: Look for it? In this crowd? It would be of no use.

TABITHA: What will Father say?

TOBIAS: You know what he will say and do!

TABITHA: Oh, Tobias, we never should have come to this wicked place!

TOBIAS: But we did! Now we're in for it! We must find some way out.

TABITHA: But there isn't any way out. He will never forgive us for losing the money.

WASHINGTON: But it was an accident!

TOBIAS: You don't understand. My father does not approve of street fairs. He . . . he especially told us not to come this way!

TABITHA: And you said he'd never find out!

TOBIAS: And he never will. We won't let him.

TABITHA: But what can we do?

TOBIAS: We'll run away. That's what we'll do.

TABITHA: Where would we go? What would we do?

TOBIAS: We could join the jugglers or the clowns! Surely someone at the fair could find work for us. Perhaps even you, sir, might help us. I am strong. Could I join your surveying party?

WASHINGTON: Nay, lad. There would be no place for you or your sister.

TOBIAS: Aye, I forgot about the lass.

WASHINGTON: Even if I could find a place for you, my friend, I would not do it.

TABITHA: But you are so kind. You gave us a bun. I thought you liked us.

WASHINGTON: I do. But I would not help you run away from your father.

TOBIAS: But you don't understand. He will be furious. I well remember the birching I got last year for coming to the fair! And now to have lost the money! No, this time, I will run away.

WASHINGTON: You are thinking so much about your father that you are forgetting about your mother. How would she feel if you were to run away?

TABITHA: I had not thought of Mother. Aye, she would be sore distressed.

WASHINGTON: I know how mothers feel, lass. When I was your brother's age, I yearned to go away to sea. But I could not break my mother's heart.

TOBIAS: So you stayed at home?

WASHINGTON: I obeyed my mother.

TABITHA: There is that word *obey!* If only we had obeyed Father and gone straight to the Captain's office!

TOBIAS: You might understand Mother, but I know you don't understand Father or you would not think it so easy to go home.

WASHINGTON: I do not think it is easy to go home and confess a fault, but I do think I understand your father. He is a hard man who deals out justice with a heavy hand, but he wants a son he can be proud of.

TOBIAS: He's not proud of me.

WASHINGTON: All fathers are proud of their sons, even when they make mistakes. My own father is no longer living, but if he were, I should stop at nothing to make him proud of me.

TOBIAS: How could he be proud of me, after this?

WASHINGTON: A father is always proud of the son who proves his courage and remains true to his conscience.

TABITHA: Mother tells us about listening to our conscience, Toby.

WASHINGTON: An angry conscience can cause you more pain than an angry father.

TABITHA (*Pointing*): Look! Look, Tobias! There's Father!

TOBIAS: Where?

TABITHA (*Pointing offstage*): He's come to look for us.

TOBIAS: Do you think he has seen us yet?

TABITHA: Not yet! We can still get away. If we run now, he'll never know we lost the money at the fair.

TOBIAS (*Thoughtfully*): But *we'll* know, Tabitha, and we'll remember, long after we've forgotten Father's anger and the punishment. (*Starts to leave*)

TABITHA: Tobias! Where are you going?

TOBIAS: I'm going straight to Father and tell him what happened.

WASHINGTON: Wait a minute. You're a lad of spirit! I'd like to know your name.

TOBIAS: Tobias Fremont, at your service. And this is my sister, Tabitha.

WASHINGTON: My name is George Washington—George Washington of Virginia. We're not likely to meet again, Tobias, but I'd like to give you something to remember me by. (*Reaching in pocket*) It's a shilling—my lucky shilling, I call it. My brother gave it to me on the day I had the painful duty of telling my mother I had caused the death of one of her most valuable horses. I have often held it in my hand when I had something hard to do. The feel of it in my fingers gave me courage. Maybe it will do the same for you. Good luck, Tobias. Goodbye, Tabitha.

TABITHA (*With a curtsy*): Goodbye, sir.

TOBIAS: Goodbye and thank you. I'll never part with this shilling—never! And every time I look at it, I'll remember the name, George Washington, and what it stands for. (*Calling*) Father! Father! Here we are! Come on, Tabitha, he sees us. Come on. (TABITHA *and* TOBIAS *run off left as* WASHINGTON *exits right. After a brief pause, the curtains open.*)

* * *

SCENE 3

SETTING: *Same as Scene 1.*

AT RISE: TOBY, TABBY, *and* MAC *stand in the same positions as at end of Scene 1.*

MAC: So that's how it happened. That's how your family got the Washington shilling.

TABBY: It's been handed down from father to son ever since. Some day it will belong to Toby.

TOBY: Not any more—not unless I get it back. But I can see what you mean, Tabby. Even if I never see the shilling again, I can't run away. I'll have to tell Dad. (MR. *and* MRS. FREMONT *enter.*)

MR. FREMONT: What's this you'll have to tell Dad? Been up to some of your tricks again, Toby? Hello, Tabby. Hello, Mac.

TOBY: You—you're home early, aren't you, Dad?

MR. FREMONT: Yes, for once I got a break and could leave the office ahead of time. I picked up your mother at the Watsons'.

MRS. FREMONT: You all look so serious. Is anything wrong?

TABBY: Yes, there is something wrong. But maybe Toby would like to talk to Daddy alone.

TOBY: No, I wouldn't. I'd rather have it out right here. Mac knows all about it, anyhow. You see, Dad . . . I did a terrible thing.

MRS. FREMONT: You're not hurt, are you?

TOBY: No, nothing like that. Much worse. I took the Washington shilling to school without asking you, Dad . . . and now . . . now . . .

MR. FREMONT (*Calmly*): You've lost it!

TOBY: How did you know?

MR. FREMONT: Doesn't something like that always happen when you break the rules?

TOBY: Yes, but . . .

MRS. FREMONT: Oh, Toby, how could you do such a thing! You could at least have asked permission.

TOBY: I was afraid you'd say no, and I wanted to show the kids at school that we really had it. They wouldn't believe me. Dad, I know you'll never forgive me. It was an awful thing to do.

MR. FREMONT: Yes, it was. It's always an awful thing to take someone else's property without permission. And the Washington shilling is something that can never be replaced.

TOBY: Dad, I don't understand you.

MR. FREMONT: What don't you understand?

TOBY: Well, I thought you'd be a lot madder. In fact, well . . . I've been scared to death to tell you. I was even going to stay overnight at Mac's house, hoping the janitor might find the shilling by morning.

MR. FREMONT: And why didn't you?

TOBY: It was Tabby. She reminded me of the first Toby Fremont and how he happened to get the shilling in the first place. It just didn't seem right for anyone who was brought up on the story of the Washington shilling to run away.

MR. FREMONT: I'm glad you remembered, Toby. Very glad. But you might also remember something else.

TOBY: What?

MR. FREMONT: That shilling was called the *lucky* shilling. Have you forgotten the luck it brought to that other Toby so long ago?

TABBY: That's right, Toby. The shilling *did* bring him luck. Mr. Fremont had forgotten to put the doubloon in his son's purse. He started out to look for him because he knew he would be scared stiff when he discovered it was missing.

TOBY: That's right! The money wasn't lost after all.

MR. FREMONT (*Producing the shilling*): And neither is

the Washington shilling! Here it is. (*All gather around in amazement.*)

TABBY: How did you ever get it? Where did you find it?

TOBY: Then you knew all the time?

MR. FREMONT: Miss Parsons phoned me at the office. She found it only a few minutes after school closed. She tried to call here, but our phone was out of order.

MRS. FREMONT: Dear me! Hasn't that been fixed yet?

TABBY: Oh, Daddy, Daddy! This is the most wonderful news in the world!

TOBY: But what happened to the shilling? Where was it?

MR. FREMONT: It was one of those freak accidents. One of your classmates had a pair of gym shoes beside his desk. When he dropped the shilling, it fell inside one of the shoes. As soon as the boy discovered it, he gave it to Miss Parsons.

TOBY: Then you're not angry, Dad?

MR. FREMONT: I think you've learned a big lesson, son. But just to clinch it, there's something I'd like you to memorize.

TOBY: Anything you say, Dad.

MR. FREMONT: It's a rule George Washington wrote in his copybook, when he was a schoolboy, not much older than you are now.

TABBY: What is it, Dad?

MR. FREMONT (*Slowly*): "Labor to keep alive in your breast that little spark of celestial fire—conscience." It has some big words in it, but I think you will understand what they mean.

TOBY: I think I do, Dad . . . especially that word "conscience."

MRS. FREMONT: I believe it's a rule we all should learn.

MAC: I agree with you, Mrs. Fremont.

TABBY: What do you say we all repeat it together, sort of like a promise from us to George Washington?

ALL: We solemnly promise that we will labor to keep alive in our breasts that little spark of celestial fire called *conscience.* (*Curtain.*)

THE END

Dolly Saves the Day

Characters

CAPTAIN LIVINGSTON
MRS. LIVINGSTON
A HESSIAN CAPTAIN
DAVID LIVINGSTON
DOLLY LIVINGSTON
GENERAL WASHINGTON
MARY ANNE, *the doll*

SETTING: *A corner of the yard of the Livingston farmhouse.*

AT RISE: DOLLY LIVINGSTON *is hopping up and down screaming for help as her brother pretends to drown her favorite rag doll in the well.*

DOLLY: Help! Help! Oh, please, Davy, please don't drown my Mary Anne. Please! Please! Oh, help, help!

DAVID: Stop screaming, you little goose; 'twon't do a mite of good. Mary Anne is not a patriot and I am going to drown her dead for good and all.

DOLLY: She is! She is! Please! Oh, you wouldn't dare do this if Father were here.

DAVID: Wouldn't I? And why not, pray tell? I'd dare to drown a wretched Tory no matter who was here.

DOLLY: You would not. Father wouldn't let you. And he'd punish you good and proper if he knew how you teased me.

DAVID: And I suppose you're going to be a tattletale and tell him when he comes home so I'll get a birching. In that case, I might as well be thrashed for something as for nothing. So here goes your precious Mary Anne . . . down . . . down . . . down . . . to a watery grave. You better say goodbye to her forever.

DOLLY: Oh, Davy, please spare her life. (*Kneeling before him*) I'll give you anything you want or do anything you want.

DAVID: Can I trust you to keep your word?

DOLLY (*Jumping up in relief*): Of course, Davy, just give me back my darling Mary Anne. (MR. LIVINGSTON *enters, sees what is going on, and stands quietly left stage, watching the following scene.*)

DAVID: Nope! Girls always tell.

DOLLY: But I wouldn't tell. Honest, I wouldn't.

DAVID: Oh, yes, you would. And if you didn't tell about this, you'd tell how I ran away yesterday to go swimming instead of working in the field.

DOLLY: No, I wouldn't, Davy. Cross my heart and hope to die.

MR. LIVINGSTON: Your sister won't have to tell me about your wrongdoings, David, and I think I came home just in time to administer a little justice. (*Brandishing his riding crop in a threatening manner.*)

DAVID: Father!

DOLLY (*Running to his side*): Oh, Father! I'm so glad to see you.

MR. LIVINGSTON (*Patting her head*): I'm sure you are, my dear. But I fear your brother will not be so glad when I have finished with him. Come, sir, take that wretched doll baby out of the well bucket and return it to your sister. Then you and I will settle our accounts.

DAVID (*Obeying his father's orders*): Here's your toy, Dolly. I wasn't going to drown her for real.

MR. LIVINGSTON: Just going to tease your little sister, and make her cry, eh? Humph! I daresay she'll be able to hear you yelling a-plenty till I get through with you. Now, march!

DOLLY (*Taking hold of her father's arm*): Oh, please, Father. Don't be harsh with Davy. All boys love to tease and he is no worse than the rest. Besides Davy worked hard while you were away.

MR. LIVINGSTON: Worked hard, did he? I heard him boasting just now of going swimming, when he was needed on the farm. That is something else he must answer for. Sorry, my dear, your plea for mercy won't do your brother a bit of good this time. (*He crosses to* DAVID, *seizes him by the collar and prepares to march him off stage when* MRS. LIVINGSTON *enters, very much out of breath from excitement.*)

MRS. LIVINGSTON: Oh, George, hurry, hurry. You must leave at once. The hired boy just told me the Hessian soldiers are coming up the road. They are as far as the spring house and headed this way. You must escape at once.

MR. LIVINGSTON (*Releasing his hold on* DAVID): I guess you are not sorry to hear that, are you, my boy?

DAVID (*Quickly*): I wouldn't want to see the Hessians catch you, sir.

MR. LIVINGSTON (*Relenting*): But you are glad enough to have them save you from punishment.

DAVID: I know I shouldn't tease Dolly the way I do, but she is such a little goose about that old rag doll. And as for the swimming, it was such a hot day, and I had worked hard all morning.

MRS. LIVINGSTON: Davy is a good lad, George.

MR. LIVINGSTON: Well, I hope so, for I must have someone to help me now that the Hessians are so close.

DAVID: Oh, please, Father, let me help you. I know I am an idler and a tease, but there is nothing I wouldn't do for our noble cause.

MR. LIVINGSTON: I believe you mean every word you say, lad, and I am going to place my confidence in you as if you were a grown man. Your mother will have to go with me as far as the old mill so she can bring my horse back. You and Dolly will have to face the enemy alone.

DOLLY: I am not afraid.

MR. LIVINGSTON: I don't think you will have cause to be afraid, Dolly. Surely the enemy would not harm a little mite like you. But there is something you and David must do for me.

DOLLY: I hope it is something big and brave.

MR. LIVINGSTON: General Washington is coming here this afternoon.

DAVID: To this house?

DOLLY: Goody! goody! Just listen to that, Mary Anne.

MRS. LIVINGSTON: My patience! How am I to entertain such a fine gentleman on such short notice?

MR. LIVINGSTON: The general is not looking for entertainment, my dear. He is to use this house as a meeting place with General Wayne. There are important plans on foot and I have the papers in my dispatch case.

DAVID: Are they very important, sir?

MR. LIVINGSTON (*Seating himself at the table and producing the papers*): I cannot even describe their importance. General Wayne has been ordered to attack tomorrow morning. But these papers order him to postpone his attack because of the increasing number of the enemy. Unless he receives these orders, he will make the attack and be wiped out. He must get these papers within the hour and report here to form new plans with General Washington. Now do you understand how important it is?

DAVID: Indeed I do. But where shall I find General Wayne?

MR. LIVINGSTON: He is staying with Mr. McClellan at the top of the hill. The old stone house in the oak grove. If I am captured these papers will never reach him and his army will be destroyed.

DAVID: Give them to me, sir. Dolly and I will see that they are delivered safely.

MR. LIVINGSTON: I don't see how you will manage, for all the roads will be guarded. Even the most innocent looking people will be searched. You cannot afford to let these papers fall into enemy hands.

DOLLY: Davy and I will look after everything.

MR. LIVINGSTON (*Rising*): You are a brave little maid, and your brother is a staunch lad, even if he is a rascal at times. Now I must leave you. Good luck to you and to our righteous cause. (*Father exits left.*)

MRS. LIVINGSTON: Good-bye, my dears. I trust you will be safe. I will see your father to the old mill. As soon as the soldiers are gone, Uncle Peter will kindle a fire in the wash house and when Father sees the smoke signal, he will come home. (*Mother exits left.*)

DOLLY (*Perching herself on the table with* MARY ANNE): How long will it be till the soldiers come, Davy?

DAVID (*Busy reading the plans*): I don't know. But we must think of a way to fool them and find a place to hide these papers.

DOLLY: As long as I have Mary Anne and you, Davy, I am not one bit afraid, and Mary Anne isn't afraid either. Aren't you ashamed, Davy, that you called her a Tory? Why, there isn't a more loyal doll in the colonies than Mary Anne.

DAVID (*Getting idea as he looks at the doll*): Say, Dolly, I have an idea! We'll use Mary Anne to fool the soldiers.

DOLLY (*Jumping off table*): How?

DAVID (*Producing pen knife from pocket*): You run and get Mother's sewing basket. Be sure to bring a needle with a good strong thread. We'll cut a slit in Mary Anne's back and sew the papers inside with her stuffings.

DOLLY (*Screaming*): No, no, no! Not my Mary Anne! Oh, Davy, you're a cruel, wicked boy! Why, that's a million times worse than drowning her in the well.

DAVID: Now, listen, Dolly. Be sensible. Mary Anne is only a rag doll. She can't feel a thing!

DOLLY: She can too. She's my very own child and I'm her mother. I won't stay here to see her tortured.

DAVID (*Catching hold of* DOLLY *as she tries to run away*): Aw shucks, Dolly. Give me that doll and let me hide those papers. (*Kneels before her and speaks in a coaxing voice.*) Look, then she'd be a hero and save the whole army. You said just now she was loyal to the cause. Now's her chance to suffer for her country just like a soldier on the battlefield.

DOLLY: Would she really be a hero, Davy?

DAVID: Sure she would. And maybe General Washington would even give her a medal for bravery. Now be a good girl and let me have her before the soldiers arrive.

DOLLY (*Kissing* MARY ANNE *before she hands her over to* DAVID): Now don't you be scared, Mary Anne. Davy says it won't hurt a bit. Here she is, now mind you be careful. I'll go get the needle and thread. (DOLLY *exits left.*)

DAVID (*Pretending to slit the doll and stuff the papers inside*): There, Mistress Mary Anne, you have a brand-new set of insides. Now you are a servant of General Washington under his orders. I must say you were a brave patient. Not a peep out of you. (DOLLY *enters with needle and thread.*) You better do the sewing, Dolly, you'll do a neater job.

DOLLY (*Covering her eyes as she sits at the table*): Oh, I couldn't. You do it, Davy. Her dress will hide the stitches. I can't bear to look.

DAVID (*Sits on floor and sews up the doll*): I always said you were a silly little goose. Now I am sure of it. I bet I'll sew her so that she stays sewed for good. (*As he is sewing* DOLLY *becomes conscious of the sound of riding. She crosses right stage to listen.*)

DOLLY: Hurry, Davy, someone is coming. Someone is riding up the drive.

DAVID (*Runs right to look out*): You're right, Dolly. It's a Hessian Captain. Now remember—not a word about Father's being here.

DOLLY: Oh, Davy, I'm scared.

DAVID: Nonsense! I have a plan and you must show me what a good little play actress you can be.

DOLLY: I don't know how to be an actress.

DAVID: Oh, yes you do. Look, I'm going to pretend to drown Mary Anne in the well, just as I did before. And I want you to scream and holler and carry on for dear life—just the way you did when Father caught me.

DOLLY: Oh, I will. I will.

DAVID: Mind—if you don't, I'll throw her in the well for real.

DOLLY: Oh, I'll scream and cry as loud as I can.

DAVID: You let me do the talking. I'm going to pretend that you are not my sister at all. I'll say your name is Betty McClellan. Understand?

DOLLY: No, but I know enough to scream and cry. (*Off stage—"Squad, halt. Ground arms. Surround the house. Let no one escape. I'll search the yard myself."* DAVID *seizes* MARY ANNE *and approaches the well.* DOLLY *goes into her act, paying no attention to the* CAPTAIN *who enters and stares at them in astonishment.*)

DOLLY: Help! Help! Oh, please, Davy, please don't drown my Mary Anne. Please, please. Oh, help, help!

DAVID: Stop screaming, you little goose. 'Twon't do a mite of good. Mary Anne is not a patriot and I'm going to drown her in the well for sure.

DOLLY: Oh, please, please. Oh, you wicked boy. You'll pay for this. I'll tell your father. Oh, please, help, help, help.

CAPTAIN: Well, upon my word! What goes on here? Stop, you wretched boy! What are you doing with this child's doll?

DAVID: I'm going to drown her in the well because she's a wicked Tory and loyal to King George, that's what I'm going to do.

CAPTAIN (*Rescuing doll*): You're going to do nothing of the sort. Here, child, take your doll (*Seizing* DAVID *by the collar*) and tell me what to do with this young ruffian. I think the flat of my sword is what he needs, and he shall have it, if you say the word.

DOLLY: Oh, thank you, kind sir. (*Curtsies*) Thank you very much.

CAPTAIN (*Shaking* DAVID): Speak up, you young rascal, and tell me what you mean by such treatment. Is this the way George Washington teaches his rebels to behave?

DAVID: You let me go. You're on *her* side. That's Betty McClellan and she has no business playing in our yard. I was only teasing her so she'd take her old doll and go home.

CAPTAIN: And so she shall. (*To* DOLLY) Where do you live, little maid?

DAVID (*Quickly*): In the big stone house on the hill near the oak grove.

CAPTAIN: Are you sure you can find the way there safely?

DOLLY: Oh, yes, sir.

CAPTAIN: I have a little maid at home about your age. She has a whole family of dolls. Now run along. Don't be afraid of the soldiers. They will do you no harm. Just tell them you have Captain Parr's permission to go to your home.

DOLLY: Thank you, sir.

CAPTAIN (*Examining the doll, much to* DAVID'S *alarm*): What a pretty doll you have there! What is her name?

DOLLY: Mary Anne, sir. Mother gave her to me last Christmas.

CAPTAIN: No wonder you love her so dearly.

DOLLY: She's my favorite child, sir. Thank you for saving her.

CAPTAIN: You're welcome, child. Don't dawdle on the road. Your mother will be worried about you.

DAVID: Yes, and run all the way or I'll catch that old doll and drown her in the deepest well I can find. (DOLLY *runs off left.*)

CAPTAIN: Are all you rebels so bloodthirsty? Aren't you ashamed to tease so small a child? But 'tis none of my business how you savages treat each other. Come, what is your name and where are your folks?

DAVID: My name is David Livingston and my mother and father are not at home.

CAPTAIN: Where are they?

DAVID: They took the road to Philadelphia.

CAPTAIN: I don't mind telling you, boy, we are on the lookout for some important papers which we have reason to believe are in this neighborhood. Do you know anything about them?

DAVID: Nothing, sir. And Father and Mother are really not at home. You are welcome to go into the house and see for yourself.

CAPTAIN: I'll soon make a thorough search. As for you—if you stir from that spot, I'll skin you alive. (CAPTAIN *exits left calling over his shoulder, "This way, men. We'll search the house."*)

DAVID (*Wiping his brow*): Phew! That was a close call. I wonder if Dolly will reach the McClellan home in safety. If only there was some way to be sure. Oh, well, I must appear cool and collected. Poor Father. If they catch him, it will go hard with him. I believe my friend, the Captain, is returning. (*Hastily sits on chair.*) Did you find anyone at home?

CAPTAIN (*Reëntering left*): No. Perhaps you are telling

the truth after all. You can tell your father when he comes home that he has furnished the Hessian army with five hams and two saddle horses.

DAVID (*Rising in anger*): You thief!

CAPTAIN: Be careful of your language, son. War is war. You should have thought of that when you patriots started this war.

DAVID: That's all right. We patriots are ready to sacrifice anything for our independence.

CAPTAIN (*Laughing*): Independence! What does a lad your size know about independence?

DAVID: I know plenty about it. I know that just last year in Philadelphia our statesmen signed a paper that declared our colonies free and independent of the British crown. But you wouldn't understand that, since you are being paid to fight for King George.

CAPTAIN: And whom would you fight for?

DAVID: For General George Washington and freedom.

CAPTAIN: You are as likely to find freedom in this war as I am to find a fortune in this old well. One of these days we'll catch your fancy General and send him back to England in a cage. In the meantime, don't let me catch you teasing any more little girls or I'll give you the trouncing you deserve.

DAVID: I guess my father can take care of that.

CAPTAIN: And I hope he does—with a good stout switch. Sorry I can't be here to see it done. Until then—my compliments. (*Bows stiffly.*) Good day to you. (CAPTAIN *exits right. Off stage—"Squad—attention! Shoulder arms! Forward march!"*)

DAVID (*Watching them from right*): Thank goodness, they are going. Really going! Now I can tell Uncle Pete to light the signal in the wash house for Father. (*A *few seconds after* DAVID *has made his exit right,* GENERAL WASHINGTON *enters right.*)

GENERAL: What a pleasant spot to rest awhile. Surely my old friend will not keep me waiting long. (*Gets a drink from the dipper at the well.*) In the meantime, I can sit down here and go over these dispatches. (*As he goes over his papers,* DAVID *enters right.*)

DAVID: Good afternoon, sir. Are you waiting for someone?

GENERAL: As a matter of fact, I am. Is this not the home of Captain Livingston?

DAVID: Indeed, it is, sir, and I am his son, at your service, sir.

GENERAL: I had no idea the Captain had so grown-up a son. I am General Washington, at *your* service, sir.

DAVID: General Washington!

GENERAL: You seem surprised. Perhaps your father was keeping my visit a military secret.

DAVID: I am surprised and overwhelmed, sir. I have long waited to meet you and be of service to you.

GENERAL: Well, now that you have met me, you can be of real service to me by calling your father.

DAVID: Oh, that I have already done, sir. At least I have signalled for him to come home.

GENERAL: Signalled? I do not understand.

DAVID: Well, you see, sir, just before you came, a detachment of Hessian soldiers was here looking for Father. He had to hide in the old mill until they had gone. Just now I gave the signal that the coast was clear.

GENERAL: But the dispatches for General Wayne? Did your father deliver them safely?

DAVID: Alas, no, sir. He had to flee before he could reach the General.

GENERAL: Then it is too late! Wayne will attack. We stand to lose everything.

DAVID: I don't think so, sir—not if my plans turn out all right.

GENERAL: Your plans! What do you have to do with it?

DAVID: Well, sir, you see, I sent my little sister.

GENERAL (*In disgust*): Your little sister! Lad, lad, this war is for men and boys, not for little sisters.

DAVID: But you see, sir, she had her doll. . . .

GENERAL: Her doll! Boy, have you lost your senses?

DOLLY (*Entering from left stage—very much excited. She runs straight to* DAVID *without noticing the* GENERAL.): Oh, Davy, I did it! I did it! I gave Mary Anne to the General, and he ripped her open and read the papers and told me to tell you to tell General Washington that everything will be all right. (*Catching sight of* WASHINGTON) Oh, I beg your pardon, sir. I did not see we had a guest.

DAVID: Dolly, this is General Washington.

DOLLY (*Dropping a curtsey*): How do you do, sir. Mary Anne and I are at your service.

GENERAL: Delighted, my child. And who is Mary Anne?

DOLLY (*Showing him the doll*): Mary Anne is my favorite child. And she has done a brave deed for you this day. She let herself be cut by a cruel knife and never cried once.

GENERAL: Indeed! I wish all my military plans might turn out so successfully. I am greatly indebted to you young patriots. By your wit and courage you have done our cause a great service. I scarcely know how to thank you.

DOLLY: Oh, I do, sir.

DAVID (*Reproachfully*): Dolly! Remember your manners.

GENERAL: Let the child speak.

DOLLY: Well, you see, sir, it was really my dolly, my precious Mary Anne who had all the pain and suffering to bear. Davy said that she would be a hero and that you might decorate her for bravery, just the way you do your own soldiers. That would thank us very, very much.

GENERAL: Would it indeed, child? Then it shall be done. (*He picks up doll and* MARY ANNE *and perches them on the table beside him. Removes medal from his own coat.*) It gives me great pleasure to be able to present this medal of my own to Mary Anne, the bravest doll in the colonies, for her courage under the knife and for her devotion to her country.

DOLLY: Oh, thank you, sir. Mary Anne and I will treasure it forever.

DAVID (*Solemnly*): And I promise on my sacred word of honor never to try to drown or in any way molest this doll that has been decorated by our General—the doll that saved an army.

THE END

Washington's Leading Lady

Characters

Laurie
Barry
Dwight
Amelia
Mary
Mitzi
} *the playwriting committee*

Miss Mifflin, *the teacher*
Mary Ball Washington
Washington, *as a boy*
Mary Phillipse
Sally
Betty
} *Mary's friends*

Martha Custis Washington, *as a young woman*
Washington, *as a young man*
Betsy Ross
Nelly Custis
Martha Washington, *as a grandmother*
Washington, *as a grandfather*
America

Before Rise: *At one side of the stage, before the curtain, stands a table with six chairs grouped around it, repre-*

senting a classroom. (The tableaux are enacted center stage as the curtain opens and closes.) The playwriting committee is grouped around table.

LAURIE: The meeting will please come to order. We will now have the reading of the minutes by the secretary.

AMELIA: How can we have any minutes when this is our first meeting?

LAURIE: All right, Miss Smarty. You can be the secretary from now on, and write all the minutes. Be sure you don't leave anything out.

AMELIA: When you write minutes, you only write down the most important things that happen.

LAURIE: Everything that happens at our meetings will be important, because writing a play for George Washington's Birthday is a very important job.

BARRY: I think the first thing we should do is to decide who will be George Washington.

MARY: You're not supposed to pick the characters till you write the play, silly.

BARRY: But everybody knows there has to be a George Washington in a George Washington play, so why not pick him now and get that settled?

DWIGHT: I think that's a good idea, Barry. Maybe we should pick all the characters before we write the play. Then we'd know whether to write hard or easy parts for them. I heard Joe Smith say he'd like to be Lafayette.

LAURIE: Charlie Naylor would make a good Lord Fairfax. Besides, his father knows a lot about surveying. He might help us write some of the speeches.

BARRY: We ought to have someone play the part of Washington's brother, Lawrence, because he was very important in Washington's life.

DWIGHT: Phil Saunders is the biggest boy in the room. Maybe he should be George Washington.

BARRY: Don't forget we'll need another big boy to play Lord Cornwallis. And we must have someone who can get a sword. We'll need a sword for the surrender scene.

LAURIE: And we'll need a whole lot of boys for the men who signed the Declaration of Independence.

AMELIA (*Rising*): Just a minute! Aren't you forgetting the most important thing of all?

BOYS: What's that?

AMELIA: Who's going to be the leading lady?

BOYS: The what?

AMELIA: The leading lady. Every play has to have a leading lady.

MITZI: To hear you talk, you'd think we were having an all-boy play for Washington's Birthday.

DWIGHT: Well, you can't very well have girls playing Benjamin Franklin, John Adams, Thomas Jefferson, and Patrick Henry, can you?

MARY: Of course not, but there are plenty of important girl parts to be filled. Amelia is right. Every play has to have a leading lady.

LAURIE: Why?

MITZI: Because it's more interesting, that's why!

MARY: Besides, what do you think the girls in our class are going to say when they find out we've written a George Washington play without any parts for them?

LAURIE: This doesn't sound very much like a business meeting. I hereby call the meeting to order. From now on, everything must be done in a businesslike way.

AMELIA: Very well, Mr. Chairman. I move that we decide on a leading lady for our play right now.

MARY: I second the motion.

LAURIE: It has been moved and seconded that we decide on a leading lady for our play right now. All those in favor signify by saying aye.

GIRLS (*Loudly*): Aye.

LAURIE: Opposed?

BOYS (*Loudly*): No!

LAURIE: I don't see how we can settle this by a vote. It will always turn out to be a tie.

DWIGHT: We could ask the class to decide or call on Miss Mifflin to settle it.

LAURIE: If we're the committee, we're supposed to settle everything ourselves. That's why we were selected.

MITZI: Why don't you listen to a few of our suggestions for leading lady?

MARY: Maybe you'd approve after all.

AMELIA: It won't hurt to listen, will it? Then, maybe we can vote again.

DWIGHT: O.K., I'm willing to listen, if the rest of you are.

BARRY: So am I. But I still don't think you need a leading lady for a George Washington play.

LAURIE: Go ahead, girls. We'll listen. What's your first suggestion?

AMELIA: Well, everyone who has ever read the life of George Washington knows that his real leading lady was his mother, Mary Ball Washington. From the time his father died until after his victories in the Revolution, he loved and honored her. As long as his mother lived, he tried to respect her wishes, and do her bidding. (*Curtain opens.*)

AT RISE: MARY BALL WASHINGTON *is seated, reading a letter. Young* GEORGE *is standing beside her.*

GEORGE: You sent for me, Mother?

MARY BALL WASHINGTON: Aye, there is a serious problem we must discuss.

GEORGE: I hope I have done naught to displease you, Mother.

MARY BALL WASHINGTON: Nay, 'tis quite another matter. I have here a letter from my brother in London.

GEORGE: From Uncle Joseph?

MARY BALL WASHINGTON: As you know, your Uncle Joseph is a very wise man, a lawyer. He has great knowledge of the world.

GEORGE: Perhaps when I go to sea, I might stop at London and visit him.

MARY BALL WASHINGTON: It is of that matter I wish to speak. Your Uncle Joseph does not think it wise for you to become a sailor.

GEORGE: But Brother Lawrence says it is a fine life, Mother.

MARY BALL WASHINGTON: Your Uncle Joseph is older and wiser. He says 'twere better you should become a tinker than to sail on a ship.

GEORGE: But many of our family have been sailors, Mother.

MARY BALL WASHINGTON: The life is not for you, my son. You know I wish only the best for you. Your Uncle Joseph and I both want you to become a gentleman and carry on the affairs of our family.

GEORGE: But, Mother, my heart is set on it.

MARY BALL WASHINGTON: Would you break *my* heart to follow the desires of your own?

GEORGE: You know I would not go against your wishes, Mother.

MARY BALL WASHINGTON: Then it is my wish you remain in Virginia! Stay with your brother Lawrence for a time, if you wish, but learn the arts of living the life of a Virginia gentleman, and the skills necessary to running a plantation.

GEORGE: It is a great disappointment to me, Mother, but if this is your wish, it shall be mine.

MARY BALL WASHINGTON: This is my wish, my son. (*Curtain closes.*)

BARRY: I can see what you mean about Washington's mother being a leading lady in his life. If he had gone to sea, our history might have been different.

MARY: I think a leading lady should be young and beautiful like the movie stars.

DWIGHT: Did Washington know any girls like that?

MARY: He certainly did. Lots of them.

LAURIE: You mean he had dates with them?

MARY: They didn't call it "having dates" in those days, Laurie. They called it "paying court" to a lady. One of the prettiest girls he knew was Mary Phillipse from New York. I think she would make a beautiful leading lady. (*Curtain opens.*)

AT RISE: MARY PHILLIPSE *is trying on a new dress to show her friends,* SALLY *and* BETTY.

MARY PHILLIPSE (*With a twirl of her skirts*): Do you think the skirt is full enough?

SALLY: It's beautiful! The prettiest dress I ever saw.

BETTY: That young Colonel Washington will be dazzled!

SALLY: The Colonel is such a handsome man, and so very tall. I wish he would take me to a party.

MARY PHILLIPSE: Maybe he will, if I ask him.

BETTY: He has eyes for no one else in New York but you.

SALLY: Are you going to the ball with him this evening, Mary?

MARY PHILLIPSE: Nay, the Colonel is in Boston Town.

BETTY: When he returns, he'll be taking you to all the parties.

MARY PHILLIPSE: Nay, I think not, Betty.

BETTY: Surely you would not refuse him?

MARY PHILLIPSE: But you forget, I know dozens of other young men.

BETTY: But none like Colonel Washington.

MARY PHILLIPSE: One even nicer than Colonel Washington.

SALLY: You mean you like someone else better than the handsome soldier from Virginia?

MARY PHILLIPSE: Aye, and he is also a Colonel. Colonel Morris is his name.

BETTY: Poor Colonel Washington!

SALLY: He will be disappointed.

MARY PHILLIPSE: Perhaps. But only for a time. One day, when I am Colonel Morris's lady, we might even go and visit him. (*Curtain closes.*)

BARRY: She won't do at all for a leading lady, even if we decide to have one. In all the movies I've ever seen, the leading lady marries the hero. This Mary Phillipse married someone else.

MITZI: Then we should choose Martha Custis because she really did marry George Washington, and they lived happily ever after, just the way they do in story books.

LAURIE: How could they live happily ever after, when Washington was always away at the wars or tending to affairs of state?

MITZI: That was sad for both of them. But I think Martha Custis should be the leading lady. When she and Washington were first married, they had a beautiful time together. One of the things that pleased her most was when her husband would order presents from London for her and his two step-children, Jack and Patsy. (*Curtain opens.*)

AT RISE: GEORGE WASHINGTON *is seated at a small table, with quill and paper, making out a list.* MARTHA *is looking over his shoulder.*

GEORGE (*Leaning back, after writing the last item*): There! 'Tis finished. I hope I have remembered everything.

MARTHA: There are so few things you've ordered for yourself, George. Most of the goods are for me and the children.

GEORGE: That is as it should be, Martha. "Women and children first," they always say. Besides, I have taken care to order myself two new beaver hats, a light summer suit, and a new sword belt.

MARTHA: I scarcely see how I can wait six months for the arrival of my new salmon-colored silk with real Brussels lace!

GEORGE: We had best not tell the children about their presents until they arrive. They will tire of waiting.

MARTHA: You are so generous, George! Ten shillings' worth of toys for each child! You could not be kinder if you were their real father.

GEORGE: I hope they will always think of me as their real father, Martha. How do you think Patsy will like the six little books I ordered for her?

MARTHA: She will love them. But I should like to see her

face when she sees the "fashionably dressed baby" you have ordered. That will please her most.

GEORGE: Every little girl loves a dolly, Martha, and our Patsy shall have the prettiest poppet in London town. (*Curtain closes.*)

MITZI: I think you will agree with me that Martha Washington should be our leading lady.

LAURIE: Martha is a very good suggestion, but if you're determined to have a leading lady, I think it should be someone more important in history.

MITZI: Who could be more important than Martha Washington?

LAURIE: Well, someone like Betsy Ross, for example. (*Curtain opens.*)

AT RISE: BETSY ROSS *is seated beside her sewing basket, a flag draped across her lap.* WASHINGTON *stands beside her.*

WASHINGTON: 'Tis a beautiful piece of work, Mistress Ross. The colors are extremely well chosen.

BETSY ROSS (*Holding up a piece of red*): This red I chose with special care.
It stands for bravery,
The courage that our country needs
To keep it ever free.
(*Holds up white strip*)
The white I chose for purity,
For love, and faith, and trust,
That men may live in honor,
And do the things they must.
(*Holds up blue strip*)
This hue I chose for loyalty

To all that's good and true.
The stars came straight from heaven, Sir,
Upon this field of blue.
(*Curtain closes as* WASHINGTON *and* BETSY ROSS *display the flag.*)

BARRY: Make sure our Secretary writes down the name of Betsy Ross as a possible leading lady.

LAURIE: Are there any more suggestions?

DWIGHT: In all the plays I ever saw there was at least one wedding scene.

AMELIA: We have already had the name of Martha Washington.

MARY: If you want a young and lovely bride, I can suggest the name of Nelly Custis, the daughter of Washington's stepson, Jack Custis. On Washington's last birthday, she married Lawrence Lewis at Mount Vernon and Washington himself gave the happy bride away. (*Curtain opens.*)

AT RISE: NELLY CUSTIS, *in her wedding dress, is talking to her grandmother,* MARTHA WASHINGTON.

MARTHA: "Happy is the bride the sun shines on," my dear. And this is a beautiful bright day for February.

NELLY: I'd be happy today, dear Grandmother, if there were a blizzard! Tell me, do you think our General will wear his handsome new uniform?

MARTHA: I don't know, child. The General has not told me what he intends to wear.

NELLY: He will look so fine in the splendid new headgear with the three white plumes.

MARTHA: Aye, he is still a handsome man.

NELLY: And just as dear and good as he is handsome. The

only cloud in my happiness is to think of leaving him and you.

MARTHA: Nonsense, child. Every girl grows up and moves away to a home of her own.

NELLY: But ever since I was a little girl, Mount Vernon has been my home, and you and Grandpapa have been as parents to me.

MARTHA: Hush, child. Here comes the General now!

NELLY: And see what he is wearing! 'Tis his old buff and blue of the Revolution!

WASHINGTON (*Carrying three white plumes in one hand and an old hat with a black cockade in the other*): Happy wedding day, Nelly! I have a present for you!

NELLY: But you have already given me a wonderful present, Sir—twenty-five hundred acres of the Mount Vernon estate to build our new home on.

WASHINGTON: This is different. (*Handing her the plumes.*) These will look better on you than they do on me. Wear them with your new white ball gown.

NELLY: Thank you, Grandpapa. They are from your new uniform, aren't they?

WASHINGTON: They are! I find them entirely too fancy for my taste!

MARTHA: So you decided to wear your old uniform after all.

WASHINGTON (*To* NELLY): I hope you are not disappointed, child. Somehow I feel more at home in this uniform which has stood me in such good service.

NELLY: Disappointed? Indeed not! I feel truly honored, sir, that you should wear the most noble uniform in the whole nation at my wedding. (*Taking his arm*) Truly, I am the happiest and proudest bride in the United States of America. (*Curtain closes.*)

MISS MIFFLIN (*Enters. Joins group before curtain*): And how is my playwriting committee coming along?

LAURIE: Not too well. We have a problem.

MISS MIFFLIN: I am not surprised. What is it?

BARRY: Oh, the girls have decided we must have a leading lady.

MISS MIFFLIN: Any suggestions?

DWIGHT: Lots of them. Too many, in fact.

MISS MIFFLIN: Who are they?

AMELIA: Mary Ball Washington, Washington's mother.

MARY: The beautiful Mary Phillipse.

MITZI: Martha Custis, his devoted wife.

LAURIE: Mistress Betsy Ross.

AMELIA: And Nelly Custis, Washington's beloved granddaughter.

MISS MIFFLIN: They are all excellent nominations. But I think you've forgotten the most important one.

MARY: You mean Washington's sister, Betty?

MISS MIFFLIN: Washington loved his sister very much, but I was not thinking of her as his leading lady.

ALL: Who could it be?

MISS MIFFLIN: I am thinking of the one for whom George Washington made every sacrifice. The one for whom he left his home, risked his life, and served with all his heart.

ALL: Who is she?

MISS MIFFLIN: Let her speak for herself. (*Curtain opens.*)

AT RISE: *A girl is posed on a pedestal. She wears a long white robe; on her head is a laurel wreath and a flag is draped across her shoulders and chest. She carries an arm bouquet of red roses. All the boys who played* WASHINGTON *kneel at her feet as she speaks.*

AMERICA: I am the one Washington loved most.
For me the young boy faced hardship and danger.
For me the young man took up the sword.
For me the young husband left his home and family.
For me the General fought and prayed.
To me George Washington gave the strength of his hands, the power of his mind and the love in his heart.
I am America.

LAURIE (*Rising and striking the gavel*): We have decided. America and only America can be George Washington's leading lady.

ALL (*Sing, as curtain closes*):
"America, America, God shed his grace on thee,
And crown thy good with brotherhood
From sea to shining sea."

THE END

Bunnies and Bonnets

Characters

MISS AMBROSE, *a receptionist*
MRS. MURPHY, MRS. ROSS, MRS. FULTON — *ambitious mothers*
FLOPSY, MOPSY, COTTONTAIL — *tap dancers*
PETER COTTONTAIL, *a trumpeter*
OSWALD, THE RABBIT, *a one-man band*
MISS BLOSSOM, *a dancing teacher*
THE BUNNY BALLET, *toe dancers*
BUGS BUNNY, *who does imitations*
THE WHITE RABBIT, ALICE — *mind readers*
MR. HUNTER, *a producer*
THE EASTER BUNNY

SETTING: *Waiting room of the Bluemont Television Studios.*

AT RISE: MRS. MURPHY *is talking to* MISS AMBROSE, *who is seated at the desk. With* MRS. MURPHY *are* FLOPSY, MOPSY *and* COTTONTAIL. PETER COTTONTAIL *and* MRS.

Ross *occupy one of the benches in the rear of the stage; on the floor is a trumpet case.*

MRS. MURPHY: Will you please tell Mr. Hunter that the Bunny Hug Tappers are here? They're billed as Flopsy, Mopsy and Cottontail. He's no doubt expecting them.

MISS AMBROSE: I'm sorry, ma'am, but Mr. Hunter isn't here.

MRS. MURPHY: But you said he would be out for lunch from twelve to two. We've already waited more than an hour.

MISS AMBROSE: It's too bad, ma'am, but I have no way of knowing when Mr. Hunter will return. Will you please fill out these cards for the children and wait your turn?

FLOPSY: Can't we go home now, Mamma? I'm tired.

MOPSY: So am I. And besides, I'm hungry.

COTTONTAIL: Me too! And these tap shoes hurt my feet! I don't want to be in television!

MRS. MURPHY: Don't be silly! Everybody wants to be in television! (*Opening paper bag*) Here, eat a cookie if you're hungry. Cottontail, put your foot up here in my lap. I'll loosen that strap for you. There! Isn't that better?

COTTONTAIL: No! It still hurts!

FLOPSY: I'm sleepy. Can't I lie down, and put my head in your lap?

MRS. MURPHY: No, indeed! You'll muss your costume. Now sit up like a good girl. Mr. Hunter will be here any minute and I want him to see a nice big smile. (*To* MRS. ROSS) I always think a smile is half the battle, don't you?

MRS. ROSS: Yes, indeed. But the more I try to get Peter to smile, the more he scowls.

PETER: I don't feel like smiling. I got to get home. The Midgets are playing this afternoon, and they need me to pitch.

MRS. ROSS: But Mr. Hunter needs you too, Peter. Remember, he's casting the Easter Bunny show.

PETER: Oh, gee whiz! I wish I had never learned to play that old trumpet in the first place. It's ruining my sports career.

MRS. ROSS: Children are so ungrateful these days! That's all the thanks I get for giving you lessons and making your costumes. (*To* MRS. MURPHY) But he does play a mean trumpet, when he wants to.

MRS. MURPHY: I'm sure he does. Is his name really Peter?

MRS. ROSS: Yes. Peter Cottontail we call him, and his trumpet fits inside that artificial carrot. I'm sure Mr. Hunter will be wild about him.

MRS. MURPHY: I can't get a word out of that girl about when he'll be back. I guess we'll just have to wait.

MRS. FULTON (*Enters carrying a big guitar case. She calls over her shoulder*): Come on, Oswald. This is the place. (*To* MISS AMBROSE) Is Mr. Hunter in?

MISS AMBROSE: No, he isn't, ma'am. But come in and wait. These other people are waiting for him too.

MRS. FULTON (*Calling*): Oswald, come on in. I told you this is the right place. Oh, dear! That wretched boy has run off again. (*Puts guitar case down in front of bench*) Now I'll have to go after him. (*Steps off stage and reappears with* OSWALD, *who is lugging a bass drum*) Oswald, you come right in here. Mr. Hunter will be here any minute.

OSWALD (*Dressed in rabbit suit*): I'm coming! I only stopped to get a better hold on this drum. It's heavy.

MRS. FULTON: Well, put it down and get organized. (*To*

MRS. ROSS) My little boy is a one-man band. It takes him quite a while to get everything hooked up. My husband says he looks as if he's wired for sound, but you know how men are about such things. Oswald, where's your mouth organ?

OSWALD: In my pocket. I told you I have everything.

MRS. FULTON: Dear me! Children are such a problem! Especially when they are so temperamental. Are you sure this is the right afternoon for the Easter Bunny show?

MRS. MURPHY: Oh, yes. The agency said definitely today's the day.

BUGS BUNNY (*Enters left and presents his card to* MISS AMBROSE): What's up, Doc? My card, Miss! The one and only Bugs Bunny at your service! Mr. Hunter is expecting me.

MISS AMBROSE: And we are expecting Mr. Hunter but we don't know when.

BUGS BUNNY: You mean he isn't in?

MISS AMBROSE: That's right. You'll have to wait.

BUGS BUNNY: Very well. (*Looks around in surprise*) Good grief! This looks like a rabbit convention of some sort. I only hope Bluemont has enough lettuce to go around. (*To* MRS. FULTON) Is this seat taken?

MRS. FULTON: No, it isn't. But look out! Don't sit on Oswald's guitar!

BUGS BUNNY: Heaven forbid! Hello, Oswald. What's your line?

OSWALD: I'm a one-man band. What do you do?

BUGS BUNNY: Imitations. "What's up, Doc?" . . . You should hear me do a three-way dialogue with Sylvester Pussycat and Elmer Fudd.

OSWALD: Do you take all the parts?

BUGS BUNNY: Oh, sure. I'm sensational.

MISS BLOSSOM (*Entering with* BUNNY BALLET): Oh, dear! I hope we're not late. (*To* MISS AMBROSE) Will you please tell Mr. Hunter that Miss Blossom and the Bunny Ballet are here? I know he will want to see them right away for his Easter Bunny audition. Really, Miss Ambrose, you have no idea how talented they are. Girls, girls, do an arabesque for the lady.

MISS AMBROSE: I'm sorry, ma'am. We never permit any acts in the waiting room. They are strictly reserved for the studio.

MISS BLOSSOM: Oh, I see. Well, rules are rules. But will you please announce us to Mr. Hunter right away?

MISS AMBROSE: As soon as he comes in, Miss.

MISS BLOSSOM: You mean he isn't here?

BUGS BUNNY: That's what she means, sister. Why do you suppose we're all lined up here? What do you think we're waiting for? Easter?

MISS BLOSSOM: Pay no attention to that horrid, rude person, children. Come. Sit down, and be careful! Don't crush your costumes.

FIRST BUNNY: I want to sit next to Bugs Bunny.

SECOND: And I'll sit on the other side.

BUGS BUNNY (*Triumphantly*): See! I do have my public. It's funny, but they find me absolutely irresistible!

MISS BLOSSOM: Children! Children! How many times must I tell you not to talk to strangers.

FIRST BUNNY: But he isn't a stranger, Miss Blossom. He's Bugs Bunny! He's our friend!

MISS BLOSSOM: Very well! But remember, the very instant Mr. Hunter appears, I want you to be on your toes.

BUNNIES: We will, Miss Blossom. (WHITE RABBIT *enters with* ALICE. *The* WHITE RABBIT *is looking at his watch.*)

WHITE RABBIT: What did I tell you! I said from the beginning we'd be late!

ALICE: But we're not late! We have plenty of time.

WHITE RABBIT: But see how many people are ahead of us. I should have known better than to wait for you in the first place.

ALICE: And how far do you think you'd get without me? (*To* MISS AMBROSE) Good afternoon. I am Alice Fenway and this is my brother. We'd like to see Mr. Hunter about a mind-reading act in the Easter Bunny show.

MISS AMBROSE: I'm sorry, Miss Fenway, but you and your brother will have to wait. Mr. Hunter is not back from lunch.

ALICE: But this *is* the day he's casting the Easter Bunny Revue, isn't it?

WHITE RABBIT: Silly girl! Just look around you. Why do you think all these other characters are here?

MISS AMBROSE: Yes, this is the day all right! And what an afternoon it has been! If Mr. Hunter doesn't show up soon, I think I'll go mad!

ALICE: When are you expecting him?

BUGS BUNNY: For a couple of mind readers who should know all the answers, you sure are asking a lot of questions.

WHITE RABBIT: Quiet, my dear fellow! Quiet!

MISS AMBROSE: It's all very embarrassing to keep saying that I don't know when he'll be in, but that's the truth. I've been looking for him ever since two o'clock. Something important must have . . . oh, thank goodness! Here he is now! (*Enter* MR. HUNTER, *a very busy, important man, carrying a brief case.*) Good afternoon, Mr. Hunter! All of these people are waiting to see you.

ALL (*Springing to their feet*): Mr. Hunter!

MRS. FULTON: Quick, Oswald! Go into your act! (OSWALD *starts to perform.*)

MR. HUNTER: Merciful Microbes! What is all this! There must be some mistake! Who are all these people?

MISS AMBROSE: They're from the theatrical agencies, Mr. Hunter. They've come for the Easter Bunny show!

MR. HUNTER: The what!

MISS AMBROSE: The Easter Bunny show! Your secretary sent out the notices last week.

MR. HUNTER: But there isn't going to be an Easter Bunny show!

MRS. MURPHY: Come on, children, let's give Mr. Hunter a great big smile . . . and when Mamma counts three, you begin right on the first beat! One, two, three! (FLOPSY, MOPSY *and* COTTONTAIL *start to tap and sing "Peter Cottontail."*)

MRS. ROSS (*Thrusting trumpet into* PETER'S *hands*): Never mind the rest, Peter! Blow good and loud. (*There is pandemonium in the office. The* BUNNY TAPPERS *are dancing and singing,* PETER *blows his trumpet,* OSWALD, *the One-Man Band, is in action,* MISS BLOSSOM'S *bunnies are doing ballet steps,* BUGS *is shouting his imitations and the* WHITE RABBIT *and* ALICE *are trying their mind-reading act.*)

ALICE: Think of any number, Mr. Hunter, from one to fifty, and my brother will tell you what it is. Quick, now, try to concentrate . . . any number from one to fifty.

BUGS BUNNY: What's up, Doc? How would you like to hear a one-man conversation with Sylvester Pussycat and Elmer Fudd? It begins like this . . .

MR. HUNTER: Quiet! Quiet! Miss Ambrose, get these people out of here! There must be some mistake!

MISS AMBROSE: Oh, dear, do be quiet! Mr. Hunter has something to say.

MISS BLOSSOM: Three more arabesques, children, and a pirouette!

MISS AMBROSE: Attention, please! Mr. Hunter has an announcement. (*Quiet is gradually established.*)

MR. HUNTER (*With much clearing of his throat*): I appreciate the fine talent that you have brought here today, my good people, but there has been a terrible mistake. My secretary must have made an error in her dictation! The Easter show this year is a *Bonnet Revue* . . . not *Bunny Revue,* as you have apparently been informed. It's *bonnets* we need, not bunnies!

ALL: What!

MRS. MURPHY: But that's impossible! The Agency distinctly said an *Easter Bunny Revue.*

FLOPSY: Aren't we going to be in television now, Mamma?

PETER: Hurray! Now I can get home in time for the game.

MISS BLOSSOM: This is an outrage! After I dragged these children clear across town.

MR. HUNTER: I repeat I'm terribly sorry. Believe me, I apologize to each and every one of you. And I assure you it's just as distressing for me as it is for you. Our sponsor has decreed an Easter bonnet production this year, and his word is law. Miss Ambrose, I must have a conference with the staff. I am not to be disturbed. Get rid of these people at once. (*Exit*)

MRS. ROSS: I must say this is a pretty kettle of fish!

BUGS: Please, Madame, it's rabbits—not fish that are giving Mr. Hunter the biggest pain.

MRS. MURPHY: I never heard of such a thing! He can't do this to us.

MISS AMBROSE: I'm really terribly sorry, people, but you

heard what Mr. Hunter said. He needs bonnets, not bunnies. (*Enter the* EASTER BUNNY *carrying basket of Easter eggs*)

EASTER BUNNY: Happy Easter, everybody!

MISS AMBROSE: Sorry! There's no call for rabbits today. The show has been cancelled.

EASTER BUNNY: Cancelled? But that's impossible. There's no such thing as cancelling Easter.

BUGS: She's not talking about Easter, Bud, she's just trying to tell you there's no soap! You're in the wrong department!

EASTER BUNNY: But isn't this the Bluemont Television Studio?

MISS AMBROSE: Yes, it is, but we don't need any rabbit acts today.

EASTER BUNNY: You must be mistaken. I'm not an actor.

MISS AMBROSE: It doesn't make any difference. We don't need any rabbit singers, dancers, magicians, musicians, mind readers . . .

EASTER BUNNY: But I'm not any of those things. . . .

MISS AMBROSE: Then who are you?

EASTER BUNNY: I'm the Easter Bunny.

ALL (*Laugh*): That's a good one.

MISS AMBROSE: Well, Mr. Easter Bunny, I'm sorry to tell you, there's nothing for you at Bluemont.

EASTER BUNNY: Oh, that's all right. I wasn't expecting anything.

MISS AMBROSE: Then why did you come?

EASTER BUNNY: To give out the Easter eggs of course. Isn't your name Miss Ambrose? I think I have one here for you. (*Looking in basket*) Yes, indeed, here it is. . . . *Annabel Ambrose* in pink icing. (*Hands it to her with a flourish*)

MISS AMBROSE (*Confused*): Well, thank you very much . . . but. . . .

EASTER BUNNY: Now, if you'll just call Mr. Hunter, I'll give him this big one with the yellow roses. I bet he'll like that.

MISS AMBROSE: Oh, I couldn't possibly call Mr. Hunter. He's in conference.

EASTER BUNNY: Don't worry. I'm sure I have enough to go around. Now let me see! Oh, yes! Here is one for Mamma Murphy, and here are three lovely ones for Flopsy, Mopsy and Cottontail! (*Distributes eggs*)

WHITE RABBIT (*To* ALICE): Say, what is this? Another mind-reading act?

ALICE: How does he know their names?

EASTER BUNNY: It's my business to know their names, little lady. Just as it is my business to know your name. And here is your egg with your name in Alice blue. (*Laughing*) Isn't that appropriate? The name Alice in Alice blue! There! I hope you like it.

ALICE (*Astonished*): Thank you.

EASTER BUNNY: And as for you, young man, I've kept your color scheme pink and white . . . to match your suit. By the way, that's a lovely pink coat you're wearing. I'm sure the children will love it.

WHITE RABBIT: What children?

EASTER BUNNY: Why, the children who see you in television. Dear me! How stupid! I forgot your picture will be in black and white. Oh, well! The children can imagine that they see your beautiful pink coat. (BUNNY BALLET *bursts into tears*) Now bless my whiskers! What are they crying about? I have eggs for them, you know.

MISS BLOSSOM: They're not crying about eggs. They're

crying because they're not going to be in television after all; and to tell the truth I could cry too.

EASTER BUNNY: Not be in television? What do you mean?

WHITE RABBIT: You seem to know everything else. Why don't you know the answer to that one?

EASTER BUNNY: But I don't understand!

MRS. MURPHY: Neither do we. We were given to understand that Bluemont was doing an Easter Bunny Revue.

MRS. ROSS: And now it turns out they're doing an Easter *Bonnet* Revue!

EASTER BUNNY: How very confusing!

BUGS BUNNY: Yes, isn't it?

EASTER BUNNY: Oh, well! Things will doubtless straighten themselves out. They always do! (*To* BUGS BUNNY) Here! Have an Easter egg!

BUGS BUNNY: What's the big idea? Who do you think you are . . . fiddling around with Easter eggs when we've all lost our big chance at television!

EASTER BUNNY: I've told you before. I'm the Easter Bunny, and it's my business to "fiddle around with Easter eggs," as you call it. Go on. Take one. That big one is for you.

BUGS BUNNY (*Scoffing*): You're no more the Easter Bunny than I am.

EASTER BUNNY: But you're Bugs Bunny. You said so yourself.

BUGS BUNNY: What kind of an act is this?

EASTER BUNNY: It's no act at all. I'm really the Easter Bunny, and it's really my job to distribute Easter eggs. That's why I'm here . . . to make people happy.

BUGS BUNNY: Well, you're not making me happy.

EASTER BUNNY: That's because you haven't eaten your egg.

Here, children, come and get your eggs. (CHILDREN *crowd around* EASTER BUNNY.)

EASTER BUNNY: These are for you, (*Doles out eggs to* BUNNY BALLET) and this one is for Peter Cottontail. (*Gives egg to* PETER) That's a fine rabbit suit you're wearing, young fellow. And what a big juicy carrot you have!

PETER: That's not a real carrot. It's just camouflage for my trumpet.

EASTER BUNNY (*Admiringly*): Do you play a trumpet?

PETER: Yeah, but I'd rather play baseball.

EASTER BUNNY: Now this one is for a fellow named Oswald. Oswald Rabbit.

OSWALD: That's for me. Thanks, Mister! And say, I believe you really are the Easter Bunny.

EASTER BUNNY: Thanks, Pal. I'm glad to know someone believes in me. Now, for the grown-ups. Mrs. Murphy, I see you already have yours. That leaves Mrs. Ross, (*Hands her an egg*) and Mrs. Fulton (*Hands her an egg*). And my goodness! We wouldn't want to forget Miss Blossom. Here's an especially pretty one for you. (*Hands* MISS BLOSSOM *an egg.*) I do hope you enjoy them! Now let me see! (*Looking in basket*) Oh yes! I still have Mr. Hunter's Easter egg. (*To* MISS AMBROSE) Can't you possibly call him so I can give it to him? He really should have it, you know.

MISS AMBROSE: I wouldn't dare disturb him and especially not for a silly thing like an Easter egg! Why he'd positively slay me!

EASTER BUNNY: But you want Mr. Hunter to be happy, don't you?

MISS AMBROSE: Well . . . sure . . . but I want to be happy too and stay alive.

EASTER BUNNY: You'll live all right. Now please do as I say and call Mr. Hunter. Everything will be all right, I promise you.

MISS AMBROSE: Not on your life!

EASTER BUNNY: I see. Well, I guess it's because you haven't yet eaten your eggs! Suppose we all take time out to relax and eat the eggs I brought. I see the children need no urging. They're already eating theirs. But how about the rest of you? Come on, start to nibble. You'll find them very good. And after you eat them, you'll all feel much better. (*All begin to taste their eggs.*)

ALICE: Umm! These are good! In fact, the best I ever tasted.

EASTER BUNNY: Splendid! Go ahead. Eat them right up! Every crumb! (*Watching while they eat the eggs*) Now, tell me . . . how do you feel?

FLOPSY, MOPSY and COTTONTAIL: We feel fine.

FLOPSY: I'm not tired any more.

MOPSY: I'm not hungry any more.

COTTONTAIL: And my tap shoes don't hurt one single bit. I could dance and dance and dance!

EASTER BUNNY: How about you, Mrs. Murphy? Do you feel any better?

MRS. MURPHY: Well, I don't know exactly, but somehow I don't feel quite so angry.

MRS. ROSS: It's amazing, but neither do I. I guess it isn't exactly Mr. Hunter's fault.

PETER: Say, Mom, if we get a chance to be in TV, I'll play baseball some other time.

OSWALD: And you know something? I bet that old bass drum isn't a bit heavy any more. Gee, I can hardly wait to play for all the little kids.

MRS. ROSS: What little kids, Oswald?

OSWALD: Why, all the little kids who will be watching. I bet they'll laugh and laugh to see a rabbit playing a mouth organ, a guitar and a bass drum. I just bet it will tickle them pink.

BUNNY BALLET: We feel great, Mr. Easter Bunny. When do we dance?

MISS BLOSSOM: I won't mind all this bother one bit if we just get a chance to make the children happy on Easter day.

EASTER BUNNY: That's the spirit, Miss Blossom. How about you, Bugs?

BUGS BUNNY: Say, what was in those eggs? I feel funnier than a crutch. By the way my left ear itches, I think this is going to be the happiest Easter of my life.

WHITE RABBIT: You know, Alice, you'll be the hit of our act. The children will just love you.

ALICE: Now I know these are magic Easter eggs! You always said *you* were the main attraction of our act!

WHITE RABBIT: I know, but I guess I was a little conceited. Actually, Sis, you're the brains of the act and I know it.

ALICE: But it's you the children will like best, brother mine. And anyway, who cares, just so long as they have a good time!

EASTER BUNNY: Wonderful! Wonderful! Now you're really getting the Easter spirit. You really want to make someone happy. How about you, Miss Ambrose? How do you feel?

MISS AMBROSE: I feel all bubbly and full of giggles. You know something? I'm not one bit afraid of Mr. Hunter, and I really would like him to have one of those eggs. I think it would do him a world of good!

ALL: Then call him!

ALICE: Yes, please call him, Miss Ambrose. Let's see what happens when he eats his Easter egg!

MISS AMBROSE: But remember . . . he wants *bonnets* not bunnies.

EASTER BUNNY: But it's bunnies that he's got, Miss Ambrose, and I'm sure we can make him learn to like us in short order.

MISS AMBROSE: O.K. Here goes! (*Calling off stage*) Mr. Hunter! Mr. Hunter! Will you come here, please? Someone wants to see you. (*Enter* MR. HUNTER)

MR. HUNTER: I told you I was not to be disturbed, Miss Ambrose. We're calling all over town trying to get Easter bonnets and girls to model them. I thought I told you to get rid of all these bunny characters! Any more mistakes like this, and you're fired!

MISS AMBROSE: Just a minute, sir. I told you someone wanted to see you.

EASTER BUNNY: I'm the one who wants to see you, Mr. Hunter! I brought you your Easter egg.

MR. HUNTER (*Sputtering with rage*): Why this is ridiculous! Preposterous! Get out of here! At once, I say! I will not have you in this office.

MISS AMBROSE: But please, Mr. Hunter!

MR. HUNTER: Not another word, Miss Ambrose, if you value your job!

EASTER BUNNY: Please, Mr. Hunter. Remember your blood pressure.

MR. HUNTER: What do you know about my blood pressure, you scoundrel!

EASTER BUNNY: I know it's reaching the boiling point, sir, and if you'd just calm down a minute, I'm sure I could help you.

MR. HUNTER: Help me! All you can do is help set me crazy!

EASTER BUNNY: Am I right in assuming that you are worried about your sponsor?

MR. HUNTER: That is putting it mildly.

EASTER BUNNY: And would an Easter bonnet help you out of your difficulty?

MR. HUNTER: Ha! Try and get one! At this stage of the game!

EASTER BUNNY: Mr. Hunter, you forget who I am.

MR. HUNTER: I don't care who you are! I want you to get out of here and fast!

EASTER BUNNY: You've heard of a magician taking a rabbit out of a hat, haven't you?

MR. HUNTER: Of course.

EASTER BUNNY: But have you ever heard of taking a hat out of a rabbit?

MR. HUNTER: What nonsense is this? How silly can you get?

EASTER BUNNY: Watch closely, Mr. Hunter. But first, take this Easter egg. It is the last one I have. (MR. HUNTER *takes egg. The* EASTER BUNNY *turns his empty basket upside down. It turns out to be a widebrimmed straw hat the ties of which have been used as the handle. It is beautifully trimmed with flowers*) Look, Mr. Hunter! Is this what you need?

MR. HUNTER: A hat! A beautiful hat! Why, it's an Easter bonnet.

EASTER BUNNY: Of course it is, and here is your model. (*Puts Easter bonnet on* MISS BLOSSOM'S *head*) There! Isn't that lovely?

MR. HUNTER: Why, it's splendid! Just splendid! Come right this way, Miss . . . er . . .

MISS BLOSSOM: Miss Blossom is my name.

MR. HUNTER: Come with me, my dear Miss Blossom. We'll do some shots of you right away.

EASTER BUNNY: Just a moment, Mr. Hunter. You're forgetting something.

MR. HUNTER: The fee? Oh we can talk about fees later.

EASTER BUNNY: Not the fee . . . the egg, Mr. Hunter. You forgot to eat your Easter egg.

MR. HUNTER: Don't be ridiculous! I have no time to waste.

MISS BLOSSOM: But you'll have to eat it, Mr. Hunter. I won't budge out of this room until you do.

MR. HUNTER: Another temperamental star! Well, O.K. I'll eat it. (*Takes a bite*) There! Are you satisfied?

MISS BLOSSOM: Not entirely. Eat a little bit more.

MR. HUNTER: Umm. . . . Say! This is delicious! I must get my wife some of these. Are you selling them?

EASTER BUNNY: Oh, no, sir. I only *give* the eggs to people. They're Easter eggs, you know. Now tell me . . . how do you feel?

MR. HUNTER: Wonderful! Never felt better in my life! (*Looking around*) By Jove! These are cute costumes! In fact, they're the cutest bunny costumes I've ever seen. If I hadn't promised the sponsor. . . .

MISS BLOSSOM: Have another bite of egg, Mr. Hunter.

MR. HUNTER (*Talking with his mouth full*): As I was saying . . . if I hadn't promised the sponsor to do a show on bonnets. . . . Say, I bet the little children would love all these rabbits. Who are you supposed to be, my dears?

FLOPSY, MOPSY AND COTTONTAIL: We're Flopsy, Mopsy and Cottontail. We want to dance to make the children happy on Easter Day.

MR. HUNTER: And I suppose this is Peter Cottontail.

PETER: That's right, Boss! I mean . . . Mr. Hunter.

MR. HUNTER: And who is this young man?

OSWALD: I'm Oswald the Rabbit. I'm a one-man band.

MR. HUNTER: And the rest of these characters I recognize! Bugs Bunny! The White Rabbit and Alice in Wonderland! How the children would love seeing their favorite bunny characters on Easter morning.

MISS AMBROSE: Then you'll sign them up, Mr. Hunter.

MR. HUNTER: Of course, I will! But bless my soul! What about the sponsor! He's expecting *bonnets.*

MISS AMBROSE: Well, give him this bonnet (*Pointing to* MISS BLOSSOM) and fill in the rest with bunnies!

MR. HUNTER: I do believe, Miss Ambrose, you've solved my problem. Here, Miss Blossom, you stand here. (*Poses* MISS BLOSSOM *and surrounds her with the rabbit characters*) Now the White Rabbit and Miss Alice. Now, Peter and Oswald. Now you, Mr. Bugs Bunny, and Flopsy, Mopsy and Cottontail right in front. There! Isn't that a lovely grouping for the finale?

MISS AMBROSE: It certainly is, Mr. Hunter. You have the bonnet and the bunnies! Just what people will be expecting for Easter. You always say you want to give people what they like.

MR. HUNTER: Yes, I guess that's the whole secret of television, Miss Ambrose, making people happy.

EASTER BUNNY: I wouldn't know about television, sir, but I think you're pretty close to the secret of a happy Easter. And now, good day to you, one and all.

ALL: Wait, wait!

MISS AMBROSE: Please wait, sir. I'm sure Mr. Hunter could use you.

EASTER BUNNY: Sorry, Miss Ambrose, but being an Easter Rabbit is a full-time job! (*Exit*)

MR. HUNTER: Say, who was that fellow? Haven't I seen him somewhere before?

MISS AMBROSE: He *said* he was the Easter Bunny, and you know, Mr. Hunter, I really think he was telling the truth. (*All sing "Peter Cottontail" or an Easter song as the curtains close.*)

THE END

The Bashful Bunny

Characters

MRS. COTTONTAIL, *wife of the Easter Bunny*
PETER COTTONTAIL, *the Easter Bunny himself*
PETER JUNIOR, *son of the Easter Bunny*
MRS. CACKLE, *a nosy neighbor*
SHERRY, *a bashful girl*
TOMMY, *a helpful boy*

TIME: *The morning of Easter Sunday.*

SETTING: *A small wood near a public park.*

AT RISE: MRS. COTTONTAIL *is putting the finishing touches to a row of Easter baskets on a table.* MRS. CACKLE *is helping her.*

MRS. COTTONTAIL: There! We're almost finished. I do think the baskets are prettier than ever this year. Peter will be so pleased!

MRS. CACKLE: Humph! He has a right to be pleased! We chickens do all the work and you Easter Rabbits get all the credit!

MRS. COTTONTAIL: Nonsense! It's not a question of who gets the credit! It's a question of making the children happy. Poor Peter just worries himself to death every

Easter for fear some child will be neglected or left out! He's a very conscientious Easter Rabbit. And the work gets heavier every year.

MRS. CACKLE: If it's such a big job, why doesn't he get Junior to help him? He's getting to be a big boy now and very handsome. I'm sure the children would love him.

MRS. COTTONTAIL: Oh, thank you, Mrs. Cackle. We are very proud of the way Junior is developing, but I'm afraid he's just no help to his father at all with the Easter work.

MRS. CACKLE: What's the matter? Is he lazy?

MRS. COTTONTAIL: Dear me! No! There's not a lazy piece of fur on his body! (*Shaking her head*) But he's just no good as an Easter helper.

MRS. CACKLE: Tut! Tut! Tut! That's just too bad! But then I have heard that a great many young rabbits are apt to be hare-brained!

MRS. COTTONTAIL: You're quite mistaken, Mrs. Cackle, if you think our Junior is hare-brained! He's very level-headed for his age. But he's so bashful!

MRS. CACKLE: Bashful?

MRS. COTTONTAIL: Yes. He just can't say a thing in public. Every time we go to the Briar Patch Reunions he just clings to my skirts or gets behind his father. He hardly speaks when he's spoken to, and as for taking an active part in the Egg Hunt ceremonies, that's out of the question.

MRS. CACKLE: Well, that's just too bad, Mrs. Cottontail, especially when your family is so much in the public eye. Oh well, maybe he'll outgrow it.

MRS. COTTONTAIL: I hope so. But his father and I are very much worried about him.

MRS. CACKLE: How does he get along in school?

MRS. COTTONTAIL: Oh, fine. Last year he got all A's and B's.

MRS. CACKLE: How's he doing this year?

MRS. COTTONTAIL: Well, I can't say exactly. They've changed the marking system. He should be home any minute now for the Easter vacation, and he'll be bringing his report.

MRS. CACKLE: All of *my* children do so well in school. They never cause us any worry at all. In fact, I just said to Mr. Cackle yesterday morning, we really do have something to crow about!

MRS. COTTONTAIL: I'm sure you do, Mrs. Cackle, and now if you will excuse me, I must go inside and start lunch. This is going to be a busy afternoon with the Egg Hunt going on in the park. Peter will want to have an early lunch so he won't feel so rushed.

MRS. CACKLE: You go right ahead, Mrs. Cottontail. I must run along anyhow. I promised to stop by the pond to see the new ducklings. Goodbye.

MRS. COTTONTAIL: Goodbye, Mrs. Cackle, and thanks so much for your help with the Easter baskets. (*Exit* MRS. CACKLE) Humph! That conceited Mrs. Cackle! Something to crow about, indeed! It's too bad we rabbits can't do a bit of crowing about our families! Bless my cabbages if it isn't Peter! And me without a bite of lunch on the table. (*Catching sight of* PETER *who is approaching slowly, blowing his nose and wiping his eyes on a large green handkerchief.*) Why, Peter, what in the world is the matter?

PETER (*Between sneezes*): It's this pesky carrot fever! (*Sneeze*) It came on me all of a sudden! (*Sneeze*) I can hardly catch my breath!

MRS. COTTONTAIL: Dear me! Have you seen Dr. Owl?

PETER: Yes. I stopped at his office on the way home.

MRS. COTTONTAIL: What did he say?

PETER: He said I should soak my feet in a tub of hot water, drink plenty of dandelion tea and go straight to bed!

MRS. COTTONTAIL: Good! I'll fix the tea right away. Come, let me help you. (*Takes his arm and tries to lead him to the house*)

PETER: Don't be foolish, Molly. You know I can't go to bed this afternoon. What would become of the Easter Egg hunt?

MRS. COTTONTAIL: This is no time to think about the Easter Egg hunt. Your health comes first.

PETER: But you forget, Molly. I am no ordinary rabbit. I am the Easter Rabbit and the children are counting on me. They must not be disappointed. (JUNIOR *enters. He carries a few schoolbooks, and his report card. As he enters he is eating a carrot.* PETER *sneezes violently at sight of* JUNIOR *and the carrot*) Get that carrot out of here! (*Sneeze*) Take it away! (*Sneeze*) Can't you see (*Sneeze*) it's killing me!

JUNIOR: Hello, Dad. What's the matter? Want a bite of carrot?

MRS. COTTONTAIL: Your father has an attack of his carrot fever, Junior. Throw that carrot away this minute.

JUNIOR: Throw it away? But it's delicious! So sweet and crunchy!

PETER (*Sneezing*): Throw it away, I tell you! Throw it away!

JUNIOR: Okay, Dad. Just one more bite! (*Throwing carrot offstage*) There!

MRS. COTTONTAIL: Your father must get to bed at once, Junior. He feels terrible.

PETER: Nonsense! I'll be much better after I've had my lunch. (*Sneeze*) All I need is a little food! (*Sneeze*) Besides, I must take charge at the Egg Hunt this afternoon.

MRS. COTTONTAIL: Botheration on the Egg Hunt! You come along with me, Peter Cottontail, and follow the doctor's orders. Let the Egg Hunt take care of itself.

PETER: Egg Hunts *don't* take care of themselves. They depend entirely on the Easter Rabbit. For generations our family has supplied the eggs, the prizes and the baskets. We are not going to fail now just because (*Sneeze, sneeze*) of a little old carrot fever. (*A bad series of sneezes*)

MRS. COTTONTAIL: There now! You're making yourself worse! Who ever heard of a sneezing Easter Rabbit? Besides, the children might catch it from you!

PETER: That would be terrible. I never thought of that, Molly. What can I do?

MRS. COTTONTAIL: Now you're being more sensible. I know you wouldn't want to make the children sick. Now come along to bed.

JUNIOR: I'm sorry you're sick, Dad. Do you feel too bad to look at my report card?

PETER (*Sneeze*): Of course not, Junior. Let me (*Sneeze*) see it! Umm! Very good! Very good indeed. (MRS. COTTONTAIL *looks too.*)

MRS. COTTONTAIL: Why, Junior! This is splendid. Your teacher says you have good work habits, you observe safety rules, and you take good care of your supplies and materials.

PETER: And you're doing splendid work in running,

jumping and scouting for rabbit traps. But (*Sneeze*) —dear me! What's this?

MRS. COTTONTAIL: Where?

PETER: Right here, where it says "Social Adjustment."

MRS. COTTONTAIL (*Reading*): "Junior would get along better with the other bunnies if he could overcome his shyness. He refuses to take part in group activities and hangs back from many experiences because he is so bashful. The rest of the class have named him 'the bashful bunny'!"

PETER: That settles it! No son of mine is going to be called a bashful bunny. Molly, I have made up my mind. Go brew my dandelion tea and prepare the hot foot bath. I am going to bed.

MRS. COTTONTAIL: But, Peter! What about the Egg Hunt?

PETER: I am placing Junior in full charge!

JUNIOR: Who? Me?

PETER: Yes, *you!* It's high time you took on the responsibilities of being the son of the Easter Rabbit.

JUNIOR: You mean I'll have to give out the eggs this afternoon?

PETER: Exactly!

JUNIOR: In front of all those people?

PETER: That's right.

JUNIOR: But I can't! You know I can't! I'm too bashful. I'd die of fright!

PETER: Nonsense!

JUNIOR: But what will I say? What will I do?

PETER: That's your problem. (*Sneeze*) Come along, Molly. I'm ready for that dandelion tea.

JUNIOR: Mother! Mother! Help me! Get me out of this. Tell him I can't do it!

MRS. COTTONTAIL: You're a big bunny now, Junior. You'll

have to learn to depend on yourself. Besides, you've watched your father give out the eggs ever since you could hop. Now don't bother me. I must help your father. (MRS. COTTONTAIL *and* PETER *exit sneezing.*)

JUNIOR: Oh dear, oh dear! What shall I do? (*Looking at the baskets*) The very sight of those baskets gives me the chills. My heart is beating so fast it's almost jumping out of my skin. I know what I'll do! I'll hop away and hide so they'll never find me. That's what I'll do. (*Starts to exit left just as* SHERRY *enters. She almost runs into him, but he dodges her, and then hurries to get out of the way of* TOMMY, *who is running after her.* JUNIOR *watches them curiously; they do not notice him at first.*)

TOMMY: Sherry! Sherry! Wait for me! Wait a minute. Please. I have something to tell you.

SHERRY: There's no use following me, Tommy. I'm not going back.

TOMMY: But Sherry, you *must* go back. They're all counting on you.

SHERRY: Then let them count! I'm not going back there and say that piece for the Egg Hunt!

TOMMY: Why not?

SHERRY: You know why, so don't ask me.

TOMMY: Sure, I know why. You're not going to say your poem because you're scared. You're nothing but a scared rabbit.

JUNIOR (*Enraged at the term "scared rabbit"*): Now look here, boy, that's no way to talk about us rabbits! I've known quite a number of brave bunnies in my time. In fact, some of them are real heroes!

TOMMY: My goodness! Who are you?

JUNIOR: I'm Peter Rabbit Junior, that's who I am. The Easter Bunny is my father.

TOMMY: You'll have to excuse me for saying what I did about scared rabbits. It's just an expression.

JUNIOR: Yes, I know. I've heard it before. But it's not fair to us rabbits.

TOMMY: I guess rabbits are braver than most people. I know they're braver than Sherry.

JUNIOR: What's the matter with her? Why is she scared?

SHERRY: I'm *not* scared, at least not in the usual way. I—I—just have a bad case of stage fright.

JUNIOR: What's stage fright?

TOMMY: Oh, she's supposed to recite a poem at the Easter Egg Hunt this afternoon and she's running away rather than face all those people.

JUNIOR: Running away?

SHERRY: Yes, is that so terrible? They can have their Easter Egg Hunt without my poem.

TOMMY: But it will spoil the program. The class elected you to say the poem.

SHERRY: They shouldn't have elected me. They know how bashful I am!

JUNIOR: Bashful?

SHERRY: Yes, bashful! I can't help it. I've always been bashful. Even when I was a small child I was bashful with strangers or in a crowd.

TOMMY: Well, you're not a small child any more, Sherry. You're a big girl now. It's high time you got over being bashful.

JUNIOR: Bless my long ears, but you sound exactly like my mother! She said almost those same words to me just a few minutes ago!

SHERRY: About being bashful?

JUNIOR: Yes . . . you see . . . well, maybe Tommy was right. Maybe I am just a scared rabbit after all! You see—I'm bashful too!

TOMMY: I don't believe it.

JUNIOR: But I am! It says so right here on my report card. (*Shows* TOMMY *and* SHERRY *his report card.*)

SHERRY: My teacher wrote something like that on my report card, too. Isn't that funny? I'm acting like a scared rabbit . . . and you . . .

JUNIOR: I'm acting like a scared girl!

TOMMY: We'd call that being a sissy!

SHERRY: Stop using that word, Tommy! It's not the same thing at all. Being bashful is different from being scared.

TOMMY: I don't see any difference. You were running away, weren't you?

JUNIOR: And so was I . . . or almost.

SHERRY: Why were you running away? What is there to be bashful about here in the forest?

JUNIOR: I'm just like you. I was running away from the Egg Hunt.

TOMMY (*Laughing*): Imagine that! The son of the Easter Bunny running away from an egg hunt!

JUNIOR: It's nothing to laugh about. I'm the disgrace of the family.

SHERRY: But surely you don't have to do anything as terrible as recite a poem!

JUNIOR: Is that so? I'll have you know this entire egg hunt depends on me. My father was taken sick with a case of carrot fever. Right this minute he's on his way to bed, and I have to deliver all those eggs! In front of all those horrible, grinning, giggling children!

TOMMY: Easy, boy, easy! That's no way to talk about us children, you know. We're your friends.

JUNIOR: I'm sorry. It's just that I'm so terribly bashful. I break out in goose bumps at the whole idea!

SHERRY: So do I!

JUNIOR: What are we going to do?

SHERRY: Surely you know a good place in the forest where we could hide—some place where they'd never find us!

TOMMY: Will you stop talking about running away and hiding?

SHERRY: What else is there to do?

TOMMY: Do what you're supposed to do, both of you. (*To* SHERRY) You go comb your hair and wash your face and go back there to that Egg Hunt and say your poem when it's your turn, the way the class and Miss Deering expect you to. And you (*To* JUNIOR), get busy with those Easter baskets and deliver the goods the way your father would deliver them if he were on the job.

SHERRY: It's easy to tell us what to do, but you're not bashful.

TOMMY: There's a cure for everything else, so there's a cure for that, too.

SHERRY: You mean you can take shots for it, like whooping cough?

TOMMY: Don't be silly! It's a lot easier than that. All you have to do is to help somebody else.

JUNIOR: How do you mean?

TOMMY: Miss Deering says that if a shy person gets interested in making another shy person feel at ease and forget his shyness, they'll both end up feeling a lot better.

SHERRY: You mean Junior Rabbit and I should help each other?

TOMMY: You could try, couldn't you? It would be better than running away.

JUNIOR: Maybe if I saw you out there when I was giving out the eggs, and you'd sort of give me a signal or something, I'd be able to keep going.

SHERRY: Giving out eggs shouldn't be so bad. You don't have to say anything.

JUNIOR: But you have to keep bouncing around, looking lively and full of capers, when you're scared to death you'll drop the basket any minute. And you have to go right up to the children and put eggs in their hands. And sometimes they try to stroke your fur or touch your ears or feel your whiskers. It's awful! I never could see how my father stands it.

SHERRY: Saying a poem is much worse. There you stand, all by yourself. Your knees shake, your hands feel cold and your throat is as dry as sandpaper. And yet you have to talk.

TOMMY: I never saw you yet when you couldn't talk.

SHERRY: But suppose I forget?

TOMMY: Suppose! Suppose! Suppose! Suppose we had an earthquake. Suppose the trees turned upside down. Suppose the sun disappeared! Why don't you suppose something useful?

SHERRY: Like what?

TOMMY: Why don't you suppose that you and Junior are out there in the park together and figure out some way to help each other.

SHERRY: I think I could help Junior give out the eggs. I could walk beside him and carry the basket.

JUNIOR: That would make me feel a lot better. And you could help protect me from the crowd.

SHERRY: The children don't really mean to frighten you,

Junior. They just love to touch that wonderful soft white fur. But I can tell them to keep back and not come too close.

JUNIOR: I feel much better already. Just having you beside me will give me more courage. But now what could I do for you?

SHERRY: If you would stand where I could see you and wiggle your nose at me or flop those long ears, I know it would make me smile, and Miss Deering says I should smile all the time I'm saying my poem. Then at least I won't look so scared.

TOMMY: Why don't you recite your poem for Junior, just for practice?

JUNIOR: Yes, go ahead. I'd like to hear it.

SHERRY (*Reciting*): One sunny Easter, quite early, at dawn,
I saw a white rabbit come out on our lawn.
He flopped a pink ear, and he wiggled his nose,
And he struck the most curious, comical pose.
He looked all around, but he didn't see me,
And tumbled about in a frenzy of glee!
He hopped to the fish pond and stood on the rim,
As if he could see a reflection of him.
He turned himself this way, he turned himself that,
Just like a fine lady who tries on a hat!
And when he was finished, he just seemed to say,
"Behold I am ready for this Easter Day!"

JUNIOR and TOMMY (*Applauding*): Bravo! Bravo!

TOMMY: See! You remembered every word.

SHERRY: Yes, but when I get up in front of all those people, I'm afraid I'll forget.

JUNIOR: I have an idea! I'll stand where you can see me and I'll signal your lines.

SHERRY: How?

JUNIOR: Say the poem again and I'll show you!

SHERRY (*As she recites poem,* JUNIOR *pantomimes every line*): One sunny Easter, quite early, at dawn, (JUNIOR *advances cautiously.*)

I saw a white rabbit come out on our lawn. (*Advances further*)

He flopped a pink ear, and he wiggled his nose, (*Does both*)

And he struck the most curious, comical pose. (*Strikes funny pose*)

He looked all around, but he didn't see me, (*Peers all around*)

And tumbled about in a frenzy of glee! (*Acts accordingly*)

He hopped to the fish pond and stood on the rim, (*Pretends to stand on edge of pond*)

As if he could see a reflection of him. (*Leans over and looks*)

He turned himself this way, he turned himself that, (*Admires himself*)

Just like a fine lady who tries on a hat. (*Puts on imaginary hat*)

And when he was finished, he just seemed to say, (*Strikes a pose*)

"Behold I am ready for this Easter Day!" (*Holds oratorical pose to end*)

TOMMY: That does it! Sherry, you couldn't possibly forget. Together you two will be the hit of the show!

SHERRY: Oh, thank you! Thank you! I won't be one bit bashful if you're there. I'll be so busy looking at you, I won't see anyone else.

TOMMY (*To* JUNIOR): But won't you feel shy, going through all those antics in front of all those children?

JUNIOR: Of course not. I'll be too busy watching Sherry and thinking what comes next.

TOMMY: What did I tell you? You've found the sure cure for shyness. Come along, Sherry, we'll be late.

SHERRY: Goodbye, Junior, and remember, I'm counting on you!

JUNIOR: I won't fail you, Sherry. I'm counting on you, too. (*Exit* SHERRY *and* TOMMY)

MRS. COTTONTAIL (*Entering*): I just got your father settled, and he's feeling better already. It's about time you got started with those Easter baskets, Junior.

JUNIOR: I know, Mother. I was just going down to the shed to get the wheelbarrow so I can load up. (*Exits. Enter* MRS. CACKLE.)

MRS. CACKLE: Cluck! Cluck! Cluck! I just heard the bad news about your husband, Mrs. Cottontail. I rushed right over to see if there was anything I could do.

MRS. COTTONTAIL: That was kind of you, Mrs. Cackle, but it's nothing serious. Just a touch of carrot fever. He'll be all right in a few days.

MRS. CACKLE: Too bad about the Egg Hunt! The children will be so disappointed!

MRS. COTTONTAIL: Oh, the Egg Hunt will be all right, Mrs. Cackle. Junior is taking care of that.

MRS. CACKLE: Junior! (*Enter* JUNIOR, *whistling as he pushes wheelbarrow. He loads the Easter baskets on the barrow, whistling merrily.*)

MRS. COTTONTAIL: Yes, Junior.

MRS. CACKLE: But isn't he . . . well, what I mean to say is . . . are you sure he can handle it?

MRS. COTTONTAIL: Yes, I'm sure, Mrs. Cackle. Junior is his father's own son, a chip off the old Easter Bunny, if I do say so myself.

MRS. CACKLE: But didn't you yourself say that he's . . . *bashful?* (*She says the word as if it is a dreadful thing.*)

JUNIOR: Who said anything about being bashful, Mrs. Cackle? I found a sure cure for *that,* all right. And just at this minute, even though I'm a rabbit, I feel as brave as a lion! So long, Mother. Tell Father not to worry about a thing! This is going to be the best Easter Egg Hunt in history! (JUNIOR *exits pushing wheelbarrow full of baskets.*)

MRS. CACKLE: *This* I have to see! Good day, Mrs. Cottontail. Give my regards to your husband. (*Bustles off on the trail of* JUNIOR)

MRS. COTTONTAIL (*Laughing*): Good day, Mrs. Cackle! Hope you enjoy the Egg Hunt.

PETER (*Entering with a sneeze and standing beside* MRS. COTTONTAIL): Well, did Junior get started?

MRS. COTTONTAIL: Yes, he did, Peter. And from the way he *started,* I think there'll be no *stopping* him from now on. As Mrs. Cackle would say, I do believe we have something to crow about! (*Curtain*)

THE END

Mother's Fairy Godmother

Characters

SHERRY PORTER
JOEL PORTER
PATRICK PORTER
JAN PORTER
MOTHER
FAIRY GODMOTHER

TIME: *The day before Mother's Day.*
SETTING: *The Porter living room.*
AT RISE: JOEL *and* PATRICK *are working with a model plane at a card table.* SHERRY *is reading.* JAN *is sitting on the floor, cutting out paper dolls.*

SHERRY (*Looking up from her book*): Remember, boys, Mother wants you to go for the laundry.
JOEL: We will—after a while.
PATRICK: Don't bother us now.
SHERRY: Jan, you'd better go to the store. Mother needs an extra loaf of bread for supper.
JAN: After a while—when I've finished cutting these out.
SHERRY: Don't say I didn't remind you.
JAN: What about yourself? You haven't even made your

bed. Mother told you to do it right after breakfast. (*Doorbell rings*)

SHERRY: Better answer it, Jan.

JAN: Let the boys do it. I'm busy. (*Doorbell rings again*)

JOEL: My hands are sticky.

PATRICK: So are mine. (*Doorbell rings again*)

JAN: Go ahead, Sherry.

SHERRY: I don't want to lose my place. (*Enter* FAIRY GODMOTHER, *dressed in a light blue cloak and carrying a wand.*)

FAIRY GODMOTHER: What's the matter with you children? Don't you ever answer the door?

SHERRY (*Springing to her feet*): How did you get in? I'm sure the door was locked.

FAIRY GODMOTHER: Fiddle-de-dee! I'm not one to bother about locks.

JAN: Who are you?

PATRICK: We don't know you.

FAIRY GODMOTHER: But I know *you!* You're the Porter children. (*Pointing to each in turn*) You're Sherry. You're Jan. You're Joel, and you're Patrick.

SHERRY: Who are you? Mother wouldn't like a stranger in the house when she's not home.

FAIRY GODMOTHER: Fiddle-de-dum! Who's a stranger? I'm your mother's Fairy Godmother!

JAN: Grownups don't have fairy godmothers.

JOEL: They're only for children in fairy tales.

SHERRY: This is just plain ridiculous! I'm going to call the police. (*Starts for phone but stops dead in her tracks as* FAIRY GODMOTHER *waves wand.*)

FAIRY GODMOTHER: You're going to sit down in that chair, young lady, and listen to me!

SHERRY (*Sitting down with a bounce as if someone had pushed her*): Dear me!

PATRICK (*Boldly*): Look here! Our mother doesn't need a Fairy Godmother. She has Daddy to look after her.

FAIRY GODMOTHER: Your daddy is a busy man. He looks after your mother as well as he can, but, after all, he keeps his Fairy Godfather busy looking after him.

JOEL: Do you mean to say Daddy has a Fairy Godfather?

FAIRY GODMOTHER: Of course. A very good one, too. Between the two of us, I think we've done a pretty good job with this family, except for a few things that need improvement.

SHERRY: We aren't used to fairy godmothers.

JOEL: We don't believe in them.

PATRICK: They seem too much like magic.

JAN: And fairy tales.

FAIRY GODMOTHER: But you believe in electricity, don't you?

JOEL: Sure.

PATRICK: That's scientific. Are you scientific?

FAIRY GODMOTHER: Fiddle-de-foe! I should say not. But I'm your mother's Fairy Godmother and it's my job to make her wishes come true.

SHERRY: Then you're not a very good Fairy Godmother because she's been wishing for a new car and an electric dishwasher for over a year.

FAIRY GODMOTHER: I have nothing to do with wishes like that. They belong in your daddy's department. I just deal with important wishes.

JOEL: Like what?

FAIRY GODMOTHER: Like wishing children would do as they are told and remember their manners. The sort of wishes all mothers make for their children.

JOEL: Do you mean to say that every mother has a Fairy Godmother?

FAIRY GODMOTHER: Yes, indeed. You've heard how mothers always know best, haven't you?

SHERRY: Sure. Everybody knows that.

FAIRY GODMOTHER: That's because they all have Fairy Godmothers to tell them what to do. How do you suppose your mother always knows when you should wear your rubbers? How does she know the very minute you're not telling her the exact, precise truth?

JOEL: I always wondered how she knew.

FAIRY GODMOTHER: She knows because I tell her—that's why.

PATRICK: Did you tell her when I rode my bicycle on the highway? (FAIRY GODMOTHER *nods.*)

JOEL: I guess you're a pretty powerful person, aren't you?

FAIRY GODMOTHER: I guess I am.

SHERRY: I—I think I'm half afraid of you.

FAIRY GODMOTHER: There's no need to be afraid of me. I've been your mother's Fairy Godmother ever since you were born. Only now you know about me.

SHERRY: Does Mother know about you?

FAIRY GODMOTHER: No, indeed. She thinks she does all those clever things by herself.

JAN: Doesn't she ever see you?

FAIRY GODMOTHER: Never. I'm not usually this big. Most of the time I can curl up in one of the flowers on your mother's hat, or perch on one of her earrings, or sit on a bobby pin. I had to make myself bigger today so you could see me and believe in me before tomorrow.

JOEL: Why before tomorrow?

FAIRY GODMOTHER: Because tomorrow is Mother's Day, and I must see what you are doing about it.

SHERRY: We've taken care of that all right. We bought her a big, potted plant.

PATRICK: A geranium with four blooms—one for each of us.

FAIRY GODMOTHER: Just as I thought! That won't do at all.

SHERRY: But Mother loves geraniums, especially pink ones.

JAN: And it cost two dollars!

FAIRY GODMOTHER: I don't care if it cost two hundred dollars!

SHERRY: Mother never wants us to buy her expensive gifts.

FAIRY GODMOTHER: I'm not talking about gifts. Don't you want to give your mother a happy Mother's Day?

ALL: Sure we do.

FAIRY GODMOTHER: Then listen to me. Your mother has said a thousand times, "I wish for once in my life, the children would do *what* I tell them, *when* I tell them!" Haven't you heard her say that? (*All nod.*) But every single one of you is a "Putter-Offer." Every time I hear your mother ask you to do something, what do you say? (*Pause*) "After a while!" "Pretty soon!" "In a minute!" Sherry can never stop reading her book. Jan always has to put her toys away. The boys always have to play one more game of something or other. Well, all that has to stop! At least for tomorrow! So we might as well have a practice session right now. Sherry, that bed of yours isn't made!

SHERRY: I'll hop right upstairs and make it this very minute. (SHERRY *exits.*)

FAIRY GODMOTHER: What about that laundry, boys?

JOEL *and* PATRICK: We're on our way. (BOYS *exit.*)

JAN: I'll go get the bread right away, Fairy Godmother.

FAIRY GODMOTHER: Never mind, Jan. There's something more important. (*Waving her wand in the direction of the kitchen*) There! That will put a loaf of bread in the bread box in a jiffy. You have another job, young lady.

JAN: What? I don't think Mother told me to do anything else.

FAIRY GODMOTHER: What about that recitation for Sunday School tomorrow? Your mother will be so proud if you can say it without a mistake.

JAN: Oh, dear! Thanks for reminding me. I almost forgot. I'll study it right away. (*Gets paper from book on table and begins to study*)

FAIRY GODMOTHER: It looks as if this household is going to have the right kind of Mother's Day at last.

SHERRY (*Running onstage*): The bed's made, and I hung up all my clothes.

FAIRY GODMOTHER: That's the way to show your mother you really love her, Sherry.

SHERRY: We do love Mother. And we want to do what she tells us, only . . . we forget.

FAIRY GODMOTHER: Yes, I know. I'm going to take care of that before I leave.

SHERRY: You are? How?

FAIRY GODMOTHER: I'll show you as soon as the boys come home. How far did they have to go for that laundry?

SHERRY: Only across the street. Here they come now.

JOEL: The job's done, Fairy Godmother.

PATRICK: Mother will be surprised we remembered. Last week she had to tell us five times.

FAIRY GODMOTHER: There'll be no more of that, you know.

JOEL: What do you mean?

FAIRY GODMOTHER: You'll see. How are you doing with that poem, Jan?

JAN: I think I have it.

FAIRY GODMOTHER: Then come here and line up in front

of me. (CHILDREN *line up as if for inspection.*) I can see you are all good children and you really do love your mother.

ALL: Oh, yes!

FAIRY GODMOTHER: You do mean to do as you're told, only, you want to do things for yourselves first! (*All hang their heads.*)

SHERRY: Not any more! We'll be especially careful. Particularly tomorrow.

FAIRY GODMOTHER: I'm not taking any chances. Hold out your hands. (*All hold out hands a little fearfully.*) I'm going to give each one of you a present.

ALL: A present?

FAIRY GODMOTHER: Yes. I'm going to give each one of you a ring. (*Pretends to put a ring on each child*) There! How do you like them?

SHERRY (*Turning her hand this way and that*): But I don't see anything.

JAN: Not a thing. Where is it?

JOEL: I can't even feel anything.

PATRICK: Is this a joke?

FAIRY GODMOTHER: It's no joke. It's magic.

ALL: Magic?

FAIRY GODMOTHER: I have given each one of you a magic ring. You can't see it nor can you feel it, but later on, you'll know it's there.

ALL: How?

FAIRY GODMOTHER: Wait and see! And now, I must go! I've been away from your mother long enough.

SHERRY: May we tell her that we've seen you? That you've been here?

FAIRY GODMOTHER (*Laughing*): Tell her anything you like. She'll think you're dreaming or reading too many fairy tales. But one thing I'm sure of. Your mother is going to have the best Mother's Day ever because she won't have to tell you to do anything more than once.

JOEL: Can't we give her the geranium?

FAIRY GODMOTHER: Certainly, and I know she'll love it. But most of all, she'll thank you children for putting her first in your thoughts. And now:

Ish-ka-bish-ka
Dish-ka-wish-ka!
I'm off and away!

(FAIRY GODMOTHER *exits in a dizzy whirl of spins and turns.*)

SHERRY: Do you think she was real?

JAN: Maybe we just imagined her!

JOEL: She was the queerest creature I've ever seen.

PATRICK: What about those rings she gave us? I can't feel anything on my finger.

SHERRY: I'm beginning to think the whole thing was some kind of daydream.

JAN: I wish Mother would come home. (MOTHER *enters with an armload of packages.*)

MOTHER: Here I am, my dears! I had no idea it was so late. We'll have to hurry to get supper before Daddy comes home. (*Handing a package to each child*) Put these on the kitchen table, will you please?

SHERRY: In a minute, Mother. We have something . . . (*Almost drops package as she hops up and down and waves her hand in the air.*) Ouch! Ouch! My finger! Something's pricking me!

MOTHER: Let me see! How did you stick yourself?

SHERRY: Ouch! Ouch! It's hurting.

MOTHER: What is it, dear? I can't see a thing.

JOEL: Quick, Sherry! Take Mother's package to the kitchen. It's the ring.

MOTHER: What?

SHERRY: Do you really think it is?

JOEL: Of course, it is. As soon as you said "In a minute, Mother," the pricking began. We'd better all hustle these things to the kitchen this very second. (*All run to the kitchen.*)

MOTHER: I wonder what sort of silly game they've thought up now. (*Sitting in chair*) Oh, dear! I'm glad to get home. I'm tired. (CHILDREN *return*) Did you get the laundry, boys?

PATRICK: Yes, we got it.

JOEL: It's in the basement.

SHERRY: I made my bed.

JAN: The loaf of bread is in the bread box.

MOTHER: Wonderful! You didn't forget a single thing. Jan, would you please run upstairs and get my bedroom slippers?

JAN: Just as soon as I . . . ouch! Ouch! (*Sticks her finger in her mouth*) That hurts. Yes, Mother dear! I'll get your slippers right away. (*Exit* JAN.)

MOTHER: What is all this about hurting your fingers? I don't understand.

SHERRY: I don't think we do either! Mother, is it true that you have a Fairy Godmother?

MOTHER: A Fairy Godmother? I could certainly use one. I have a Godmother out in Kansas City, but she's a real flesh-and-blood person.

JOEL: Could you have a Fairy Godmother and not know you had one?

MOTHER: I suppose so. I really never thought much about it. I guess I'm too old for fairies.

PATRICK: No, you're just the right age. She said so.

MOTHER: Who said so? Dear me! Why are you all so mysterious? You've been talking in riddles ever since I came home. (JAN *enters with bedroom slippers.*) Thanks, dear. (*Puts them on.*) Oh, by the way, Joel and Patrick, please run out to the car and bring in the rest of the packages and my car keys.

JOEL: Just a second, Mother, I'd like to get this straightened out.

PATRICK: Yes, we'll go in a minute, but . . . (*Both* BOYS *begin to dance up and down and grab their fingers yelling*) Ouch! Ouch!

SHERRY: Hurry up, boys! It will stop hurting the minute you start doing what Mother asked. (BOYS *make a dash for the door*)

MOTHER: Sherry, explain all this to me. What is happening here?

SHERRY: I don't know if we can explain it, Mother. You see, your Fairy Godmother was here, and she gave us each a ring, and . . .

MOTHER: Sherry! Sherry! You've been reading too many fairy tales.

JAN: That's what she said you'd say.

MOTHER: Who said?

JAN: The Fairy Godmother. She was dressed all in blue and she looks after you all the time. (BOYS *enter with packages*)

SHERRY: We're trying to tell Mother about her Fairy Godmother, but she doesn't understand.

JOEL: We don't understand either, but from now on, we're going to do what you ask, the minute you ask us.

PATRICK: It's a sort of Mother's Day present.

MOTHER: You couldn't have thought of anything better, my darlings.

JOEL: No more of this "in a minute" or "just a second" stuff.

JAN: From now on, Mother comes ahead of anything else.

SHERRY: Look! Look!

ALL: What? Where?

SHERRY: Look at Mother's earring. It's swinging back and forth!

JAN: I do believe she hears us and understands.

PATRICK: I guess we needed a Fairy Godmother to remind us that Mother always comes first.

JAN: It's just like the poem I learned for Sunday School.

MOTHER: Can you say it for me, Jan?

JAN: Yes, I'll say it for you, Mother, and I'll make it extra loud, just in case *she* (*Pointing to earring*) might be listening.

Only One Mother

Hundreds of stars in the pretty sky,
Hundreds of shells on the shore together,
Hundreds of birds that go singing by,
Hundreds of lambs in the sunny weather.

Hundreds of dewdrops to greet the dawn,
Hundreds of bees in the purple clover,
Hundreds of butterflies on the lawn,
But only one mother the wide world over.

(*George Cooper*)

(CHILDREN *engulf* MOTHER *with hugs and kisses as curtains close.*)

THE END

The Magic Carpet Sweeper

Characters

LIDA LAWSON
JIMMY LAWSON
KAY LAWSON
JOEY LAWSON
MRS. LAWSON
TONY MARVIN

TIME: *The day before Mother's Day.*
SETTING: *The Lawson living room.*
AT RISE: LIDA, JIMMY, *and* KAY *are seated around a table composing a poem.*

LIDA: What will rhyme with Mother besides *other* and *brother?*
JIMMY: Smother.
LIDA: That won't do. Smother is a horrible word. It won't fit into a Mother's Day greeting.
KAY: How about "ruther"?
JIMMY *and* LIDA: "Ruther?"
JIMMY: I never heard of it.
LIDA: There is no such word.

KAY: There is so. And I already have it in a rhyme. *I'd ruther have you for my mother than any other!*

LIDA *and* JIMMY (*Laughing*): That's a good one!

LIDA: You're thinking of the word *rather*.

JIMMY: You'd have to say: *"I'd rather have you for my mather than any ather!"*

KAY (*Crossly*): Then, make up your own poems! Anyhow, I told you from the beginning we should have bought a Mother's Day card instead of trying to write one.

LIDA: Using what for money?

JIMMY: It's taken every cent we could scrape together to buy her the earrings and the bracelet.

KAY: Yes, I guess you're right. I never thought we'd get enough for the bracelet. I do hope Mr. Kline saved it for us.

LIDA: I'm sure he did. When we bought the earrings last week, I told him we'd be back for the bracelet if we could possibly manage.

JIMMY: Anyhow, he had several sets in stock.

KAY: Joey's been gone a long time. He should have been back by now.

LIDA: Maybe we shouldn't have let him go by himself.

JIMMY: Stop worrying. That Joey knows his way all over town and back again. Mother says he's the best errand boy in the family.

LIDA: Just the same, I'll be glad when he gets back with that bracelet.

KAY: Let's look at the earrings again. I know she'll love them.

LIDA (*Rising and going to desk*): We'll wear them out just by looking at them. (*Gets package from drawer*)

JIMMY: Why did you leave them in the desk? Mother might find them.

LIDA: I had them up in my bureau, but I brought them down this morning to show them to Ruthie Evans and I haven't taken them up yet. (*Opening box*) There! Aren't they lovely?

JIMMY: There's only one! Where's the other one?

LIDA: They're both there. They must be!

KAY: They're not. One is gone.

JIMMY: Were they both there when you showed them to Ruthie?

LIDA: I haven't shown them to her yet. She's coming over later. But they were both in the box this morning.

JIMMY: Are you sure? Did you look?

LIDA: No, I didn't look, but where else would they be? No one has had the box out of my bureau.

KAY: I did. Last evening I brought the box down to show the earrings to Daddy. But I'm sure they were both in the box when I put it back.

JIMMY: This is a fine note. You two girls should have kept your fingers off that box. Now what are we going to do?

KAY: Don't blame us. I saw you showing the earrings to Danny Martin yesterday after school.

JIMMY: That was before you showed them to Daddy, so I'm in the clear.

LIDA: This is terrible. Who could have taken it?

JIMMY: Probably nobody. It's just lost.

LIDA: One of us must have dropped it.

JIMMY: Let's look. (*Starts looking around on the floor*)

LIDA: I'll look on the stairway.

KAY: I'll look in the bedroom. (*As* LIDA *and* KAY *start to exit,* JOEY *enters. He carries a hand carpet sweeper clumsily wrapped in brown paper.*)

JOEY: Surprise! Surprise! Look what I have!

KAY: Joey, something terrible has happened.

LIDA: One of Mother's earrings is gone.

JIMMY: Did you get the bracelet?

JOEY: What bracelet?

ALL (*In amazement*): What bracelet!

JOEY: You mean that old bracelet down at Mr. Kline's? No, I didn't get that. I saw something Mom really wants.

LIDA: Joey, what are you talking about? You know perfectly well you were supposed to get that bracelet to go with the earrings.

KAY: That's what we wanted.

JOEY: Sure, that's what *you* wanted. But I got something Mom wants.

JIMMY (*Looking at the awkward package*): What is it? It looks like a floor lamp.

KAY: Or a giant umbrella!

JOEY: You're wrong. You're wrong. Look! (*Removing paper*) It's a carpet sweeper! A "Magic Carpet Sweeper"!

ALL (*Dumbfounded*): A carpet sweeper!

LIDA: Joey Lawson! How could you do such a thing!

JIMMY: A dumb old carpet sweeper!

KAY: That's a terrible Mother's Day present! Besides, she has a sweeper.

JOEY: It's not just an ordinary sweeper. It's a *magic* carpet sweeper.

LIDA (*Scornfully*): Magic! Magic! Who ever heard of a magic carpet sweeper?

JOEY: But it is. It is. It says so. Look! (*Points to the word "Magic" pasted in gold letters on base of sweeper.*) There's the label.

JIMMY: Joey, you don't understand. That's the trade-name.

JOEY: What's a trade-name?

JIMMY: Just a name the manufacturer made up. They could have called it the "Golden Sweeper" or the

"Diamond Sweeper" or "Little Gem." The label doesn't mean it's really magic.

KAY: You take that thing right back.

LIDA: And get our money refunded.

JOEY: I can't. I bought it at the second-hand store, and there's a big sign that says "No Goods Exchanged."

LIDA: What got into you, Joey? What made you do such a crazy thing?

JOEY: It's what Mom wants. She always says she wishes there was some magic way to keep this house clean; and when I saw this "Magic" sweeper in the window, I went right in and bought it. It was a real bargain.

KAY: Bargain, my foot!

JOEY: It was. Tony Marvin sold it to me and he gave me a special price. When he found out I had two dollars and a half, he said I could have it for that.

KAY: Joey, you spent our good money for a broken-down, second-hand carpet sweeper.

JIMMY: You are the prize dope of the family!

LIDA: We should never have sent you on such an important errand.

KAY: You're too little.

JOEY: Is that so? I'm not too little to know what Mom wants. She wants some kind of magic to help her with the housework and that's what I got. She'd much rather have that than any old bracelet.

LIDA: Is that so?

JOEY: Yes, that's so. And I don't care what you say about trade-names, this is a *real* magic sweeper.

JIMMY: How do you know?

JOEY (*Grabbing hold of sweeper's handle*): I—I can feel it. When I take hold of this handle, it feels like magic.

(*Very impressively*) There are little tingles running up and down my arm. And when I push it (*Pushes it back and forth*) the tingles get bigger and bigger.

LIDA: I don't believe you. (*Watches him for a minute as he pushes sweeper. She is impressed by the blissful expression on his face.*) Here . . . let me try.

JOEY: Keep away. You'll spoil it.

LIDA (*Eagerly*): Come on, Joey. Let me try.

JOEY: O.K. Only for a little while. (LIDA *takes hold of handle very gingerly and pushes sweeper around the room.*)

JIMMY: Do you feel anything?

LIDA: I—I'm not sure. (*After a few more tries*) Yes, yes. I believe I do. (*Sweeps harder*) Now I'm sure of it. (*Pushing sweeper toward others*) Get out of my way. Let me sweep over there near the table.

JIMMY: Aw, go on. You're as simple-minded as Joey. I bet you don't feel a thing.

KAY: Let me try, Lida. Let me sweep a little bit.

LIDA: After a while. Stand back. I want to sweep under the sofa. (*Much sweeping as cast dart here and there getting out of the way of the sweeper.* KAY *follows* LIDA.)

KAY: Let me try. It's my turn.

JOEY: Let her have it, Lida. Let her have it.

JIMMY: You'll wear out the rug with all this sweeping.

KAY: Let me try it out in the dining room. Mother said this morning there were some crumbs on the floor.

LIDA (*Reluctantly*): All right, but be careful. I'm beginning to think maybe there is something magic about it.

KAY: Nonsense. I don't believe a word of it, but let me see for myself. (*Takes handle and sweeps back and forth a few times*)

LIDA: How does it feel?

KAY: I can't exactly say. It doesn't feel like an ordinary sweeper.

JOEY: The harder you push it, the better it feels.

KAY (*Sweeping more vigorously and heading toward dining room*): Yeah. I see what you mean. I'm going to give it a real workout in the dining room. (*Exits with sweeper*)

JIMMY: What is all this, Joey? What are you trying to give us anyhow?

JOEY: Nothing. It's really true, Jimmy. It's really a *magic* carpet sweeper. The sign says so.

JIMMY (*Patiently*): I've explained to you, Joey. The sign doesn't mean a thing. It's only a label.

JOEY: That's what *you* think.

LIDA: Just wait till you try it.

JIMMY: Who? Me? Can you imagine me pushing a carpet sweeper?

LIDA: It wouldn't hurt you for a change. You're always trying to get out of work.

KAY (*Entering with sweeper*): Joey, Joey, I believe you're right. There *is* something magic about this carpet sweeper. I'm going to take it upstairs and try it in my room.

JIMMY: Are you serious, Kay? Do you really mean it?

KAY: Sure, I mean it. This carpet sweeper is definitely different.

JIMMY: Let me try it.

KAY: Not till after I've used it in my room. (*Moves toward door*)

JIMMY: My room's dirtier than yours. Let me try it first.

KAY: I'd better show you how to use it. Boys are so awkward at this sort of thing. (*Exit* KAY *and* JIMMY)

LIDA: I don't know what to think. Joey, you've upset our whole Mother's Day surprise.

JOEY: I don't see why. I've brought the biggest surprise of all.

LIDA: Joey, you know that carpet sweeper couldn't be real magic.

JOEY: You said yourself you felt tingles up and down your arm.

LIDA: Yes, I know it *felt* like magic. But my common sense tells me it couldn't be true.

JOEY: I'm glad I don't have too much common sense to believe in magic.

LIDA: Now you've spent all our money on the carpet sweeper and we can't get the bracelet.

JOEY: You still have the earrings.

LIDA: That's the worst part of it. We don't have the earrings. One of them is missing!

JOEY: Missing! What became of it?

LIDA: We don't know. I had them in my bureau drawer, but we've been taking them out and showing them around so much that somehow or other one has disappeared.

JOEY: Golly, that's too bad. But you should be thankful we have the magic carpet sweeper to give Mother.

LIDA (*Stamping her foot*): Stop calling it a *magic* carpet sweeper. It's not anything of the sort. (KAY *and* JIMMY *return with sweeper*. JIMMY *is excited.*)

JIMMY: Boy, oh, boy, this is really something. It tore around my room like all possessed. I never had such a good time cleaning my room.

JOEY: Do you really think it's magic?

JIMMY: I don't know. But it's something special.

LIDA: Did you feel the tingles?

JIMMY: I sure did.

LIDA: I don't know what to think.

KAY: It doesn't really make much difference what we think. It's the only present we have for Mother. We don't have the bracelet, one earring is lost, so this is all we have left.

JIMMY: O.K. Then what are we waiting for? Let's get out the fancy paper and ribbon and make it look like a real present.

LIDA: We should empty it first. Mother always empties her electric cleaner before she puts it away.

KAY: I'll get a newspaper and lay it on the floor. (*Gets paper and spreads it out on floor.*)

JOEY: With all the sweeping we've done, it should be pretty full.

JIMMY: Here, (*Taking sweeper and emptying it*) let me do it. (*As dirt spills out on paper,* KAY *spies the earring.*)

KAY: Look! Look! What's that sparkling in the dust?

LIDA: Where?

KAY: Right there.

JIMMY (*Picking it up*): Why, look, it's Mom's earring.

JOEY: Now, maybe you'll believe this sweeper is really magic. It finds lost articles.

JIMMY: I lost a dime somewhere yesterday. I wonder if that's in here.

KAY: Look! There's the gold button off my good dress. I've looked every place for it.

JOEY: I told you! I told you it was magic.

JIMMY (*Squatting down and poking at the dirt on the paper*): I'd still like to find that dime. (*As children are crouched around the paper,* MRS. LAWSON *enters.*)

MRS. LAWSON: What in the world are you children doing?

ALL (*Jumping up, startled*): Mother! Where did you come from?

LIDA: You weren't supposed to come home for another hour.

MRS. LAWSON: I got an earlier bus. What's wrong? Aren't you glad to see me?

KAY: Sure, only . . .

JIMMY: You walked in right in the middle of our surprise.

MRS. LAWSON: I'm sorry, but it's surprise enough to find you working with a carpet sweeper. Don't tell me you've been cleaning your rooms!

JOEY: It's your present, Mom. Look . . . a "Magic Carpet Sweeper."

MRS. LAWSON: A carpet sweeper! For me! But darlings, I have a carpet sweeper.

JOEY: I know, but this is different. It's a magic carpet sweeper, Mom . . . real magic.

LIDA: Mother, it was all Joey's idea. He thinks it's magic because it says "Magic" on the label.

JOEY: It really is, Mom. You wait till you try it.

JIMMY: It really does feel different, Mom. I noticed it when I cleaned my room.

MRS. LAWSON: When you what?

JIMMY: When I cleaned my room! It felt sort of tingly.

KAY: And I noticed the same thing when I used it in my room and in the dining room.

MRS. LAWSON: You mean you actually swept the dining room and your bedroom?

KAY: Sure.

LIDA: When I did this room, I must admit I felt little tingles up and down my arm.

MRS. LAWSON: Then there's no question about it. This sweeper really is magic.

LIDA: Do you really think so, Mother?

MRS. LAWSON: I certainly do. Any sweeper that could get you children to clean your rooms without being told is real solid gold magic, and no mistake.

JIMMY: It didn't seem like work at all. It seemed more like fun.

KAY: Jimmy and I even fought over taking turns.

MRS. LAWSON: Then it must be real magic. Joey, it's a wonderful present. Where did you find it?

JOEY: It was in the second-hand store window. A boy in our school sold it to me . . . Tony Marvin. (*Doorbell rings.*)

TONY (*Offstage*): Hey, Joey, may I come in? (TONY MARVIN *enters, cap in hand.*)

JOEY: Hy'a, Tony. What are you doing here? Mom, this is Tony, the fellow who sold me the magic carpet sweeper.

MRS. LAWSON: Hello, Tony.

TONY (*Shuffling in embarrassment*): Glad to meet you, Mrs. Lawson.

JIMMY: Mom loves her sweeper, Tony.

TONY: That's too bad . . . I mean . . . that's swell, Mrs. Lawson, but, well, my mother sent me over to bring the sweeper back.

KAY: But you can't do that. Joey paid you for it.

JIMMY: Two dollars and a half.

TONY: Yeah, but, you see . . . the sweeper wasn't for sale. It was just sittin' there in the window. Mom had been cleanin' up and someone called her at the back door . . . and well . . . when she came back I had sold her sweeper. She was plenty cross.

MRS. LAWSON: It was a natural mistake, Tony, and I think you were a very good little salesman.

JOEY: Then . . . then it isn't really magic?

TONY: Magic? Gosh, no. Who ever said it was?

JOEY (*Kneeling in front of it and pointing to the letters*): But the gold letters say "Magic."

TONY: You can't believe everything you read, Joey. Look, I'm sorry. But here's your money. I must get back with this so Mom can finish her cleaning. Nice to have met you, Mrs. Lawson. So long, everybody. (*Picks up sweeper and exits*)

LIDA (*With a shrug*): There goes your Mother's Day present!

KAY: I was beginning to think it really was magic.

JIMMY: It was magic enough to find the missing earring.

LIDA (*Getting both earrings*): Yes, Mother, at least we have these for your Mother's Day surprise.

MRS. LAWSON: How beautiful. (*Putting them on*) And they're so comfortable. Just what I wanted.

JOEY: One was lost but the magic carpet sweeper found it.

JIMMY: Aw, stop talking about that old carpet sweeper. It wasn't magic or any such thing.

KAY: It wasn't even for sale.

LIDA: Only a little boy like you would have been fooled.

JOEY (*Angry*): I don't care what you say. It was magic. It was, it was, it was!

MRS. LAWSON: Don't be so upset, Joey. I think you're right. I think there really was magic in that carpet sweeper.

JOEY: You do?

MRS. LAWSON: Yes, I do.

JIMMY: Mother, you heard what Tony Marvin said.

MRS. LAWSON: Just the same, it turned work into play. Every week, I coax and plead, and beg, and order, and command until I get you children to do your household chores.

ALL (*Sheepishly*): I guess you're right.

MRS. LAWSON: The magic of the sweeper made the work easy because you *wanted* to do it.

LIDA: But those mysterious tingles.

MRS. LAWSON: A little imagination is a wonderful tingler, Lida. You'd be surprised how many tingles there are in our old carpet sweeper, if you'd use it more often.

JOEY: You mean there might be magic in our very own sweeper?

MRS. LAWSON: There's magic all around you, Joey, if you just look for it, and have love enough to know it, when you see it.

LIDA: Mother, I think I'm beginning to catch on. (*Running to kitchen and running back with a dustcloth.*) Look! How would you like a magic dustcloth for your Mother's Day gift? I promise to use it every day, just for the fun of feeling those magic tingles.

MRS. LAWSON: Wonderful, Lida, wonderful. Thank you a thousand times.

KAY: Wait a minute, Mother. I have a magic present for you, too. (*She darts off.*)

JIMMY: I know where there's a piece of magic you could use. (*Exits*)

JOEY: Me, too! Me, too! (*Exits*)

LIDA (*Handing money to her mother*): Here, Mother. You keep the rest of the money. I think you would rather have your magic presents than any bracelet we could buy.

MOTHER: I'm sure of it, darling.

KAY (*Entering with dish towel*): Look, Mother. Here's a magic dish towel. You won't have to tell me to dry the dishes any more. I'll dry them by magic.

JIMMY (*Entering with polishing cloth*): Here's the magic

polisher for the car. It will be so shiny, you'll never know it for the same old bus.

JOEY (*Entering with shoe-shining kit*): If I'm to be the bootblack of this family, I might as well use a magic shoe-shining kit. My magic brush will do the trick.

JIMMY: From now on you'll get your housework done by magic for sure, won't you, Mom?

MRS. LAWSON: I sure will, Jimmy, and it will be the best magic of all—the magic of love.

ALL (*Crowding around her*): We have plenty of that, Mother dear.

LIDA: Say, I just thought of the perfect rhyme to go with *Mother*.

ALL: What?

LIDA: Love her! Now we can finish our Mother's Day greeting.
The best gift for Mother

KAY *and* JIMMY: From Sister and Brother

JOEY: Is show that you love her

ALL: Each day of the year. (*All crowd around saying "We do, We do."*)

THE END

Lacey's Last Garland

Characters

CINDY RANDOLPH
CARLTON RANDOLPH } *Cindy's cousins*
LACEY RANDOLPH }
AUNT EMMELINE
LIBBY TREVOR
MRS. RANDOLPH
JUDGE HENDERSON

TIME: *Spring, 1867*

SETTING: *The Randolph living room, in a small Southern town.*

AT RISE: CINDY *and* CARLTON RANDOLPH *enter.* CINDY *carries a folded parasol and an empty flower basket.* CARLTON *carries a bugle.*

CINDY: It feels so good to get into this nice, cool house! I'm just about melted! I hope to goodness this parasol kept the sun off my nose, or I'll be full of freckles tomorrow.

CARLTON: You girls! Can't you ever think of anything except how you look . . . even in the cemetery?

CINDY: I wasn't thinking of my freckles during the services, silly! Wasn't it wonderful, Carlton? All the flowers and the flags? And the girls in their white dresses! Everybody looked so pretty!

CARLTON: There you go again! Thinking about your looks! That's all Decoration Day means to you!

CINDY: Why, Cousin Carlton! What a mean thing to say! You know I think the Decoration Service is the most thrilling thing in the world! And so sad! Did you see all the ladies wiping their eyes when I said my poem—"The Soldier's Wife"? I declare I can hardly say it myself without crying. (*Reciting*)

"Away where the bugles are sounding
At morning and evening their call,
My hero, my soldier is guarding
The Land that was dearer than all.
Though he wears not a bar on his shoulder,
Nor glittering star on his breast,
Yet my heart in its fond worship crowns him,
The noblest, the bravest, the best!" *

I bet I'll remember that poem when I'm a hundred years old! (*As an afterthought*) Your bugle sounded mighty fine, too, Carlton.

CARLTON: I was pretty nervous there for a while. But I hope it came out all right.

CINDY: It did. I heard Uncle Will tell Lacey it was a shame your mamma didn't get back from Columbus in time to hear you.

CARLTON: Maybe it's a good thing Mamma wasn't there, after what Lacey did.

CINDY: I guess you're right, Carlton. Poor Aunt Dora would have gone through the ground! Truth to tell, I

* The verses are from *"The Soldier's Wife"* by Mrs. Emily Huntington Miller, published in *The Ladies' Repository,* April, 1863.

almost fainted myself when I saw Lacey walk over there to the Union plot and lay her last garland on that grave! In front of all those people! Mamma is so mortified she vows she'd go straight home if she hadn't promised to stay here with you and Lacey till Aunt Dora comes back from Columbus.

CARLTON: Poor Lacey! I bet Aunt Emmeline will just about skin her alive!

CINDY: You don't need to sound so sorry for her! After all, she has disgraced the whole Randolph family! What would your mamma say?

CARLTON: That's just it! I don't know what Mamma would say. But I know Aunt Emmeline will say plenty. (AUNT EMMELINE *enters. She is overheated, excited, and angry.*)

AUNT EMMELINE (*Fanning vigorously with a palm leaf fan*): Mercy me! I'm plain tuckered out! Cindy! Carlton! Where are you?

CINDY: Right here we are, Mamma. My sakes, you're just about ready to drop. Let me get you a glass of water.

AUNT EMMELINE: Not now, child. Just let me sit down and catch my breath! (*Sits down.*) Carlton, my footstool, please. (CARLTON *puts stool in place*) Cindy, my smelling salts! (CINDY *takes her mother's bag and finds bottle of smelling salts which she holds so that her mother may sniff from time to time.*) There! That's better. (*Coughs as she gets too strong a dose of the smelling salts*) Not so close, Cindy. Not so close! Carlton, run get my slippers, please. My feet are killing me!

CARLTON: Yes, Aunt Emmeline. (*Runs offstage*)

CINDY: I'll help you undo your shoes, Mamma. (*Kneels and removes shoes.*)

AUNT EMMELINE (*Blissfully*): Ummm! That feels good!

(*Leaning her head back*) Now, Cindy, I think I could drink a glass of water, if it's good and cold.

CINDY (*Running to table and pouring a glass of water from pitcher*): It's just like ice, Mamma. (*Gives her the water*)

AUNT EMMELINE (*Sipping the water*): That's very refreshing, dear. Thank you.

CARLTON (*Entering with slippers*): Here you are, Aunt Emmeline. (*Helps her put on slippers.*)

AUNT EMMELINE: Thank you, Carlton. You're a good boy. (*Straightening up.*) And now, if you will tell your sister to come down here, I think I feel strong enough to deal with her.

CARLTON: Aunt Emmeline . . .

AUNT EMMELINE: Send Lacey down here at once, Carlton. At once, you hear me. (*Grimly*) There's a little lady who needs a firm hand, and I'm just in the humor to cope with her.

CINDY: Mamma, Lacey isn't here.

CARLTON: She hasn't come home yet. We thought she was in the carriage with you.

AUNT EMMELINE: In the carriage with me, indeed! After what that child did this morning, I wouldn't be seen driving home with her in an open carriage, even if she is my own niece! It's bad enough that she has disgraced us in front of the whole town!

CARLTON: Aunt Emmeline, you sound as if Lacey committed a crime or something! After all, she's only a little girl!

AUNT EMMELINE: She's old enough to know friend from foe! She knew perfectly well what she was doing when she laid her garland on the grave of a Union soldier!

Think of it! The war hardly over! Her own father and uncle, her brother, her cousin all slain by the enemy and she would dare do a thing like this!

CARLTON: Maybe she doesn't understand, Aunt Emmeline.

AUNT EMMELINE: She'll understand when I finish with her! Why, if Cindy had done a thing like that I could never hold up my head again. Your mamma will simply die of shame! Lacey must be made to understand what she has done.

CINDY: Where is Lacey, Mamma? The services have been over for an hour.

AUNT EMMELINE: Probably hiding somewhere on the place . . . afraid to face the music.

CARLTON: No, ma'am. I don't mean to contradict you, Aunt Emmeline, but Lacey wouldn't hide. She never runs away, even when she knows she's going to be punished. I'm worried about her. Maybe something has happened to her.

CINDY: Shall we go look for her, Mamma?

AUNT EMMELINE: Carlton may go, if he likes. After all, he's her brother. I'm getting one of my headaches, and I'm going to lie down. I want you to sit by me.

CINDY: Very well, Mamma. (*Collects her things*) I'll go upstairs with you right away. (AUNT EMMELINE *prepares to exit.*)

AUNT EMMELINE: Mind you, Carlton, when you find Lacey, send her straight upstairs to me.

CARLTON: But your headache, Aunt Emmeline!

AUNT EMMELINE: Headache or no headache, I want to see her the minute she comes in. Now come along, Cindy. (CINDY *and* AUNT EMMELINE *exit.*)

CARLTON: Aunt Emmeline is sure upset! I'll be glad when

Mamma comes home. Being the man of the house is getting to be a bigger job than I ever expected. Well, I guess I'd better start looking for Lacey or there'll be more trouble when Aunt Emmeline gets up from her nap. (*Exit* CARLTON.)

LIBBY (*Entering from opposite side of stage*): Oo-hoo! Lacey! Anybody home? (*Looking around*) My goodness! Where is everybody? (*Running to door and calling*) Oo-hoo! Lacey! Anybody home?

CINDY (*Entering with small basin and towel*): Sh! Not so loud! Mamma has one of her headaches. Oh, it's you, Libby. Where's Carlton?

LIBBY: I have no idea. I just came in the back door. Where's Lacey?

CINDY: That's what we're all wondering. Mamma says she's afraid to come home after what happened this morning.

LIBBY: Dear me! I don't see it's anything to make such a fuss about! All she did was to lay one of her garlands on a Union boy's grave!

CINDY: Libby Trevor! How can you say such a thing! Lacey Randolph was just the same as a traitor, putting flowers on an enemy's grave!

LIBBY: Mercy me! You sound just like Mamma. She told me not to dare come over here, but . . . well . . . Lacey and I are best friends, and I just had to come over and tell her I'll stick with her no matter what the rest of the folks in this town say about her.

CINDY: You'd better not let my mamma catch you saying such things. Lacey ruined our whole Decoration Service doing what she did. I declare I'm ashamed she's my cousin.

LIBBY (*Defiantly*): Well, I'm not ashamed she's my friend, so there, Cindy Randolph! I think she did a fine thing, and I'm going to stay right here and tell her so.

CINDY: Then you can stay here by yourself, because I'm going back upstairs and put cold compresses on Mamma's head. (*As she starts to flounce out she bumps into* LACEY, *entering with a basket of fresh flowers.*)

LACEY: Excuse me, Cindy. I almost knocked that basin out of your hand.

CINDY: So! You've come home at last!

LIBBY: Lacey, are you all right?

LACEY (*Laughing*): Of course, I'm all right. What's the matter with you two? You look upset! What's wrong?

CINDY: As if you didn't know. You've sent poor Mamma to bed with one of her nervous headaches, that's what's wrong!

LIBBY: I just came over to tell you that I'll stand by you, Lacey, no matter what!

LACEY: That's very sweet of you, Libby, but what have I done that I need standing by? And how could I possibly have given Aunt Emmeline a headache?

CINDY: Lacey Randolph, you are impossible! Don't you know you have disgraced the whole family?

LACEY: Don't be silly!

CINDY: Silly? You call it silly! Well, maybe you'll feel pretty silly yourself when Mamma gets done with you.

LACEY: Libby, you're the only sensible one here. Maybe you can explain all this. After all, I've only been out picking some more flowers.

CINDY: Flowers! Flowers! How can you stand there and talk about flowers after what you did?

LIBBY: It's the garland you put on the Union soldier's

grave, Lacey. Your Aunt Emmeline is in a dreadful state over it.

LACEY: You mean she's angry?

LIBBY: Angry? She's practically sick in bed according to Cindy.

CINDY: It's not only Mamma. The whole town's talking about it. You've brought shame and disgrace on the Randolph name.

LACEY: Cindy, don't you dare talk to me like that. You know I'd rather die than do such a thing.

CINDY: You've done it just the same. Putting a garland on the grave of an enemy. And your own father and brother killed in the war!

LACEY (*Angry*): I'm warning you, Cindy Randolph, not another word!

CARLTON (*Entering*): I just can't seem to find her. I've looked everywhere. (*Seeing* LACEY) Why, Lacey! Where on earth have you been?

LACEY (*Running to her brother*): Oh, Carlton! Carlton! What is the matter with everyone in this house? Cindy says I've disgraced the family by putting my wreath on that Yankee soldier's grave. She's talking about Papa and Bill . . . and . . . (*Starting to cry*) Oh, Carlton. You understand, don't you? I did it for them!

CINDY: How can you say such a thing? Did it for them, indeed!

LACEY: I did! What's more, I went out and picked all the flowers I could find so I can decorate all the rest of the Yankee graves.

CINDY: Wait till Mamma hears this!

LACEY: She won't have to wait because I'm going straight upstairs and tell her myself. (*Enter* AUNT EMMELINE)

AUNT EMMELINE: Just what are you going to tell me, Lacey?

LACEY: Aunt Emmeline, I want you to understand. I want you to understand that I put my garland on that Yankee soldier's grave because of Papa and Bill and Uncle David, and all our brave men who were killed. When I looked at the Yankee boy's grave, I suddenly realized he might have been the same age as Bill. Maybe he has a sister up North who would give anything to be able to lay flowers on his grave, only it is too far away. Some of our men, too, are buried far from home. Wouldn't you like to think that someone would remember to put some flowers on *their* graves at a time like this? (*Stops and looks at everyone on stage*) I don't think you understand one word I've been saying! (*Bursts into tears*) Not one of you! If only Mamma would come home. I know she would understand. (*Exits in tears.*)

LIBBY: I think I understand what Lacey was trying to say.

CARLTON: So do I, Libby. Please, Aunt Emmeline, try to understand. Lacey would never do or say a disloyal thing —not ever.

AUNT EMMELINE: I am sure she had good intentions, my boy, but Lacey is such an impulsive child. She doesn't stop to think . . .

CINDY (*Looking offstage*): Quick! Quick! Mamma, straighten your hair. Judge Henderson is coming up the walk and there's a lady with him. I must get rid of this basin. (*Exits*)

AUNT EMMELINE: Mercy on us! What can bring the Judge here at this hour? And who could be with him?

LIBBY (*Peering offstage*): Why, I declare to goodness, it's Mrs. Randolph! Carlton, it's your mother.

CARLTON: It can't be! But it is! It is! (MRS. RANDOLPH

enters with JUDGE HENDERSON *carrying her bags. There is a great flurry of excitement and greeting.* CINDY *returns onstage to join in the general commotion.*)

AUNT EMMELINE: I can hardly believe you're home, Dora. We weren't expecting you till next week.

MRS. RANDOLPH: I know! I know! But I suddenly got so homesick I just couldn't stay away another minute. Oh, Carlton, you look wonderful. And how you've grown. Where's Lacey?

CINDY: She's upstairs, Aunt Dora. I'll call her.

AUNT EMMELINE (*Hastily*): No, no, Cindy. Just a minute. Let Aunt Dora catch her breath first. Judge Henderson, won't you sit down and have some lemonade? It's such a warm day.

JUDGE HENDERSON: No, thank you, ma'am. I haven't been home myself as yet. I came up from Columbus on the same train as your sister, and so I had Josh drive the carriage straight up here from the station.

CARLTON: We missed you at the Decoration Services this morning, Judge. No one can take your place, sir, when it comes to oratory.

MRS. RANDOLPH: The services! Don't tell me they're over! They were supposed to be next week.

AUNT EMMELINE: It was because of Reverend Hastings, Dora. He's leaving town and we wanted him to conduct the services.

MRS. RANDOLPH: I declare I'm so disappointed I could cry.

AUNT EMMELINE: I know how much the services mean to you, Dora, but there wasn't time to let you know. I didn't want to spoil your visit.

MRS. RANDOLPH: I would have given anything to have

helped with the services this year, Emmeline. You see . . . well, I had something different to propose.

AUNT EMMELINE: Something different?

MRS. RANDOLPH: Yes, you see, Emmeline, this week, I attended the services in Columbus. Oh, Emmeline, they were beautiful . . . If only I could tell you.

AUNT EMMELINE: More beautiful than ours, Dora? Everybody says we have the loveliest flowers in this section.

MRS. RANDOLPH: Not the flowers, Emmeline. The services. You see, there were three wonderful women, Miss Moreton, Mrs. Fontaine, and Mrs. Hill, who are really responsible for starting the services in Columbus at Friendship Cemetery. Over fourteen hundred of our Confederate dead are buried there. And in the same cemetery, a little apart from the rest, are the graves of about forty Northern prisoners of war. Last year, Emmeline, and this year too, the women of Columbus laid their flowers on *all* the graves.

AUNT EMMELINE *and* CINDY: On all the graves! (LIBBY *and* CARLTON *exchange looks.*)

MRS. RANDOLPH: They honored the men of the North and of the South. Oh, Emmeline, it was the most noble thing I've ever seen. That's what I wanted to do this year here at home. I remembered those few lonely graves in our cemetery, all covered over with vines. I wanted our women to follow the example of the women in Columbus.

AUNT EMMELINE: Dora, what would folks say?

JUDGE HENDERSON: They would say just what the whole nation is saying about the women of Columbus . . . "These are the noblest of them all." They would say in their hearts what Francis Miles Finch said with his pen when he heard the story. (*Takes paper from pocket and reads*)

"By the flow of the inland river,
Whence the fleets of iron have fled,
Where the blades of the grave grass quiver,
Asleep are the ranks of the dead:
Under the sod and the dew,
Waiting the judgment day:—
Under the one, the Blue;
Under the other—the Gray.

"From the silence of sorrowful hours,
The desolate mourners go,
Lovingly laden with flowers,
Alike for the friend and the foe;—
Under the sod and the dew,
Waiting the judgment day;—
Under the roses, the Blue;
Under the lilies, the Gray.

"Sadly, but not with upbraiding,
The generous deed was done;
In the storm of the years that are fading,
No braver battle was won;—
Under the sod and the dew,
Waiting the judgment day;—
Under the blossoms, the Blue;
Under the garlands, the Gray."

(*There is a pause after the poem. Then* AUNT EMMELINE *clears her throat.*)

AUNT EMMELINE: Carlton, will you please ask Lacey to come down?

CARLTON (*Quickly*): Yes, Aunt Emmeline. (*Exit*)

AUNT EMMELINE: Dora, I have something to tell you.

MRS. RANDOLPH (*Alarmed*): About Lacey? Is something wrong?

AUNT EMMELINE: It's about Lacey, Dora, but there's nothing wrong. You say you wanted the women of our town to decorate the graves of North and South alike? Well, Dora, your wish has been granted.

MRS. RANDOLPH: I knew our women would find it in their hearts to remember the brave men of both sides.

AUNT EMMELINE: Not our women, Dora. Just Lacey.

MRS. RANDOLPH: Lacey? What could Lacey do? She's only a child!

AUNT EMMELINE: She's only a child, Dora, but she set us all an example. She stood there at the ceremony, with one garland remaining in her hand after the services. Suddenly she walked over and laid it on the grave of a Yankee Drummer Boy.

MRS. RANDOLPH: How wonderful!

AUNT EMMELINE: The rest of us weren't wonderful, Dora. At least, I wasn't. I was angry and ashamed. I felt she had disgraced us all. I—I'm afraid I didn't understand.

LIBBY: There were other people who didn't understand either, Mrs. Randolph, but I am sure they will, when they have time to think about it.

JUDGE HENDERSON: The whole country will soon be ringing with the news of Columbus. This poem, this beautiful poem will tell the story to generations yet unborn. I prophesy that a day will be set aside for the whole nation to pay tribute to our fallen heroes. (LACEY *rushes in and runs to her mother.*)

LACEY: Mamma! Mamma! They've told you what I did? They've told you about the horrible disgrace?

AUNT EMMELINE: If there's any disgrace, my child, it was not yours—but mine.

LACEY: Aunt Emmeline!

AUNT EMMELINE: You were right, child. I did not understand. Grief and despair sometimes make us slow to understand and to forgive.

CARLTON: Mamma has been telling us about the ceremony in Columbus, Lacey. The women there did the same thing you did, and the whole town approved.

JUDGE HENDERSON: Not only the whole town, my child, the whole nation.

LIBBY: Judge Henderson has been reading us a poem, Lacey, a beautiful poem written in honor of their action.

JUDGE HENDERSON: It was published in the *Atlantic Monthly* for the whole country to read.

LACEY: Then I haven't disgraced you after all.

MRS. RANDOLPH: You've made me very proud and happy, Lacey.

AUNT EMMELINE: I'm sorry I spoke so sharply, Lacey, and to prove to you that I really do understand, I have a suggestion.

LACEY: Anything you say, Aunt Emmeline.

AUNT EMMELINE (*Indicating basket of flowers*): These flowers . . . you intended to put them on the rest of the Union graves?

LACEY: Yes, yes, I did.

AUNT EMMELINE: Then I suggest that we all go with you —that we all share in your gesture of love and forgiveness.

LACEY (*Running to her aunt and putting her arms around her*): Oh, Aunt Emmeline, thank you, thank you.

AUNT EMMELINE (*To* JUDGE): And that poem, Judge

Henderson, I should like to hear you read it, as we lay the flowers on the graves of those men and boys who lie so far from their loved ones.

MRS. RANDOLPH: Oh, Judge Henderson, if you only would!

JUDGE HENDERSON: I will be honored, ma'am. I would especially like to read the last stanza. (*Reads from paper*)

"No more shall the war cry sever,
Or the winding rivers be red;
They banish our anger forever
When they laurel the graves of our dead:—
Under the sod and the dew,
Waiting the judgment day;—
Love and tears for the Blue,
Tears and love for the Gray." (*Curtain*)

THE END

The Talking Flag

Characters

NARRATOR
THE FLAG
JAMES
BETTY
JANE
RUTH
MIKE
JOHNNY
TOM
SALLY
GRACE
FRANK
MARY
BOB
DICK
OTHER CHILDREN

BEFORE RISE: *The* NARRATOR *enters in front of the curtain.*

NARRATOR: Did you hear about the amazing thing that happened in our school? We hope you didn't because we're just dying to tell you about it. Maybe you won't

This play was inspired by *Makers of the Flag,* an address delivered by Franklin K. Lane, Secretary of the Interior, June 14, 1914.

even believe it, when you do hear it, but we're going to tell you the story just the same.

It all began . . . let me see. . . . Today is (*Name day*) Well, it must have been at least a week ago. We pupils were all gathered in our assembly hall and were just giving the pledge to the American Flag. I remember thinking: "The stars never seemed brighter. The blue was never more brilliant! The white never more dazzling!" I was thinking all this to myself, but I was saying the pledge right along with the rest.

SETTING: *A school room. Across the center opening at rear hangs an American Flag behind which a child is concealed.*

AT RISE: *A group of children, representing each grade in the school, stand on the stage. They salute the flag and repeat the Pledge of Allegiance, then sit down.*

NARRATOR: Well, that's when it happened. Just as we said the last word, the Flag began to speak.

FLAG (*As the voice of the* FLAG *begins to speak, the flag should be spotlighted*): Good morning, my little Flag-Makers.

NARRATOR (*The children look about them in bewilderment*): We were speechless, until James Kelly, from fourth grade, stood up and said:

JAMES: You must be mistaken, sir. We are not Flag-Makers.

FLAG: Oh, yes, you are. You are, indeed.

BETTY: But we're not taxpayers or lawmakers. We're not even grownups. We're just pupils of the (*Insert name*) school.

FLAG: I know who you are, and I mean what I say. Every

day you are helping to make the flag, and I am very grateful to you.

JANE: But we girls can't even sew very well. Mother says my stitches look terrible. They're too big and uneven. The stitches in the flag are so little you can hardly see them.

RUTH: Once I tried to cut out some stars and they were all crooked. I could never cut out five-pointed stars like those in the flag.

FLAG: There's more to making a flag than sewing stripes or cutting stars, my little friends. Right here in (*Insert name*) School you are learning to believe in the things the flag stands for.

RUTH: I certainly never knew I was a Flag-Maker.

MIKE: Me either! It makes me feel important.

FLAG: It *should* make you feel important. Going to school and making the flag are just about the two most important jobs in the world.

JANE: I'm afraid I still don't understand what you mean.

FLAG: Very well, I'll try to explain. See that little boy in the second row?

JANE: That's Johnny Jones. He's in first grade. He's too little to be a Flag-Maker.

FLAG: That's where you're wrong. Let me talk to him. (*Louder*) Johnny, Johnny Jones, can you hear me?

JOHNNY: Yes, I can hear you, Mr. Flag.

FLAG: What have you learned in school so far this year, Johnny?

JOHNNY: Oh, I've learned a lot of things. I've learned how to read, and I've learned how to print my name.

FLAG: Think of that! You've learned the magic of words. Someday you may write a great book, or make a fine speech that will help to make better citizens. That's being a real Flag-Maker.

TOM: We're learning fractions in our grade, and they're awfully hard. How does that make me a Flag-Maker?

FLAG: America needs more scientists, more men and women who can figure out the mysteries of our wonderful world of nature, and invent new ways of helping mankind. Fractions are just the beginning. The arithmetic you are learning today may help to make America a stronger nation tomorrow.

BETTY: I never thought about it before, but I guess you're right. Going to school *is* an important job.

FLAG: And a school is a mighty important building. Next time you pass a school, look up at the flag waving on the flagpole, and remember that it is a *free* flag waving over a *free* school. (*The children sing any flag song familiar to them.*)

SALLY: I know we are learning many lessons in school that will help us become good citizens. Our teacher calls some of these lessons *Our American Heritage.* She says it is not only our duty, but our *privilege* to learn such immortal words as the preamble to the Constitution of the United States.

ALL (*Rising*): We, the people of the United States, in order to form a more perfect union, establish justice, insure domestic tranquility, provide for the common defense, promote the general welfare, and secure the blessings of liberty to ourselves and our posterity, do ordain and establish this constitution of the United States of America. (*Sit down*)

FLAG: Those are wonderful words for every Flag-Maker to know, boys and girls. I believe you are beginning to understand that by learning these lessons here in school you are helping to make the flag.

GRACE: We just finished a unit on South America in our grade. We learned some Spanish songs and dances. Would you like us to do them for you?

FLAG: That would be fine. (*South American song, dance or both*)

TOM: When we learn the songs and dances of another country, are we still helping to make the flag?

FLAG: The American Flag flies in every quarter of the globe. Learning the customs of another country helps you to understand the people of that country. Through exchanging language and customs, through sharing music and dancing, the nations of the world learn to like each other. They learn to be friends. When you learn to make friends with other nations, you are helping to make the flag.

FRANK: We are learning about Democracy in school and I am sure that is helping to make the flag.

FLAG: Right! Tell me what you are learning about Democracy in your school.

FRANK: We are learning to talk things over and settle our problems by group discussion.

MARY: We are learning to vote on matters of importance and abide by the will of the majority.

BOB: We elect our school officers and help make our school laws.

BETTY: We learn to work together on committees and put our heads together when we make our plans.

DICK: We learn to enforce our laws as well as to make our laws. Would you say the members of the Safety Patrol are also Flag-Makers?

FLAG: Yes, indeed. Every member of the Safety Squad is doing his bit to make America strong by making America safe. So every boy or girl who practices the rules of safety is a first-class Flag-Maker. (*The children sing any safety song.*)

FLAG: Learning to obey traffic laws is one of the first lessons for a good citizen. I'm glad to see you Flag-Makers at (*Insert name of school.*) are off to such a good start.

JAMES: You make it sound as if everything we do in school helps to make the flag.

FLAG: That's what I've been trying to say, James. I'm glad you understand.

JAMES: I guess we're helping to make the flag even when we're on the playground.

FLAG: I should say so. Learning to win and lose, learning to play a clean game, learning to be a good sport, all of these lessons are a part of flag-making.

MARY: I'm glad you're talking to us, Mr. Flag. I never knew you could talk at all.

FLAG: Maybe you just never listened, Mary. The Flag has something to say to everyone.

MARY: I knew the flag had a special message for soldiers and sailors and great patriots, but I never knew it had anything to say to school children.

FLAG: The flag that flies over an American public school or hangs in an American classroom is a very lucky flag indeed. You are making me very proud and happy by telling me all of the fine things you are doing here in your school.

SALLY: Excuse me, sir, but I have a very important question to ask.

FLAG: Speak up so all can hear.

SALLY: I want to ask if our parents know we are Flag-Makers.

BETTY: I'll bet my daddy doesn't know we're learning flag-making at school.

FLAG: Every parent wants his child to learn everything he can in school. In fact, here in our country the schools belong to the people. They really own them.

JOHNNY: Then why don't they come to visit more often?

RUTH: We'd love to have them.

FRANK (*With a sigh*): I guess it's because they're too busy!

ALL: Too busy!

MARY: Yes, too busy! When some parents receive an invitation to visit the schools, this is what they say (*Children sing to the chorus of "Short'nin' Bread"*):

Mamma's much too busy, busy, busy,
Mamma's much too busy, not today!
Daddy's much to busy, busy, busy,
Daddy's much too busy, not today!

RUTH: But if they knew we were learning to be Flag-Makers, they'd have a different answer. Then they would say:

Mamma's not too busy, busy, busy,
Mamma's not too busy, I'll be there!
Daddy's not too busy, busy, busy,
Daddy's not too busy, I'll be there!

BOB: Then all we have to do is to tell them we're helping to make the flag and ask them to come and see for themselves.

FLAG: And when they do visit your school, young man, I know they will be pleased with what they see, just as I am pleased, and just as America is pleased. You know that's the most important job of all.

ALL: What?

FLAG: To make America proud of you.
You're proud of your land, your own U.S.A.
You're proud to be living the American way.
You're proud of your flag, every stripe, every star,
You're proud of your country, wherever you are.
You're proud of the colors, the red, white, and blue,
But can your America be proud of you?

ALL: We hope so. Tell us how.

FLAG: It's not always easy, it takes lots of work.
It's a task you must labor, and never must shirk.
It takes lots of courage, and patience and skill,
It takes lots of trying and plenty of will.
But learn to be brave, and loyal, and true,
And the country you love will be proud of you.
(*The children sing "Make America Proud of You."* *)

CURTAIN

NARRATOR: Well, that's what happened in our school just a week ago. Ever since then, we've been trying our best to be better Flag-Makers and make America proud of us. But we need lots of help and encouragement, especially from our parents. You can help us most by visiting our schools and learning about our activities. We hope you'll come again soon and often. You can be sure you are always welcome, and by helping us, you may become a Flag-Maker too.

THE END

* *"Make America Proud of You" by Jack Fulton and Lois Steele. Published by Randolph Music.*

Production Notes

The Greedy Goblin

Characters: 6 male; 3 female.
Playing Time: 25 minutes.
Costumes: The Goblin is dressed in solid green. A hooded mask covers his face; the mask should have large phosphorescent eyes painted on it. A long loose duster covers the Goblin from head to heels, and he carries a green feather and a note (to leave on the table) in his pocket. Mr. Strudel wears the traditional white baker's cap and apron. All the other characters wear everyday dress.
Properties: Coat and hat for Mr. Whitman; doorbell; pumpkin pie and serving knife; flashlight for Joe; tray for paper plates, napkins, forks and cinnamon shaker.
Setting: The Whitman living room. The room should contain a tabouret or small stand center stage, at least four chairs, a telephone, a table with black silk thread in the drawer, and a desk with paper on it and four flashlights in a drawer. There is an entrance from the outside and one leading to the kitchen.
Lighting: Stage lights out and up at Goblin's entrance and exit.

A School for Scaring

Characters: 9 male; 8 female.
Playing Time: 10 minutes.
Costumes: Miss Goblin wears a long, dark brown dress with long sleeves and a peaked hood. Professor Owl wears a feathered costume and spectacles. Beulah Banshee wears a long, slim-skirted black dress and has very long, stringy black hair. Danny Demon wears a red devil costume. Fanny Phantom, Gregory and Gracie Ghost, Gloria Ghoulie, Harry Haunt, and Solomon Spook wear white ghost costumes. Helen Hobgoblin wears a brownie suit with a pointed hood. Johnny Jack-o-Lantern wears a pumpkin-head mask and an orange and black costume. Sammy Scarecrow wears an old baggy suit and an old battered straw hat, with straw sticking out from his suit and hat. Girl witches wear traditional black witches' costumes and pointed hats. Boy witches wear black tight-fitting brownie suits and pointed hats. Solomon Spook wears ordinary boys' school clothes.
Properties: Books and a roll sheet

for Miss Goblin. Brooms for the witches. Large piece of sheet metal for Harry Haunt and Fanny Phantom. Chains for all pupils except Harry and Fanny. Record book for Professor Owl. Books for all students.

Setting: Miss Goblin's classroom at Scare 'em School. The pupils sit at desks, and Miss Goblin has a large desk or table. In one corner of the room is a broom closet. There is an entrance on one side of the room.

Lighting: No special effects.

The Mystery of Turkey-Lurkey

Characters: 4 male; 2 female; Speaker may be male or female; as many male and female extras as desired for Chorus, Ducks, Geese, Chickens, and Turkeys.

Playing Time: 15 minutes.

Costumes: Alice, Fred, Betsy, Mike, and Chorus wear everyday modern dress. Policeman wears appropriate uniform. Turkey-Lurkey wears paper-bag mask, a bright scarf around his neck, and a fringed brown crepe paper costume to suggest feathers; his tail may be made of cardboard covered with crepe paper. The Ducks, Geese, Chickens, and Turkeys wear paper-bag masks.

Properties: Rhythm instruments for Chorus; a few turkey feathers; dish of water.

Setting: The barnyard. At center stage are low primary chairs for the Chorus. Downstage left is an empty cardboard coop bearing a sign: TURKEY-LURKEY. Downstage right is a long cardboard cage marked MARKET HOUSE, large enough for eight children, and cut so that each child can stick his head out of a hole in the cardboard. Further right is a stepladder camouflaged as a cardboard tree. A few turkey feathers are scattered on floor near tree. There are exits at right and left.

Lighting: No special effects.

Strictly Puritan

Characters: 3 male; 9 female.

Playing Time: 25 minutes.

Costumes: Modern dress. Officer Kerr wears a police uniform.

Properties: Dried corn, stone, books, groceries, small covered basket, fishing equipment, large gunny sack.

Setting: A recreation room of a home. Upstage center is a large fireplace. An improvised spit has been placed in the fireplace, and on the spit is a chicken leg. A long table and several chairs are at center. On the table are some books. Other furnishings—lamps, easy chairs, pictures, etc.—may be added if desired.

Lighting: No special effects.

Thanks to Butter-fingers

Characters: 2 male; 3 female.

Playing Time: 20 minutes.

Costumes: Modern everyday dress. Charlotte wears a ruffled apron over her dress. Betsy has on blue jeans. (If possible, Charlotte should have blonde curls, Betsy, dark pigtails.) Dean wears glasses. When Mrs. Upton re-enters with Dr. Rinehart, they wear coats.

Properties: Centerpiece of fruit and autumn leaves, electric coffeepot, stack of plates, trays with glasses and silver, dustpan, broom, long piece of plywood, extension cord, large cold cream jar, dish cloths, sugar bowl, ring. (Note: the breaking of the glass and the damaging of the sugar bowl lid should be faked. The sugar bowl can be equipped with a false lid which is already equipped with a loose knob.)

Setting: The dining room of the Upton home. At center is a large table covered with a cloth. Chairs are placed around the table. There is a small side table near the big table, and a china closet against the upstage wall.

Lighting: No special effects.

Mr. Snow White's Thanksgiving

Characters: 3 male; 4 female.

Playing Time: 25 minutes.

Costumes: Modern dress. The children and Mr. Foster wear dungarees. Mrs. Foster wears a simple gingham or calico dress. The Blodgets are a bit more dressed up, but still simple. All of the characters have outdoor clothing.

Properties: Blue ribbon, newspaper clippings, medal on a ribbon, a gift-wrapped book, typed letters and document, envelopes, pen, two white turkey feathers.

Setting: Comfortable farmhouse living room of the Fosters. Left stage is a small desk or table with a typewriter on it. A few big chairs, a clothes tree, and possibly a couch are in the room. Exit at right leads out to front of house; at left to back.

Lighting: No special effects.

Mary's Invitation

Characters: 3 male; 6 female; male or female extras for chorus.

Playing Time: 15 minutes.

Costumes: Modern dress.

Properties: 3 envelopes, for girls; pile of school books, notebook and pencil, for Mary; bag of newspapers, for Tim; packages and a grocery cart, for Mrs. Cook and Mrs. Barry; rolled rug, for Mr. Leskov.

Setting: Scene 1 is in a small park in the midst of a business area. There is a park bench at right center. A painted backdrop of trees may be used. Scene 2 is in a classroom.

Lighting: No special effects.

Turning the Tables

Characters: 15 male; 10 female; extras, if desired, for other children in library.

Playing Time: 20 minutes.

Costumes: Children wear everyday modern dress. Miss Warren wears a smock over tailored clothes. Hobgoblin wears long black gown and hood. Consult illustrated editions of the books concerned for suggestions on costuming the Book Characters.

Properties: A dozen books and sign: CHOOSE A PAL FOR BOOK WEEK for central table; several books for children; pencil, card file, etc., for Miss Warren; name cards for children and Head Hobgoblin.

Setting: The Children's Room of the Cardiff Public Library. Prominently displayed on a long table at center is a collection of books with a large sign: CHOOSE A PAL

FOR BOOK WEEK. At right stands Miss Warren's desk. Another table, with chairs, stands at downstage left corner.

Lighting: If possible, there should be complete blackouts before the appearance and disappearance of the Book Characters, as indicated in the text. A curtain may be used instead at these two points, if desired.

THE MIRACULOUS TEA PARTY

Characters: 7 male; 8 female.

Playing Time: 15 minutes.

Costumes: Mrs. Stevens wears modern, everyday clothes, and an apron. Minty wears an everyday dress, her mother's hat, fur piece, and high-heeled shoes when she first appears; she slips into her own shoes later on in the play. The boys and girls wear everyday modern dress. The book characters wear appropriate costumes; illustrated editions of these books will give costuming ideas.

Properties: Sewing materials, six books, plate of cookies for Mrs. Stevens; hat, fur piece, high-heeled shoes, tray of lemonade and cookies for Minty; skipping rope for Janie West; baseball and bat for Billy Evans; several hats for Bartholomew Cubbins; toy telephone or bicycle bell for sound of telephone offstage; cymbals for sound of thunder offstage.

Setting: The front lawn of the Stevens home. There is a large umbrella table to the right of stage center with six or seven small chairs standing near it. At downstage left, a few feet from edge of stage, is a picket fence. The boys and girls enter from left, from stage steps or from an entrance located in front of picket fence. Another exit at right leads into house.

Lighting: If possible, lights should go off for a few seconds at third clap of thunder, as indicated in the text.

THE FORGOTTEN HERO

Characters: 5 male; 5 female.

Playing Time: 20 minutes.

Costumes: Modern dress. Students wear school clothes; Miss Merryweather wears a dress. Mr. Caufield wears overalls or work clothes.

Properties: Small bench and note for Mr. Caufield; black metal box containing first-aid equipment, bandage, scissors, and a small case with a medal in it, for Helen and Mary.

Setting: The stage of a school auditorium. The stage may be bare or decorated with streamers and banners with a patriotic theme.

Lighting: No special effects.

VICKY GETS THE VOTE

Characters: 8 male; 5 female.

Playing Time: 25 minutes.

Costumes: Everyday modern dress.

Properties: Ten flashlights, newspaper for Jim, paper and pen for Vicky.

Setting: A comfortable living room furnished with a couch, chairs, tables, lamps, etc. A writing table or desk should be downstage, a telephone on a small table upstage.

Lighting: The lights go off and then come up as indicated in the text.

THE CHRISTMAS UMBRELLA

Characters: 7 male; 7 female; Ting, Ling and the eight Neighbors may be male and/or female.
Playing Time: 25 minutes.
Costumes: Ting and Ling wear green and red elf costumes. Santa and Mrs. Santa are dressed in traditional costumes. The older Umbertos wear modern, everyday dress, while the younger seven wear pajamas and bathrobes. The eight Neighbors wear coats and hats.
Properties: Large box, toys, crossword puzzle, pencil, dishes, teapot, cakes, two signs with the word "Invisible" printed on them in tinsel, large box containing nine umbrellas, Christmas tree lights, balls, tinsel, cotton, an umbrella stripped of its covering, a stand to hold umbrella in upright position, star, small radio.
Setting: Scene 1: Santa's Workshop. There is a door at right. The upstage wall is lined with almost empty shelves. Workbenches stand at left and right. Upstage center are a small table and a rocking chair. Scene 2: The Umberto living room. The room is plainly furnished with couch and a few easy chairs. There is a door at right. Upstage center is a large table.
Lighting: No special effects.

SOFTY THE SNOW MAN

Characters: 9 male; 4 female.
Playing Time: 25 minutes.
Costumes: Santa Claus and the six store Santas wear the traditional costumes. The store Santas are not padded and do not have beards. They wear placards announcing the names of the stores. The Snow Man wears a battered silk hat, a white padded costume, and carries a broom. Spunky and Mrs. Santa can wear red and green costumes. The girls wear everyday modern dress.
Properties: Mechanical toy, bell, record book, white teddy bear, small black paper hat, black paper buttons, pins.
Setting: A display room. Santa's desk is at upstage center. On the desk is a bell. Shelves of toys, signs and Christmas decorations may be added.
Lighting: No special effects.

THE BIRDS' CHRISTMAS CAROL

Characters: 8 male; 10 female; Narrator may be male or female; there can be any number of Carolers, both male and female.
Playing Time: 25 minutes.
Costumes: Everyday dress. The Carolers wear outdoor winter clothing. Carol wears a bathrobe and pajamas. The Nurse can wear a uniform. The Ruggles children are dressed as indicated in the text; the whole Ruggles family should have on rather elaborate, odd-looking clothing.
Properties: Letter; large paper bag of oranges, watch, dolls, various packages wrapped in Christmas paper for the Ruggles.
Setting: If desired, the entire play may be produced without using a curtain, or any of the scenes indicated in the text may be

played before the curtain. If a curtain is used, the settings may be as simple or as elaborate as desired; however, it is suggested that a minimum of furniture be used so that the scenes may be changed quickly and easily. Scene 1: A chair for the grandmother, plus Christmas presents and perhaps a small decorated Christmas tree. Scene 2: A wheel chair, chaise-longue or bed for Carol, a chair for Uncle Jack. Carol should be covered with a blanket and propped up on pillows. (Uncle Jack might sit on the bed.) Scene 3: Seven chairs, a wood box and a coal hod (or any combination of chairs and boxes). Scene 4: A bed for Carol.

Lighting: No special effects.

The Christmas Runaways

Characters: 4 male; 2 female.

Playing Time: 25 minutes.

Costumes: Joey and Doodles wear heavy winter coats over their overalls and sweaters. The three boys wear hiking clothes—heavy woolen shirts and flannel trousers, etc. The Lady wears a blue raincoat with a hood.

Properties: Doll wrapped in blanket for Doodles, bundles containing sandwiches for Joey and Doodles, candy bar for Joey, flashlight for Brad, thermos jug, camping equipment including cups, plates, forks, cans of beans, a jar of pickles, etc., for the boys, lantern, letter (in pocketbook) for the Lady.

Setting: A stable. At center is a bale of hay. Nearby is a manger. The furnishings include a few rough benches, an old wheelbarrow, some barrels and other equipment that might be found in a stable. A lantern is on one of the benches.

Lighting: The lighting should be dim at rise. Stage lights should come up full when Pokey lights the lantern. When Doodles sings "Away in the Manger," a spot light might be used on the group, emphasizing the blue of the Lady's coat.

The Santa Claus Twins

Characters: 9 male; 4 female; the Weigher and the Measurer may be male or female; male and female extras.

Playing Time: 10 minutes.

Costumes: Miss Jingle and some of the children wear everyday clothing. The costumes of the other characters may be as simple or as elaborate as desired (these characters might wear everyday clothing and carry props or wear hats, etc.). The Christmas Fairy should have a wand and a crown, the Toy Soldier a sword and gun. Ned and Fred wear identical Santa Claus costumes.

Properties: Scales, tape measure, telegram.

Setting: A bare stage with a decorated Christmas tree in one corner.

Lighting: No special effects.

Santa Claus for President

Characters: 6 male; 1 female; 11 characters, either male or female.

Playing Time: 10 minutes.

Costumes: The Prologue and the elves should be dressed in red and green. Santa wears the traditional red and white costume.

The reporters can wear suits; they should also wear hats with "Press" signs stuck in the brims. The foreign children might wear costumes suggesting the countries they represent.
Properties: Telegrams, pencil and paper, big red notebooks and large green pencils for reporters, banners with names of foreign countries, American flags.
Setting: Santa's workshop. This can be as elaborate or as simple as desired, and might contain a few tables, chairs, tools, wood, paper, toys, etc.
Lighting: No special effects.

Mystery at Knob Creek Farm

Characters: 6 male; 5 female.
Playing Time: 20 minutes.
Costumes: Modern, everyday dress for all characters except the Boy from Kentucky, who wears a coonskin cap, a long rough brown hunting shirt, and no shoes.
Properties: Picnic basket, sandwiches, pickle jar, potato chips, lemonade; maps, cameras, Lincoln souvenirs; small stone, camera for Mary; pen and autograph book for Penny; wooden bucket for the Boy; automobile horn.
Setting: A picnic grove on Knob Hill Farm, Kentucky. There are a picnic table and benches near center stage, strewn with picnic equipment, cameras, maps, and a general assortment of Lincoln souvenirs.
Lighting: No special effects.

Melody for Lincoln

Characters: 2 male; 6 female.
Playing Time: 20 minutes.
Costumes: Modern dress. When characters enter from outside, they wear hats and coats or jackets. Spanish costume, with ruffled skirt and lace shawl, for Theresa.
Properties: Small dressing case, for Miss Lucinda. At the beginning of the play, Theresa's Spanish costume is inside the case.
Setting: The living room of the Alvarez home. There is a piano, with a piano stool, at right center. The room is furnished comfortably, with a sofa, several chairs, end tables, lamps, etc.
Lighting: No special effects.

The Tree of Hearts

Characters: 5 male; 3 female; male and female extras.
Playing Time: 25 minutes.
Costumes: King, Prince, and Chancellor wear appropriate court clothes. Mr. and Mrs. Gooseberry and Goldie wear peasant clothing. Dale and Gail wear everyday, modern dress. Children of Valentia wear peasant skirts, shorts, etc.
Properties: Scroll and quill for Chancellor; spade for Mr. Gooseberry; market basket for Mrs. Gooseberry; large straw hat for Goldie; guide book for Dale; folding screen; sign: HAPPY BIRTHDAY, YOUR HIGHNESS!; trumpets; small bare tree; green tub; decorated red paper hearts with wire hangers attached.
Setting: Scene 1: Near the Head Gardener's hut, in the Palace Garden of Valentia. A painted backdrop of flower beds and Mr. Gooseberry's marvelous trees may be used. Scene 2: Same as Scene 1, except for a folding screen

placed at center stage bearing the sign: HAPPY BIRTHDAY, YOUR HIGHNESS!

Lighting: No special effects.

Crosspatch and Cupid

Characters: 7 male; 6 female.

Playing Time: 15 minutes.

Costumes: Modern, everyday dress for Teacher and children. Crosspatch wears black shorts and shirt, black patch over one eye, and black pirate hat. Cupid wears white shorts and shirt, small golden wings, and a golden quiver slung on his back containing red paper darts.

Properties: Scoreboard, black crayon, for Crosspatch; scoreboard, quiver filled with red paper darts, red crayon, picture of Cupid, for Cupid; bell, large heart-shaped wire frame, book, for Teacher; red paper, crayons, drawing paper, paste, for children.

Setting: A classroom. Two long tables are placed at stage right and left respectively, the foot of each table facing the audience. Five chairs are placed at the outer side of each table. The Teacher's desk stands at center stage. Two stools and scoreboards mounted on easels stand upstage right and left. There is one exit.

Lighting: No special effects.

The Washington Shilling

Characters: 8 male; 6 female; Actors, Street Criers, may be male or female; male and female extras.

Playing Time: 25 minutes.

Costumes: Modern, everyday dress for present-day characters. The colonial children wear appropriate costumes of the period. George Washington wears hunting shirt, knee breeches, and coonskin cap. Clowns, Juggler, and Actors wear bright carnival clothes and masks. Street Criers wear ragged clothes and hold trays suspended around their necks.

Properties: Jewel case for Tabby; overnight case, note, for Toby; telephone, bench; sign: STREET FAIR—COME ONE, COME ALL!; recording of carnival music; balls for Juggler; hand puppets for Actors; trays loaded with meat pies, sweets, toys, buns for Street Criers; 3 buns, shilling, for George Washington; purse for Tobias; shilling for Mr. Fremont.

Setting: Scene 1: The Fremont living room. At center stands a small table. Other appropriate furniture is placed around the stage. Exit right leads to outdoors. Exit left leads to other rooms of the house. Scene 2: This scene is played before the curtain. A bench is placed to one side of the apron stage, and the sign, STREET FAIR—COME ONE, COME ALL! is placed at center. Scene 3: Same as Scene 1.

Lighting: No special effects.

Dolly Saves the Day

Characters: 4 male; 2 female.

Playing Time: 20 minutes.

Costumes: Characters may be dressed in clothes of the period. Washington wears the uniform of a Continental General, and the Captain that of the Hessians.

Properties: A rag doll; riding crop; papers for the plans; pen knife; dipper; medal.
Setting: There is an old well at the right, and a rustic table and chair at the left.
Lighting: None required.

Washington's Leading Lady

Characters: 7 male; 13 female.
Playing Time: 15 minutes.
Costumes: Modern, everyday dress for playwriting committee and Miss Mifflin. America wears a long white robe with a flag draped across her shoulders and chest. She wears a laurel wreath on her head and carries an arm bouquet of red roses. The historical characters are dressed in appropriate clothing of the period.
Properties: Gavel; letter; quill and paper; small table; sewing basket; American flag; three white plumes; black cockade; bouquet of red roses; one or two chairs; pedestal.
Setting: At one side of the stage, before the curtain, stands a table with six chairs grouped around it, representing a classroom. The tableaux are enacted center stage as the curtain opens and closes.
Lighting: No special effects.

Bunnies and Bonnets

Characters: 6 male; 9 female; number of girls in Bunny Ballet optional.
Playing Time: 25 minutes.
Costumes: Flopsy, Mopsy and Cottontail wear glorified bunny tap-dancing costumes. The Bunny Ballet wear bunny ballet costumes. Alice is dressed as Alice in Wonderland. Peter Cottontail, Oswald, Bugs Bunny, White Rabbit, and Easter Bunny wear bunny suits. Peter Cottontail carries a large artificial carrot; Oswald carries large drum; White Bunny wears a watch; Bugs Bunny may carry a real carrot; Easter Bunny carries decorated basket of Easter eggs. The others wear modern clothes. Mrs. Fulton enters with big guitar in a case, Mrs. Murphy has a paper bag; Mr. Hunter carries a brief case.
Properties: Wide-brimmed straw hat trimmed with flowers with ties to be used for handles when it is used upside down as Easter Bunny's basket; Easter eggs for all, with appropriate decorations; trumpet in case; mouth organ; calling card.
Setting: Waiting room of the Bluemont Television Studio. There is a receptionist's desk left stage and benches at rear of stage for prospective talent. There is a stage entrance at right.
Lighting: No special effects.

The Bashful Bunny

Characters: 3 male; 3 female.
Playing Time: 20 minutes.
Costumes: Peter Cottontail and Junior may wear white pajamas trimmed with a big pastel bow at the neck, tails of cotton, and ears. Mrs. Cottontail may wear white pajamas with tail and ears also, with an apron added. Mrs. Cackle's costume should suggest feathers and wings; the effect may be achieved very simply with a brown sweater and skirt,

kerchief, and "wings," consisting of a fringed brown triangle of cloth attached at the wrists and back of the neck. Mrs. Cackle wears an apron, also. Sherry and Tommy wear everyday school clothes.

Properties: Easter baskets; large green handkerchief for Peter Cottontail; carrot, school books, report card, and wheelbarrow for Junior.

Setting: A small wood near a public park. Trees, shrubbery and rocks may be suggested. There is a table near stage center, with a row of Easter baskets on it.

Lighting: No special effects.

Mother's Fairy Godmother

Characters: 2 male; 4 female.

Playing Time: 25 minutes.

Costumes: Modern, everyday clothes for Mother and the children. Fairy Godmother wears a long, blue cloak over a full-length dress.

Properties: Model plane, paper dolls, scissors, book, wand, several packages, bedroom slippers for Mother, keys.

Setting: A modern American living room. There are two comfortable chairs, a sofa, an occasional chair, tables and lamps. There is a card table set up downstage left.

Lighting: No special effects.

The Magic Carpet Sweeper

Characters: 3 male; 3 female.

Playing Time: 30 minutes.

Costumes: Everyday modern dress.

Properties: Paper and pencil, small box containing earrings, carpet sweeper wrapped in brown paper, gold button, dustcloth, dish towel, polishing cloth, shoe shine kit.

Setting: A comfortable living room with sofa, several chairs, a desk, end tables, lamps, etc.

Lighting: No special effects.

Lacey's Last Garland

Characters: 2 male; 5 female.

Playing Time: 30 minutes.

Costumes: Dress of the Civil War period.

Properties: Parasol, flower basket, bugle, palm leaf fan, pocketbook containing small medicine bottle, slippers for Aunt Emmeline, small basin and towel, basket of fresh flowers, two suitcases, folded sheet of paper.

Setting: A simple living room, furnished with rather heavy Victorian furniture. There are several small tables placed about the room, with a pitcher of water and several glasses on one.

Lighting: No special effects.

The Talking Flag

Characters: 9 male; 6 female; male or female extras as desired.

Playing Time: 15 minutes.

Costumes: Everyday school clothes.

Properties: A large American flag.

Setting: A school room. Across the center opening, at rear, hangs a large American flag behind which a child is concealed. There are chairs or school desks for the children.

Lighting: No special effects necessary, but flag should be spotlighted, if possible.